SCOTLAND

ENGLAND

.Rotterdam
Cleves

HOLY

Brest

SPAIN

Hampshire.

MY LORD OF CANTERBURY

My Lord

of

Canterbury

GODFREY TURTON

GARDEN CITY, NEW YORK

DOUBLEDAY & COMPANY, INC.

PREFACE

The purpose of this book is to try to show what it felt like to be Thomas Cranmer, to see the events, ideas, and people of his time through his eyes. Where historical evidence is available I have not consciously departed from it, and I have omitted nothing known to me which has an important bearing for good or ill on his character. There are occasions however in his life of which no record exists, and many of these are indispensable to the story. To fill the gaps I have treated conjecture as fact, rather as an antiquary fitting together the fragments of an ancient jar makes up with putty where a piece is lost. I have tried to shape my putty as closely as possible to recorded circumstances.

Even if I were capable of a convincing pastiche of sixteenth-century English the effect would be to put an unnecessary barrier between Cranmer and the reader, so I have translated his thoughts into modern speech, extending the licence, for the sake of consistency, to his use of titles of honour. Men in the sixteenth century were more ceremonious than today, and Cranmer would have spoken of Anne Boleyn's father as "my Lord of Wiltshire," even of her brother George Boleyn as "my Lord of Rochford"; following modern custom I have made him speak of the older man as "Lord Wiltshire," of the younger as "Rochford." There is anachronism too in the titles "Princess Mary" and "Princess Elizabeth." The King's daughters were known at the time as "the Lady Mary's Grace," "the Lady Elizabeth's Grace"; but the ancient forms would be out of place in a narrative written in modern language.

I owe a great debt to Mr. Jasper Ridley's *Thomas Cranmer* (Clarendon Press, 1962), which provides an indispensable frame of events on which to hang my story and a wealth of references from which to seek supplementary details. I owe a similar debt for my account of the reign of King Edward VI to Mrs. Hester Chapman's *The Last Tudor King* (Cape, 1958). Other secondary authorities which I have used are Paul Friedmann's *Anne Boleyn* and the relevant volumes of Froude's *History of England* and of Agnes Strickland's *Lives of the Queens of England*. The reason given for Anne Boleyn's execution is propounded and supported with much evidence by Margaret Murray in *The Divine King in England* (Faber, 1954).

The main contemporary sources which I have been able to consult are Morice's anecdotes and the anonymous life of Cranmer from *Narratives of the Days of the Reformation* edited by Nichols, Foxe's *Acts and Monuments*, Cavendish's *Life of Thomas Wolsey*, Cranmer's letters mainly from the collection edited by Jenkyns, and such extracts from the letters of Chapuis as are quoted by Friedmann in his copious footnotes.

G. T.

SOME RELEVANT DATES

1485 Battle of Bosworth, death of Richard III, end of the Wars of the Roses and accession of Henry VII, the first Tudor King.

1489 Birth of Thomas Cranmer.

1509 Death of Henry VII and accession of Henry VIII.

1547 Death of Henry VIII and accession of Edward VI.

1553 Death of Edward VI and accession of Mary I.

1556 Death of Cranmer.

1558 Death of Mary I and accession of Elizabeth I.

Throughout Cranmer's life Calais with its surrounding territory belonged to the English Crown, sole remnant of the dominions formerly held in France by the Plantagenet kings. It was lost to the French in the latter part of Queen Mary's reign, after Cranmer's death.

"My Lord of Canterbury is too old a truant for us twain."

– King Henry VIII to Stephen Gardiner,
Bishop of Winchester.

Maiden sweet and lovely, listen to my prayer.
I offer you my heart and my archdiocese to share.

– Old Song

MY LORD OF CANTERBURY

1

Dusk has fallen early this evening. They have just rung the angelus in St. Michael's church next door, and at this time of year, the spring equinox, there should be another hour still of daylight. But these dark wet days draw in quickly, as I have learnt here. There seems to have been no break in the clouds since this year 1556 began, a spring as stormy and gloomy as my own fortunes. No doubt the weather has been the same elsewhere, but when my imagination travels to Cambridge it evokes memories of blue sky swept clean by the east wind blowing in from the sea. Places where one has been happy live bathed in fabulous sunshine. I have no need of invention to create an appropriate atmosphere for Oxford.

There is just enough light outside when I look through the window to show the college of Balliol with its low tower and oriel window looming through the rain, a frontage of grim stone almost as forbidding as its neighbour, this Bocardo prison which I inhabit. The intervening ground is the usual waste of rubbish and weeds that one finds around a city's precinct. The rain has turned it into mire, and the open drain beneath the wall has swollen into a torrent deep enough to soak a man to the thighs if he had the boldness to wade among the argosies of drowned cats, rotten vegetables and accumulated filth crowding the stream. I cannot see whether it has blocked the conduit yet and flooded the main road coming in from the north. The corner of the gatehouse projects too far and hides the view. But if Oxford has acquired a new moat it does not seem to deter the traffic. I can hear the usual clatter of hooves and wheels on the cobbles, townspeople hurrying home before dark and many strangers as well, I suspect, visiting the town to watch the spectacle tomorrow.

Tomorrow's spectacle in which I play the chief part, yet am still uncertain what the part will be. Is Oxford looking forward to hear a Protestant recant or to see an Archbishop burnt alive? I have signed so many recantations in the past month. Shame overcomes me at the thought of them. Men far less responsible for the reformed religion than I am, men whom I myself led into these ways of thinking, have died without flinching for their convictions. I admire their courage and envy them their singlemindedness. It is right to die for what one believes, but it is necessary to be sure of one's belief before dying for it. If I go to the stake only to emulate others, to escape the stigma of cowardice, I am not a martyr but a hypocrite. My martyrdom will be founded on a lie.

I have never found certitude easy. Beliefs grow slowly in my mind, changing shape as they gain a fresh insight or shed what seems to be an error. It is not a process that leads naturally to conclusion. This can often be an advantage in the ordinary intercourse of life. One is better able to understand other people if one's ideas have not yet hardened and can be stretched without loss of integrity to accommodate theirs. The difficulty is to know when the limits of understanding are reached. There always seems to be one more step that can be taken without danger in fellowship. Harmony is a great good, but there are others greater for whose sake it must in the last resort be renounced. If only I could see them more clearly I could, I hope, find the courage to die for them; but my mind still gropes in vain. It is an agonising task to define the principles for which a man must condemn his living body to the flames.

For more than two years while I have been in prison I have struggled to find an answer to the question, and with this end in view I began to write a theological treatise, a rejoinder to the views affirmed by my old colleague and adversary, Stephen Gardiner, Bishop of Winchester, in his defence of the Real Presence. But that work was too limited in scope to satisfy me. I have to assure myself not only that my arguments are sound but also that my life has not been lived in vain. In my sixty-seventh year I see the destruction of nearly everything that I helped to build. Were my efforts deluded from the outset? Are the Queen and her advisers right in wanting to undo the fruits, to start again? I cannot know for certain unless I go back over the events and weigh each in turn.

So in time spared from more serious writing I have set out the story of my life, beginning from the earliest that I can remember.

Now except for this introductory chapter and some pages at the end it is finished. Even if I myself am the only reader, if the work is lost after my death, it will have served its purpose to clear my mind for tomorrow's ordeal. That is my chief task in recalling the past, to judge myself; but if in spite of all likelihood the manuscript is preserved and finds others to read it I cherish the hope that it will lead them to sympathise with my difficulties, perhaps condone my offences. At any rate, before condemning me, let them answer honestly what they would have done themselves if they had been in my place.

It is growing very dark and I can hardly see to write. God grant that on this of all nights they do not mean, as on many occasions before, to leave me without candles. No, I hear a step that I recognise in the passage. It is the little maid who waits on me, a friendly sweet-tempered child, gay even in these grim surroundings; but to-night she is constrained and silent, checking her tongue, as I can guess, from talking of the excitement in the town and the mounting pile of fagots outside Balliol. She is the same age as my own daughter, not unlike her in face and gestures. Among my troubles there is always comfort in the thought that Margaret, my wife, is safe with both children in Germany.

Good girl. She has put a lighted candle on the table, with two more unlit beside it to use if I work on late, a more generous supply than I have known for a long time. The night lies before me in which to write undisturbed, in which to gather my courage to face the morning.

2

Aslockton, where I was born on the 2nd July 1489, lies in the basin of the Trent on the borders of Nottinghamshire and Lincolnshire. The Smite, a small tributary of the Trent, divides it from its sister parish of Whatton. All the country here is very flat so that the merest knoll becomes an eminence commanding a wide view, and in most years in winter an island in a lake of flooded fields. The embankments enclosing the Smite and other watercourses are seldom able to stem the torrents invading us when the snow melts. Not far from our house there is an artificial mound, an earthwork dating, I believe, from prehistoric times and now overgrown with grass and scattered thornbushes. It used to be my favourite walk when I was a child, particularly when I had to wade to it through the floods and climbed up out of the shallow water into a kingdom of my own enisled from earthly concerns. On one side I looked across at the thatched roofs of Aslockton with the stone walls and red tiles of our own house overtopping them, on the other at the tower of Whatton church with its tuneful bells; but between them and me lay an ocean as ultimate to my imagination as if no shores bounded it, no willows protruded their trunks and branches from the surface.

Hillmen are said to pine when they are away from their native hills. I who was born and bred in the low country live happiest under a sky whose great dome lies bare from horizon to horizon. It was one of the main reasons why I settled down so quickly at Cambridge when I went to live there, that it offers views as unconstricted as at home and a similar fascination in the changing moods of the light.

As soon as I could ride a horse I looked forward eagerly to the occasions when my father allowed me to follow him to market at Bingham or to visit a neighbour in another village. I have two brothers, John who is older and Edmund younger than myself, and four sisters, Dorothy, Agnes, Alice and Emmet; but none of them at that age loved riding as I did, so when the chance of an expedition arose it was I who implored and usually managed to be taken. While my father bargained with a drover at the market or sat in a farmer's kitchen drinking ale or mead (the latter especially I liked, and there was usually a small mug of it for me, with sweet cakes) I could listen or not as I wished to their conversation. There were times when I came home filled with rumours of violence and danger on the western outskirts of the kingdom and thanksgiving for good King Henry's victory over the rebels, whose baseborn leader pretended to be the heir of the Plantagenets. While I understood little of the meaning I enjoyed the thrill of contact with great events.

My father was lord of the manor of Aslockton, but his property was of no great size, lying in a part of the country divided into many small manors surrounding and scattered among the estates of the Abbey of Welbeck.

He looked after his land and tenants, attended church regularly—walking into Whatton for the purpose on the frequent occasions when there was no priest at Aslockton—and asked nothing better of his neighbours than that they should no more meddle in his affairs than he did in theirs. To us children he was unfailingly kind when he had time to spare for us. I have described how he used to take me with him on his errands about the country. He also taught me to shoot with the longbow, never losing patience on account of my shortsightedness but encouraging me till in spite of my disability I became a tolerable marksman. I owe it to his teaching that throughout my life I have enjoyed shooting as a recreation offering escape from public affairs into the quiet seclusion of the woods, and that when my rank earned me Royal permission to use the crossbow I was able as a grown man to adapt myself to the new weapon with such ease. Most of all I am grateful to him for my skill in horsemanship. I learnt to ride almost before I could walk, and he was always egging me on whether by crafty praise or by good-humoured mockery to test myself on larger and rougher horses. It is, I hope, a forgivable vanity in one who has few other causes to boast that I drew pleasure later from my reputation in the stables at

Knole and Ford. It became a byword among the grooms for a horse hard to manage that it was the Archbishop's favourite.

Country tastes I could share with my father, but he took little interest in training my mind. He seldom spoke of religion or politics, and then only in perfunctory and conventional terms. Looking back I can understand his reluctance, see in it an attitude common to the great majority of Englishmen of his time, who after more than thirty years of civil strife desired only to be left in peace to their private concerns.

There was a welcome for my young brother Edmund and me at most doors both in Aslockton and in Whatton, but our favourite haunt was the blacksmith's forge, at any rate it was mine. A smithy is the main centre for exchange of news in a country parish. Everyone who keeps a horse whether for tillage or for travel has occasion to visit it, and at almost any time of the day a group of men can be found there busy in conversation while they wait for their turn. At Aslockton they were for the most part local people. I listened to them eagerly, looking forward as one does as a child to the time when I myself could enter the great world, distant and unknown and for that reason all the more fascinating.

When I sort these memories out in the light of later knowledge my impression of England under the first Tudor King is of a nation thankful for orderly government and anxiously hoping that it will last. There were grievances of course as there always will be, but their target was more often some local magnate than the Royal authority, and King Henry VII would have wasted money which he was little inclined to spend if he had paid eavesdroppers to watch the forge at Aslockton or any similar gathering of his humbler subjects. The rich might complain of the stern measures which he took to replenish his Treasury; but the poor were not, or believed that they were not, concerned.

There were great benefits which all enjoyed from the new dynasty. For the first time almost in living memory the country had peace both at home and abroad. Contending armies no longer used the farmer's crops as a battlefield, or the streets and houses of the towns as a fortress to be attacked or defended till all were in ruins. Unruly retainers of the barons no longer marauded with impunity.

Although the last battle of the civil war was fought before I was born I heard many stories of the misery of the years of unrest, stories told from experience. They left an impression on my mind which nothing can erase, a passionate horror of anarchy.

It has been the custom in my lifetime to condemn the Kings of the House of York and contrast their faults with the merits of the Tudors. King Richard III in particular is represented as a monster so deformed in body and soul as to be scarcely human. I myself of course can only speak of him from hearsay, but I must admit that in many of the conversations to which I listened as a boy in Nottinghamshire well out of earshot of the authorities, conversations among men to whom his reign was a recent memory, a much more favourable and more credible portrait was drawn. There was a wool merchant who used to visit us every summer after shearing-time, travelling from the north down the Fosse Way. His own home was at York, and he spoke openly of the popularity enjoyed by King Richard and the respect still paid to his memory there. He himself saw the King riding through the town, and he declared emphatically that there was no sign of any deformity, although he looked carefully, having heard tales of a weakness in one of the King's shoulders. Whatever the weakness may have been, it was not of a kind to mar the appearance of a well-set figure and stern but gentle face.

That is the evidence of an eyewitness who saw King Richard, the last of the Plantagenets, in the flesh, and it recurs to me whenever the ignorant repeat the official legend of a misshapen bogyman. I begin to wonder too how much truth there is in the moral enormities ascribed to him. The picture which I have received of his short reign from those who lived in it is of great expectations bitterly disappointed, a false dawn heralding prematurely, but nonetheless indubitably, the end of the long night of the civil war. When his brother, King Edward IV, died undisputed ruler of the country the victory of the White Rose seemed to be secure, and men at last dared to believe that peace lay ahead. The only lingering source of uneasiness, only enemy able to blight the prospect, was that very Henry Tudor whom we honour today as the founder of peace and prosperity. Whether King Richard would have jus-

tified the nation's hopes we cannot know. Henry Tudor invaded
with French support, won the battle of Bosworth and the throne of
England, and his fallen adversary has earned the ignominy due to
those who are dead and unable to reply.

The civil war was a calamity whose damage has taken a lifetime,
all my own lifetime, to make good. When authority fails the people live in misery. God's work of love cannot be accomplished without the peace and order that the King maintains. This is the true
source of the reverence owed to the Crown. They are mistaken who
attribute any sanctity to Royal birth. Hereditary succession is a
convenience ensuring on most occasions that King succeeds King
without dispute. The Tudors with little Plantagenet blood in their
veins have proved their right to rule by the best possible evidence.
They have given peace where before there was strife.

This digression has led me a long way from the smithy at
Aslockton to follow the development of ideas sown there, whose
influence has governed me all my life. I had time and leisure
to absorb them, having the fortune to enjoy longer than most boys
the careless freedom of early youth. The nearest grammar school
was that kept by the canons of Southwell more than thirty miles
away on the farther side of the Trent, and it was intended that
when I was old enough I should be sent there to be educated.
But time passed and still I remained at home. Looking back I can
guess that the reason was shortage of money.

It was soon after my tenth birthday that the news came which
heralded a change. The impact at first was harmless enough. Old
Canon Jenkins, the priest who had served at Whatton since I was
born, died at last of a lingering illness. After a short interval one
of the canons, Thomas Wilkyngton, was sent as successor. It was
a compliment to Whatton that such a man was chosen. His learning and his character alike commanded respect, and my father who
enjoyed intelligent company was delighted to have him as a neighbour. He became a frequent visitor at our house, and it is easy
to guess that in the course of conversation the problem of my
education was discussed. I do not know from which of them the
suggestion came, but the outcome was that Canon Wilkyngton's
clerk (an appointment made necessary by the prolonged vacancy at

Aslockton) was ordered to hold classes of instruction in the aisle of Whatton church, to be attended by the sons of the local gentry including not only me myself but Edmund too who was already over seven years old.

I am sure that neither my father nor Canon Wilkyngton had any reason to doubt the suitability of our schoolmaster, who was better educated than most clerks of his sort and held a licence from the Abbey to teach. In the presence of his superiors he was respectful to the point of servility, and they could have no idea how his demeanour changed when their backs were turned. Among ourselves at school we called him Friar Tuck after the well-known character in Nottinghamshire legend, and I shall use that instead of his real name in speaking of him for fear of offending any relations of his still alive. It was a nickname appropriate to his corpulence, but to nothing else. He was not of course a friar, and no one had less of the good nature of Robin Hood's jolly chaplain.

Hatred is mortal sin, but I am still guilty of it at times when I think of Friar Tuck. He suffered from a thwarted craving to dominate others. A class of small boys offered an opportunity such as he can seldom have known before to avenge humiliation and restore his self-esteem.

It was largely my own fault that the victim was so often myself. If I had stood up to the man he would have respected me and yielded. But I have never had any aptitude for sharp retort. When I am attacked I want to retire into myself, to think it over and collect my forces. His favourite form of persecution was to take advantage of my short sight. He would write a Latin sentence or similar exercise on a slate, hold it up and put me a question. As he held it too far off for me to read I was of course unable to answer, much to his feigned indignation and secret triumph. The frequent strokes of the cane which I received for this were less painful than the lash of his tongue. He excelled in a combination of menace and sarcasm.

He was not of course an ignoramus, or I should not have acquired the elements of Latin and logic as I did; but my progress came from a natural interest in these subjects and in spite of his brutality.

My father was not to blame. He had received a satisfying report of the man's abilities, and nothing had been told him since to shake his confidence. He made a point at every available opportunity of taking me with him riding or shooting, even putting himself out to do so when he had business of his own. But he never asked me about my schoolmaster. Perhaps he feared the answer and was at a loss to know what to do for the best. Even my mother was more attentive to me than usual, but her household duties kept her fully occupied. It was something in the tone of her voice, the expression of her face, that made me aware of her concern rather than her words and actions.

There came a time however in my second year at school when a graver anxiety claimed her attention. My father was a man of robust health who had scarcely known a day's illness in his life. He made light of his injuries when he arrived one evening badly scarred on the face, explaining that he had ridden home by a short cut and had to push his way through a thicket of briers, when his horse took fright nearly throwing him before he could disentangle them both from the thorns. He told the story with humorous details and we all laughed; but it was no laughing matter when the scars refused to heal and became day by day worse inflamed and discoloured. He lost his appetite for food, seemed to have no energy left for anything, and a peevish irritability appeared which alarmed us the more because it was so unlike him. At last when the symptoms were those of a high fever he was persuaded to stay in bed, and my mother distrusting the skill of the old apothecary in Bingham, who used to attend us in our childish ailments, sent to Nottingham for a doctor reputed to have studied at the famous school of Padua in Italy and to be an adept in the latest principles of medicine. She also sent a message to Dorothy and Agnes, my elder sisters who were married. Both lived within fairly easy reach, the one at Ratcliffe and the other at Ossington.

The new doctor was both learned and conscientious. He spent several days in the house, and as we tiptoed past the sickroom door we could hear his voice brisk and confident talking in low tones to my mother, who insisted on performing the greater part of the nursing duties herself. It was strange for the house to be so full. In addition to the doctor it contained Dorothy and Agnes with their husbands, Harold Rosell and Edmund Cartwright, who came promptly in answer to the summons. The interruption of routine, which in different circumstances would have been welcome to those of us who were still children, was now a constant and dreadful reminder of our anxiety. Edmund and I were even glad to go to school, and the two younger girls, Alice aged fourteen and Emmet seven, kept out of the way as much as they could in the garden. At last however it seemed that skill and care would prevail, and that the patient was out of danger. The Rosells and Cartwrights left, unable to stay away longer from home, and the doctor himself having given detailed instructions for the convalescence returned to Nottingham.

The very next night my father suffered a relapse. My mother, I am sure, did all that she had been told. We ourselves were sent to bed; but as I lay awake I listened to the footsteps of the servants hurrying up and down the stairs on her errands. There was a restless excitement in the air, a premonition of disaster.

It was almost dawn when I heard my name called, a fine May morning with haze clinging to the garden and a pink glow rising in the sky. Edmund and I who shared a room leapt from our beds as if we had been waiting for the cue. My sisters were already in the passage, and my mother was coming towards us, followed by John. Her face told us the news without need to speak, but as she met our eyes she nodded. There was a low cry quickly stifled from Alice; she grasped little Emmet's hand and they slipped away in silence. My mother never could bear any display of emotion, least of all could she have then. We others stood grouped uneasily and miserably around her in the passage, but still she said nothing. Then she left us and went downstairs. At last we could weep.

My father's death was the first great sorrow of my life. I have lost many since whom I loved, but the shock has come to me as something familiar and therefore more tolerable, as if this early experience accustomed, adapted me to bereavement. At twelve years old I had no resources in myself to soften the blow. It was not that I lacked confidence in my mother; I was fond of her and respected her, but I could not escape with her from my troubles as with my father into the fields and woods.

The only person able to fill the void in my life was my sister Alice. She and I hitherto had followed rather different paths; she was not far from me in age, but her time had been spent under my mother's supervision more indoors than out. Now whether by chance or her own intention divining my need we were brought closer together. Not only in the house either; Alice had always been more of a tomboy, a lover of the open air, than the other girls. In the long summer evenings she asked me to give her riding lessons. She had a great contempt for women who travelled riding on a pillion behind a servant. To ride with Alice was an adventure in itself. Her delight was to match our horses in a race over country abounding in obstacles. But there were times also when we trotted together quietly in conversation. I learnt then what a lifetime has confirmed, that even when we disagreed most widely I could count on her to respect and understand my point of view.

In ordinary circumstances my mother might have disapproved of what she would have regarded as Alice's neglect of a girl's proper work; but beneath her reserved manner she had penetration and sympathy, and she raised no objection to our excursions. There were other reasons too for her to pay less attention than usual to strict discipline. As soon as the funeral was over and my father had been laid in his tomb in Whatton church she had to take up his burden of responsibility. John, left heir, was younger than both Dorothy and Agnes, and had not yet come of age. He needed all her help to manage the estate. She had at least the consolation that as he was unmarried she was spared for the time being the pain of being supplanted by a daughter-in-law in her home.

So much indeed continued as before that it saddened me. I was not yet accustomed to the speed with which time closes its stream over the heads of those drowned in it. Least of all was any change apparent at school, any mitigation even for a day of the tyrant's temper. Yet release was not far off if I had only known. Already rumours heralding it had reached the smithy; but I remained ignorant of them, having neither the time nor the inclination any longer to loiter there.

My first news came from my mother. She told me that the Abbot of Welbeck had died and that our own Canon Wilkyngton had been elected to fill his place. I could see that she was distressed on both accounts. No successor to Canon Wilkyngton at Whatton had yet been appointed, and when he departed for Welbeck to take up his position the parish was left in charge of Friar Tuck. This was of course only a provisional arrangement unlikely to last long, but to Friar Tuck himself it appeared in a very different light. He believed that he had been promoted to parish priest, and his self-importance rose accordingly. It was pure mischance that brought him into conflict with Sir Robert de Whatton, the most substantial of the neighbouring landowners.

An old woman who lived by the river near his house kept a flock of ducks, and it happened one day that as these were swimming down the stream they found the gate into his garden open and filed through. He rounded them up and impounded them, killing them off one by one for his table. On his wife's insistence Sir Robert himself intervened, demanding either the return of the ducks or heavy payment in compensation.

Friar Tuck was badly frightened. He would gladly have given back the ducks if he could, but it was impossible as he had eaten them. In his agitation he made a serious mistake. Instead of confessing the truth and throwing himself on Sir Robert's mercy, he tried to defend himself by attacking the old woman whom he had wronged. He told Sir Robert with many protestations of respect that she was a witch who practised black arts and deserved no consideration.

At the hearing Friar Tuck suffered utter defeat. No evidence was offered to sustain the charge of witchcraft, but witness after witness came forward to complain of the oppression under which the parish had groaned since Canon Wilkyngton's departure. Sir Robert wrote to the new Abbot of Welbeck—his old friend, Canon Wilkyngton—telling him what had happened and asking him to recall the present clerk.

My mother was less concerned than I expected at the abrupt

end to my schooling at Whatton. Possibly she had foreseen it as she watched the course of events. Without a word to any of us she had been making her own arrangements, writing to friends who had influence and building up a reserve of money for the step that she had in mind. I was young but not too young for the university. She told me now that when the coming academic year began I should go up to Cambridge.

3

Cambridge was my mother's choice because the older university of Oxford still lay in her eyes under suspicion of heresy. The stigma was to a large extent out of date even in her own youth, completely so in mine. Wyclif had been dead for more than a century, and Oxford had long ago abjured the teaching of the Lollards. But prejudice dies hard, especially in those like my mother with little knowledge of the matters concerned. I often used to smile as I watched the direction that ideas were taking at Cambridge to think that this was the haven of orthodoxy to which she so confidently entrusted me.

But I have never regretted her decision. For the next twenty-five years Cambridge became my home, inspiring a lasting affection. My first favourable impression probably owed much to circumstance. I was leaving behind me memories of Friar Tuck and of our own house still desolate from my father's death and travelling into the unknown, a fascinating prospect to the young. It was the longest journey that I had yet made in my life, incomparably farther than any on which my father took me. One of our servants rode with me as far as Stamford, where he left me among a group of my own age waiting for a man sent from the university to escort us to Cambridge. The following morning the cavalcade set off early, but it was late at night when we approached our destination. The town glittered ahead in the darkness. I felt that I was entering an earthly Paradise, a fabled city of learning.

In the course of time I witnessed much that was inconsistent with these expectations; but there was no harsh disenchantment, and I doubt whether my illusions are wholly banished even now. I was lucky in the college in which I was enrolled. It was barely seven years since John Alcock, Bishop of Ely, founded Jesus College, dissolving the nunnery of St. Radegund and converting the buildings to academic use. Even in those days his action earned approval. The story goes that, when he sent visitors to report on the standard of religion, they found only two nuns in residence, one of whom was with child and the other a child herself.

Although since their conversion into a college the buildings were more fully occupied it was still a small community, which absorbed me on my arrival with less than usual of the sensation of plunging into cold water. It may have been partly because I was the youngest that I was treated with so much kindness, but it was also in keeping with the prevailing spirit among my companions.

From my window in Jesus I looked across open fields to the river, and as my two roommates shared my taste that was nearly always the direction that we took when we had leisure. The Cam seemed immense compared with the Smite at home. It was my first experience at such close quarters of a navigable waterway. There was seldom a reach without a boat or two, gaily painted barges trading up from the Ouse and the Wash.

Indoors and out of doors we talked. It surprises me now to reflect how much time we found for conversation, yet without neglecting our books. The questions discussed were very different from those to which I was accustomed at home at Aslockton.

It is the fashion today to sneer at Duns Scotus, and his very name corrupted into "dunce" has become a byword for ignorant stupidity. But at the time of which I write his authority was still unshaken in the schools and was the foundation of the lectures which I attended on philosophy. His faults are well known. There is no need here to dilate on his riddles and sophistry. I prefer to record the debt that I owe him for the light that he throws on the meaning of faith. Earlier teachers following Aquinas tried to link faith with reason, insisting that the highest truth is intelligible. Duns uses his weapon of subtle logic to refute them. Reason can prove neither the immortality of the soul nor the existence of God. If we retain conviction it is on the strength of faith alone.

Where then is the province of faith, over which reason has no jurisdiction? The nearest approach seems to lie in the evidence of the senses. I know immediately that I see or hear, and except in unusual circumstances no one can reason me out of the conviction.

The same immediacy belongs to faith. The presence of God is revealed by a faculty which responds as directly as the eye or ear, and the sensation that it receives is love. The part played by reason is subsequent, forming concepts, drawing conclusions from the evidence. These are subject to examination to determine whether they are right or wrong. But there is no room for argument about the sensation itself. If I am asked why I see the colour red I can only answer that I do.

The province of faith is limited to sensation. Judgments arising from it, such as that God is love, depend on reasoning, but in the example given the chain is so short that error cannot enter. Theology is founded on faith just as any study of the movement of the stars is founded on vision, but like those of natural science the doctrines which result must submit to reason to be accepted. If the logical chain breaks, nothing else can support them.

My ideas did not fall into shape at once. They were still immature even when I had taken my degree and been elected to a fellowship at my college. I was never a leader of thought at the university. My mind works slowly, and I preferred to watch rather than enlist in the controversies already fermenting in Cambridge when Luther's name was still unknown. My sympathies in those early days were if anything on the side of tradition. All my life I have had a horror of the chaos which results from collapse of authority, and it seemed better to tolerate even grave abuse of Papal power than to weaken the Church perhaps beyond recovery by encouraging doubt of the efficacy of its indulgences, private masses and other machinery of salvation. So I seldom joined the company at the White Horse, an inn in the High Street which was becoming the recognised meeting place for the discussion of advanced opinions. On the few occasions when I was persuaded to accompany a friend there I wished myself well away.

It was not that I was afraid of incurring the disapproval of the authorities. King Henry VII was more concerned to enforce political than religious conformity, and his son, the new Henry who acceded on his death, showed no signs yet of changing the policy. Within reasonable limits a man was free to criticise the Church. The only reason for the uneasiness that I felt at the White Horse—

"Little Germany" as it came to be called later after the rise of Luther—was that the atmosphere was uncongenial. Yet the material setting was agreeable enough in its lack of formality. These meetings were in fact nothing more than a gathering of friends in a public room at the inn. If the members of the public assembled there were drawn almost entirely from the university and its adjuncts, it was only because on most evenings there was no space left for anyone else.

The proceedings began with general conversation turning invariably as the room filled to religious argument. Soon a single voice, that of one or other of the leaders, rose above and dominated the hubbub to deliver what amounted to a sermon. Many of those who conducted these debates had to pay for their belief with their lives in a less tolerant world when they grew older. I who have shown none of their firmness, and cannot even make up my mind on what to stand firm, ought to be the last to deride them. Yet willing as I am to admire I cannot and never could share their assumptions. The most dangerous temptation besetting a reformer, as I know from my own experience, is to identify the reforms with himself, to cherish them as his handiwork inviolable and sacrosanct, any disparagement of which is a personal affront. It is too easy then to divide the world into black and white. There is something stifling in the society of strict enthusiasts closing their ranks in conscious rectitude against the unenlightened.

Almost the only member of the group whom I got to know well was Thomas Bilney. We became acquainted one evening when the room was particularly full and I was standing leaning against the wall. He insisted on giving up his chair to me, and before I could object he had squeezed himself into an alcove to sit on a low shelf there. He was so slight in build—his nickname, as I learnt, was Little Bilney—that he fitted in where no one else could. We left the inn together and stood talking for a time in the street before he went home to Trinity Hall and I to Jesus. But before parting we arranged to meet again, and after that I often went for walks with him by the river, a pastime more to my taste than the sessions at the White Horse.

He was much younger than I was, but I felt myself in the

presence of an older spirit. He was very earnest, almost excessively so (he had no sense of humour); but his nature was so completely free from sourness, so unwilling to judge others that I could adapt myself without oppression or impatience. At the time of our first meeting he was full of enthusiasm for the work of Erasmus, whose translation had just appeared of the New Testament into Latin from the original Greek. Bilney had managed to obtain a copy and was reading it avidly. He himself knew no Greek, and I gained prestige in his eyes when I admitted that I was learning the language and had even attended the lectures given on the subject by Erasmus in Cambridge when he was Professor of Divinity. This provoked a shower of questions, to few of which I was able to reply. Erasmus lecturing in Latin with a Dutch accent had not been easy to follow. I am afraid that it was a disappointment to Bilney that I retained less clear an impression of what the lecturer said than of his sharp pointed nose, high-pitched voice and general appearance of a disconsolate but shrewd and rather supercilious coot.

Years afterwards I met Erasmus at closer quarters when he visited me at Lambeth about the pension granted him by my predecessor Archbishop Warham. I told him of his admirer at Cambridge, and at first he was not best pleased. Battle had been joined by then between the old and the new in religion, and Bilney himself had already suffered as a heretic. Erasmus, a cautious man, was anxious not to be implicated. But suddenly, as if the name recalled something that he had heard, he smiled and his whole face was transformed, becoming understanding and gentle, while he muttered more to himself than to me in his own Latin the text from St. Paul's epistle that was always on Bilney's lips:

"This is a true saying and worthy of all men to be received, that Christ Jesus came into the world to save sinners."

It was Bilney indeed who taught me to read the Bible with understanding, and to use it as a standard by which to judge later accretions of doctrine. I have never been able to accept everything in the book as divinely inspired; many passages are mutually contradictory, others quite unintelligible, and I can sympathise with the Church in its reluctance to make it freely available to be misinterpreted by ignorance. Yet I am no less certain that the risk is worth taking, when there is so much of value of which Christians must otherwise be deprived. People should be encouraged to read the Bible, not to pick out texts to support their own prejudices or worldly interests, but to discover the nuggets of divine truth that it will yield to those who honestly seek them, gold whose gleam is recognised by the light of God shining in their hearts.

Bilney's text helped to shape and strengthen my belief in the doctrine of the Incarnation. I saw the birth of the Holy Child at Bethlehem free from incrustation of legalistic jargon and pagan symbolism. There was no bargain here, manifestly unjust, whereby the innocent suffered for the guilty, no victim to propitiate divine anger. The event was no more and no less than the Bible declares, God's revelation in the flesh of his own nature.

I owe more to Bilney than his arousing of my interest in the Bible. He himself was a living example of the validity of his ideas. One afternoon when he had pleaded an engagement that prevented him from joining me I happened to catch sight of him at the gate of the gaol. I discovered that he was a frequent visitor there comforting the prisoners, and that he was equally assiduous as a friend of the sick, even in the leper house. The poor at Cambridge had less reason to be grateful for the reluctant largesse of the clergy than for the personal care which Bilney lavished on them, listening to their troubles, cheering their despondency, bringing them small presents of food and other comforts and making up in affection for the inadequacy of his resources. If I have portrayed him at some length it is to show that not all those who frequented the White Horse were word-spinners obsessed with their own importance. Bilney had faults, but I do not think that his friends were wrong in calling him a saint. Even sanctity has its moments of weakness, of absurdity.

When Bilney suffered martyrdom more than ten years later my regard for him was increased by the very circumstances at which malice sneered. He was arrested at Ipswich where he was preaching, and brought to London on Cardinal Wolsey's orders to be tried. Wolsey was no persecutor and as long as he remained in power few heretics died at the stake. It is clear from what I heard of the trial, over which Tunstall presided as Bishop of London, that every effort was made to obtain a recantation, to avoid a death sentence. I can sympathise with Tunstall, having so often been in his position myself, desperately trying to persuade the prisoner to save his own life. There was the additional incentive that Bilney had really so little to recant. His mind had a simplicity that accepted without question the main doctrines of the Church. His only offence was to have spoken too severely against supersititious practices, the abuse in particular of images and of the worship of the saints. But there he stood firm, stubbornly refusing to retract what he had said. For hours Tunstall argued without effect, showing an invincible patience, and at last rather than admit defeat he adjourned the court so that Bilney might seek the advice of his friends. Their arguments succeeded where his own had failed. Bilney recanted.

He had to go through the humiliating ceremony at Paul's Cross, walking in front of the procession with a fagot on his shoulder and standing with it before the preacher till the sermon was over. Then he was confined in the Tower, but in less than a year he was released and allowed to return to Cambridge. Back at Trinity Hall he avoided his old companions, and I did not even know that he was there till it was too late; but those who saw him report that he was a broken man haunted by shame and penitence. He could not bear to look at his books, least of all his cherished New Testament, so bitterly they reminded him of his failure.

Then late one evening a friend met him in the street dressed as if for a journey, and when he was asked what it meant he replied with an exaltation that had long been strange to him that he was going "up to Jerusalem." He disappeared into the night, and the next heard of him was that he was travelling through the eastern counties, preaching in the fields as his licence to preach in church had been withdrawn. It was not long before he was arrested again, and this time no mercy was shown him. The relapsed heretic was condemned to be burnt. He died, it is said, with such rapture on his face as if like St. Stephen he saw heaven opened. His self-respect, his soul was restored. In a few more years all the abuses were proscribed, for denouncing which Bilney was sentenced.

My friendship with Bilney was made easier by his lack of interest in doctrinal dispute. I was unready at that time to question tradition and shrank from those who tried to thrust their opinions on me. Part of my reluctance sprang no doubt from the fact that I depended for a living on retaining my fellowship at Jesus; but I had not thought out the issues clearly enough in any case to take sides in the controversies that were debated. I preferred the company of older men, especially of Dr. Robert Ridley, a fellow of Queens', whose acquaintance I made when he was my tutor in logic. His room was a haven of orthodoxy safely cushioned from the impact of reform, and I found it very restful.

On one occasion I met his nephew Nicholas, who had come to Cambridge to visit him. He was nearly twelve years younger than myself, still attending school in the north at Newcastle-on-Tyne. Nicholas was shy in my presence, and we had little to say to each other; but I was favourably impressed by his courteous attention to his uncle, and touched by the old man's evident pride in him. When he left the room he passed out of my life for twenty years. I little guessed that when he entered it again he would become one of my closest friends, or that between us we were destined to reform the whole establishment of the Church in England. It is merciful perhaps that his uncle did not live to see this career fulfilled.

It was partly loneliness, partly a desire to assert my independence that prompted me to visit the Dolphin, a small inn in Jesus Lane. This was a very different house from the White Horse. Standing on the edge of the town it catered mostly for countrymen on their way to and from the market. As I sat listening to them I seemed to be back at the smithy at Aslockton.

At the time when I began to visit the Dolphin the French King Louis XII had just died, having been married for less than five months to our own King Henry's younger sister, Princess Mary. The marriage was unpopular in England, and its end provoked ribald jokes about elderly husbands with the implication, satisfying to national self-esteem, that England in the person of the young bride had won a suitable victory over the Frenchman.

Another sensation even more startling was to follow. I can well remember the evening when it reached the Dolphin. I was sitting listening in a corner while those around me discussed the future of the Royal widow. In the middle of the conversation a man came in who was a stranger; he remained silent at first, then as he gathered the sense of the argument he interrupted suddenly to ask whether none of us had heard the latest story current in London. His words gained him rapt attention as he announced with the pride of the informed instructing the ignorant that the "White Queen," as she was known in France, had been secretly married in Paris to the Duke of Suffolk.

The effect on the company was all that he could have wished, but the exclamations which it provoked betrayed little satisfaction with the new choice of husband for the nation's sweetheart.

This incident is engraved on my memory less because of its bearing on political events than because, almost accidentally, it brought me into contact for the first time with Joan. She was a girl in her early twenties, distantly related to the wife of the host of the inn, and she lived in the house as one of the family helping with the various duties. Her most striking feature was her jet-black hair which she wore loose over her shoulders; with her dark, almost swarthy complexion set off by a high colour it earned her from the customers whom she supplied with drinks the nickname of "Black Joan."

She was very popular among them. Without any special claim to beauty her wide mouth and fearless brown eyes were true indications of a character ready to accept everyone and everything with unfailing goodwill. To the Dolphin she was indispensable, shrinking from no work however menial when, as often happened, there was more than the meagre staff could perform. It was an advantage for this that she was powerfully built, tall and strapping. Yet there was nothing heavy in her appearance. She carried herself with a grace that delighted the eye.

I used to watch her as she came into the room with a tray of mugs and listen enviously to the exchange of raillery. She had a merry, rather saucy tongue never at a loss for an answer and well able to keep the impudent in their place. I felt as if I were an outcast contemplating across an impassable barrier a comradeship in which she and even the roughest boor were at ease, but from which I, the sober scholar, was forever excluded.

She happened to be standing near me that evening when we heard of the marriage of the Duke of Suffolk to the Queen of France, and in the hubbub that broke out I was the only person, I suppose, whom her voice could reach. So she addressed her remark to me, and I still think that it was the most sensible comment that could be made:

"A princess who doesn't want a husband chosen for her can't afford to waste time. The only safe place is in bed with the man of her choice."

In normal circumstances shyness would have prevented me from responding adequately; but I was caught out of myself, exhilarated by the feeling that we were enisled in the din around us. As we talked I forgot that I had ever been afraid to speak to her.

When I got to know her better I understood how well it was in keeping with her kindheartedness to seize the opportunity offered for that opening remark. I am sure that she had been watching me for a long time, sorry for my evident loneliness and anxious to find a way to relieve it that would not give offence. Now that we were duly acquainted she never failed to catch my eye and smile at me when she entered the room, and if she was not too busy she would come and sit beside me. Far from embarrassing, this had the effect of putting me on a surer footing with the customers at the inn. They were no longer puzzled by, suspicious of, my intrusion. They assumed, not entirely wrongly, that the purpose was Joan.

In my life hitherto there had been little contact with women. At home it was Edmund or else my father to whom I looked for companionship, and although I saw more of Alice after my father's death I reverted at Cambridge to purely male surroundings, resigned myself to celibacy. The celibate is a man who abjures not only the pleasures but the responsibilities also of an important part of human life. What understanding can he have of the problems of mankind? Is he the fittest for God's purpose who renounces the field in which it is achieved?

These questions had a peculiar urgency for me. Celibacy might be right or wrong, but it was the condition on which my place at the college depended. If I married Joan I must resign and lose my livelihood. On the other hand, if I did not, any livelihood became devoid of meaning, left with nothing but myself to support. I was certain, little as I could account for the feeling, that Joan was essential to me. My friends attributed it scornfully to physical attraction, and there was truth in much that they said; but it was not true that Joan and I had nothing in common in mind and spirit to draw us together. Even the difference of our education turned out to be less of a barrier than I feared. I found to my surprise and gratification that my intellectual interests, far from repelling her, enhanced my prestige in her eyes. For my own part I grew daily more in love with her gay lightheartedness, her courage and good nature.

When I told her of the rule of celibacy imposed by the college she was plainly astonished that I regarded it as a difficulty at all. To her the solution was obvious, for us to dispense with a marriage ceremony, and she was both puzzled and amused that I should object. But I have always been thankful that I refused to break the law of the Church, so that later when I myself had to enforce it I did not feel a hypocrite punishing others for the offence. I tried to think the issue out clearly. I believe that man was created body and soul, and that when he serves one at the expense of the other he distorts the Divine image within him. If the Church is mistaken in its praise of the ascetic, it is very right in condemning sexual promiscuity. I felt too that if I made Joan my mistress without marrying her, so as to be able to pose as a celibate, I should be defrauding the men waiting to become fellows of the college, one of whom would have the right to my place. The same difficulty arose if we contracted a secret marriage, pledging troth to each other before witnesses who could be trusted not to betray me.

I explained as much of this to Joan as I could, and she listened with easy acquiescence. She did not seem to be greatly concerned over what would happen when the college dismissed me. It was not in her nature to worry about the future. We talked sometimes of moving to Aslockton and settling on the piece of land which my father left me in his will. The idea pleased Joan, who could see herself without difficulty as a farmer's wife; but I knew in my heart that there was not land enough to support us without unremitting drudgery, and I feared even worse than the hardship the attitude of the neighbours if I returned to the country of my boyhood to live in such a style. It was painful too to contemplate leaving Cambridge which I had come to regard as a second home.

These cares were quickly forgotten in Joan's company. Her example was infectious, and I was well content to live as she did in the present, as remote from harsh reality as if we were deep in the enchanted forest of Broceliande. Few preparations were needed for our wedding. The host of the Dolphin and his wife were the only witnesses who accompanied us to the church at Barnwell Priory a mile or two out of the town, where we were married. As soon as the service was over I went straight to the Master of Jesus and told him what I had done. He accepted my resignation.

4

Joan and I were married but we had no home of our own in which to live. I had to give up my room in college and did not know where to look for another to suit our means. I had seen too much of the slums when I visited them with Bilney to be willing to expose Joan to such misery and filth. The host of the Dolphin suggested that for the time being she should live on at the inn. They were good people and asked nothing in return, but she was so ready to help whenever she was needed that the arrangement cannot have been to their disadvantage. It would have been too much however to expect them to take me in as well without payment, and I could not afford to pay the regular charge. I was lucky to find lodgings for myself with Bilney's help over a warehouse in a boatyard belonging to a man whom he had befriended in the past. The room was small and bare, but I enjoyed the view from the window beneath which the river flowed lapping against the wall.

From these lodgings it was only a short walk to the bridge, just across which stood Buckingham College, my new place of employment. My old colleagues at Jesus had been kindness itself; far from wishing to punish me for my defection they did what they could in the university to re-establish me, with the result that I was appointed a common reader here to teach novices undergoing the preliminary course in Latin grammar. Both the pay and the standard of learning were modest, but I had no right to complain. I had expected my marriage to put an end altogether to my academic career.

Buckingham was in origin a monastic foundation, but it had grown in the course of nearly a century, accepting by this time a number of secular students. It would have been better for its own sake if there had been more; they were not enough to save it when the religious houses were dissolved. I was sorry to hear

of the buildings left empty and even sorrier for the friends whom
I made there; but a few years later, I am glad to say, Lord
Audley brought most of them back when he refounded the college,
restoring the fabric and adding new. The only irretrievable loss
was the name which he changed to Magdalene. The old name
had unhappy associations since the execution of the last Duke
of Buckingham.

Although I slipped quickly enough into the routine of the
work, it was an odd and unsatisfactory way to begin married life.
I spent as much time as I could spare at the Dolphin, and owed
many excellent meals to the generosity of the house; but even
so Joan and I saw much less of each other than we wished. She
urged me to let her come and share my garret in the boatyard,
but I could not agree to that. There was no comfort, scarcely
even any furniture, and a raw damp oozed in at every chink from
the river outside. The neighbourhood moreover had none too
good a reputation, and I should have had to leave her alone there
most of the day. I assured her that the present arrangement was
only provisional and that we should soon be able to live together. We both had to exercise patience as best we could.

When I told her that our troubles would soon be over I believed what I said; but time went by, and I began to fear that
I had been too sanguine. The dilemma was hard to resolve; a
house fit for a married couple demanded a larger income, but marriage was itself an insuperable barrier to promotion in the academic
world. My brother Edmund, who had followed me to Cambridge
and was already a fellow of his college, met me one day on the
bridge as I was leaving work. He had clearly been waiting for me
there so that I should not escape him. I had avoided him since
my marriage, shrinking from contact with any of the family. I was
so sure that they would all disapprove. But when he waved his
hand and called I could not ignore him. I crossed the road to join
him, and we walked together towards the town.

As we talked I perceived how wrong I was to lack confidence
in him. We have always been a united family, and although Edmund does not share all my tastes and I often tease him for his
gravity there is a bond between us whose strength any emergency

reveals. I remember with gratitude the loyalty that he has shown me through my life, especially during the years when he was my archdeacon at Canterbury, my steadfast ally against the forces trying to subvert our policy. At the time of which I write the position was reversed, and the leading part was his; but he made it as easy as he could for me to accept advice from a younger brother. Whatever he may have thought of my behaviour he wasted no words on reproach. His whole attention was devoted to the question of saving what was left of my career. He told me that he had just received a letter from Aslockton, an answer to one which he had managed to send in charge of a man travelling that way. It shamed me to think how long it was since I myself sought news from home. If Edmund found means to overcome the difficulties of correspondence I could too; but since falling in love with Joan I had done nothing to break the silence.

I guessed that his own letter was to announce my marriage, but we spoke at first about events at home of which my mother informed us in her reply. John was married to a girl from Staveley in Derbyshire with whom everyone seemed to be pleased, and my mother had left our old house to the young couple and moved into one formerly occupied by the agent who looked after this part of the lands belonging to Welbeck Abbey. There was no resident agent any longer; one of the canons came over at intervals from the Abbey to collect the rents. Alice alone remained unmarried and lived with my mother to keep her company. It surprised me to learn that even Emmet had a husband while Alice had not. Emmet is the youngest of the family, and Alice not only her elder by more than six years but also in my opinion much the better-looking. I remarked on this to Edmund and he agreed with me. He brought out the letter from his pocket and read the relevant part aloud. It was a bare statement of fact without comment. I recognised my mother's style.

He paused in the street while he read me the letter, and when he had finished he hesitated, still holding it in his hand. A passer-by jostled him and he dropped it. I picked it up.

"You'd better read the postscript for yourself," he said. "It concerns you."

I did what he told me. The sentence was short and to the point: *"If the Abbey appoints a new agent here it might suit Tom."*
I understood Edmund's hesitation. My mother was proposing that I leave Cambridge, the academic world for good, and my heart sank at the prospect. Yet like all her ideas this abounded in common sense. It was a long way from the daydreams with which Joan and I had played, never very seriously on my own part, of retiring to Aslockton to live in a cottage, earning a meagre subsistence from the soil. Welbeck Abbey paid its agents a good salary and demanded qualifications in return, not the least of which, I had always supposed, was membership of its own order of White Canons. What chance of appointment had a layman? From my knowledge of my mother I felt sure that she would never have mentioned the possibility without satisfying herself that it was likely to be achieved.

Joan was delighted with the idea when she heard of it. She became convinced at once that its fulfilment was a foregone conclusion, and the excitement with which she began to plan our new life revealed more than she had ever admitted of her disappointment with events since our wedding. It was not in her nature to complain, and she had settled down again with apparent resignation to her old routine at the Dolphin; but it was a pitiable descent from the expectations which we both had cherished. Even I foreseeing more of the difficulties never imagined us living apart for so long, no sooner united than separated.

Seeing how my mother's letter cheered her I had not the heart to confess my own misgivings. I was ashamed of myself for hoping rather than fearing that the Abbot of Welbeck would reject my application, and little by little I grew reconciled to a change that conflicted with so many of my habits and interests. It was clear that I had to choose between Cambridge and Joan. To try to enjoy both was to retain neither. I had already lost my fellowship at Jesus, and my wife would soon tire of waiting for me. The threat of losing her came as a salutary shock, revealing how much she meant to me and how little in comparison I valued academic success. Instead of dreading exile to Aslockton I found myself looking forward to it as the beginning of domestic happiness, the vision of a home where Joan presided over a growing family of children.

Christmas was coming, and I decided to spend it in Nottinghamshire. Many years had passed since I was there last. The journey cost too much in time and money to be undertaken except at rare intervals. But now there was urgent reason to put it off no longer. Joan was pregnant, and in another month or so she would be unfit to travel. So I hired a strong horse and she and I set off together, she riding behind me on a pillion.

Looking back through the best part of four decades crowded with events I have difficulty in seeing Joan clearly as she then appeared to me. I have married twice as this story will show, and my second wife is still living. She and I have been through so much together that I can no longer adjust myself to the idea of marriage shared with anyone else. But I must put her out of my thoughts if I am to recall a true image of the past. It would be unfair to Joan and a source of confusion to draw comparisons. She cannot reasonably be judged in a setting whose emergence depended on her death. If she had lived longer my own life would have been very different. I should not have been Archbishop of Canterbury, I should not be waiting in prison in my old age to be burnt at the stake. Instead I should probably have spent the years in quiet obscurity at Aslockton, concerned with nothing graver than the problems of the farmers and cottagers placed in my charge. There would have been ample opportunity to enjoy myself with horse and longbow, to indulge my love of the country, and my intellectual interests would have withered, shared by no one around me. I wonder if I should have missed them. I am certain that I should never have sighed for the company of the eminent.

It was a destiny of this sort to which I looked forward as I rode north with Joan, and I contemplated it, if not with enthusiasm, at any rate without despondency. She herself was a powerful antidote to gloom, with her lively interest in the scene through which we travelled and her flow of comments always cheerful and amusing. I was pleased too that I was going to see my mother and Alice, so pleased that I wondered how I managed to refrain for so long. I did not feel too much anxiety about their reception of Joan.

Whatever they thought of my marriage, my mother would betray none of her feelings and Alice only such as were likely to comfort me.

We slept a night at Stamford and reached home late in the evening of the second day, so late that there was scarcely time to feel strange in the house before we went to bed. The next morning my expectations were confirmed. My mother was kind to Joan, a careful and considerate hostess particularly when I explained that a baby was on the way. Yet I knew in my heart that she did not approve of her as a daughter-in-law. I hoped that Joan did not perceive it and assured her, as I could with truth, that my mother's manner was habitually undemonstrative, but I doubt whether I succeeded in banishing the unfavourable impression. It was Alice who did most to revive Joan's spirits, letting her see that she had taken a genuine liking to her and treating her as a younger sister who shared her confidence. Alice has a nature whose warmth puts people at once at their ease.

My surprise that Alice had remained single so long turned to alarm and distress when I learnt that she was proposing to enter a religious order. I have no love of celibacy in any case, least of all for a woman so well fitted to bring happiness to the man lucky enough to marry her. I said nothing about it to Alice herself, feeling that I had no right to interfere, but one day when she was walking with Joan and me to Whatton, and we crossed the wooden bridge over the Smite, she stopped suddenly and pointed to Sir Robert's house among the trees beyond the field.

"You remember Dick?" she asked. "His younger son."

I nodded. We were fellow victims of Friar Tuck.

"Yes, of course you would," she agreed, "but you probably don't know that he was killed three years ago fighting at Flodden against the Scots. He and I were engaged to be married."

She said no more and I did not press her with questions. I guessed that she deliberately chose an occasion when Joan was present to avoid them. But I understood better the reasons that prompted her to take the veil. She gave her affections too generously to leave any for disposal elsewhere when her early love failed. She talked readily enough of her plans for a life of religion. The

Abbot of Welbeck—still our own Canon Wilkyngton—had been helpful when she applied to him, and he found a suitable house not too far off, at Stixwould in Lincolnshire, where she could undergo training to be a nun. I suspected that his exertions on her behalf were as much stimulated by her own charm as a tribute to my father's memory, and the impression was strengthened when she went on to tell me of her recent visits to the Abbey to get me myself appointed agent to administer the lands around Aslockton. This was the first that I knew of the part that she had played, and I perceived how much I owed to it. The Abbot in fact promised her that he would employ me.

The promise was kept when I went to Welbeck myself to see him. He greeted me cordially, talking of the old days at Aslockton and Whatton, and it seemed that the only question to be decided was that of the date when I should begin work. As the Abbey was in no great hurry I obtained consent without difficulty to my request for a postponement of a few months to give Buckingham College time to fill my place. I was anxious too to wait till our child was born before involving Joan in the troubles of setting up house in new surroundings. I felt sure that this was best for her, although she herself preferring to act on immediate impulse chafed at the delay. She was resolutely opposed to the idea of going back to Cambridge to fill in the time at the Dolphin, and as I had to go back myself I was at a loss to know what to do with her. I did not like to suggest that she should stay on alone at Aslockton for the rest of her pregnancy. My mother would have kept her without complaint, been a scrupulously attentive nurse, but Joan would inevitably have become aware that she was regarded as a burden.

As I worried over the problem Joan herself offered a solution. She said that she would like to join her parents in Huntingdonshire at St. Ives. It was so much the natural thing to do that it may seem odd that it had not occurred to me before; but the truth was that she spoke so little of her home, rather evading my questions about it, that I came to think that both her parents were dead and the people at the Dolphin her only living relations. When I took her to St. Ives I learnt the reason for her reticence. Her father was a cobbler living in very poor circumstances down by the bridge over the Ouse, and the cottage was so full, the quarters were so cramped that it seemed scarcely possible for anyone else to be inserted. The swarming population reminded me of the old riddle:

> As I was going to St. Ives
> I met a man with seven wives:
> Every wife had seven sacks,
> Every sack had seven cats,
> Every cat had seven kits.
> Kits, cats, sacks and wives,
> How many were there going to St. Ives?

Not of course that Joan's father had seven wives. He was a godfearing law-abiding man, and the women of all ages whom he supported were his daughters, sisters, cousins, aunts, who with as many cats and kits as the rhyme records and more, not to speak of dogs and ducks, bore witness to nothing more blameworthy than the exuberance of his hospitality. All came crowding to the door when we appeared. They greeted Joan warmly, and she herself was evidently happy to be among them. My mind was at ease when I left her in their care, impressing on them that a messenger be sent to gallop with the news to Cambridge when the birth was imminent, and giving them money to defray the cost.

Cambridge was forlorn without Joan. Time lagged when I no longer had to snatch it in precious hours as best I could to visit her at the Dolphin. I was unable even to forget her in my work which lost whatever interest it inspired now that I was so soon to abandon it altogether.

A successor was found to replace me at Buckingham, but it was agreed that he should wait till I received the summons to St. Ives. It was good of him to put my convenience before his own, and I am afraid that he suffered much trouble in consequence. The messenger came for me suddenly in the middle of the night and I left at once, pausing only outside the Buckingham gatehouse to shout till the porter awoke and looked out, and I told him to warn the new reader to take my class in the morning. Then I galloped away.

My alarm sprang less from what the messenger said than from his urgent yet furtive bearing. Indeed he hardly spoke except to tell me to make haste. When I asked after Joan he either remained silent or answered at random. He was very evidently unwilling to talk, and I gave up trying to force him. I held my thoughts tightly in check as we galloped in silence through the night along a road built long ago by the Romans relentlessly straight to the horizon across the fens. The moon had risen and shone intermittently through scudding clouds.

The distance from Cambridge to St. Ives is thirteen miles, and it is level going all the way. I do not like to urge a horse beyond its strength, but I was in no mood then to be considerate, and we seldom even dropped into a trot till we reached the bridge over the Ouse. A faint glow flickered from the window of the cottage, and as I glanced through I saw that it came from a fire piled with logs, the only illumination. I walked straight in without knocking. At first I could distinguish no one in the room in the firelight. Its former population human and animal had vanished, and the emptiness oppressed me the more because it was in such contrast with what I expected. Then I saw Joan's mother. She was standing alone in the corner beside the bed beckoning to me, and as I approached she lifted the coverlet without a word. Joan lay there motionless. She was pale, but she still retained traces of her naturally rich colouring. Her glossy black hair scattered in tangled skeins over the pillow wreathed her face like the petals of a drooping flower. Her eyes were closed, but I felt in her expression, her whole posture an unfathomable peace. She was dead.

"And the child?" I asked the old woman.

"Dead too," she told me and added dully: "It was a girl."

Among the Psalms my favourite is that which declares: "He giveth his beloved sleep." None can afford greater consolation to the mourners at a funeral, and years later I was anxious to appoint it for the purpose when I was helping to compile a book of common prayer in English on the orders of King Edward VI. I refrained for fear of offending the habits of the devout by introducing too many changes into the forms translated from Latin. So the Psalm retains its traditional place in the order of service for the last Sunday of the Church's year. As each year ends I think of Joan as I recite the verse:

"It is but lost labour that ye haste to rise up early and so late take rest, and eat the bread of carefulness, for so he giveth his beloved sleep."

I left my wife and daughter buried at St. Ives and returned to Cambridge without purpose or prospects. My successor had already taken over my Buckingham duties, and there could be no question of upsetting the arrangement. Yet I was unable to bear the thought of going to Aslockton alone to make my career there. The whole reason for the plan had been Joan, and without her every moment would be desolate. I wrote to the Abbot of Welbeck explaining what had happened and asking him to excuse me and cancel my appointment. My mind was too distracted to think clearly. I perceived only when it was too late that I had cut myself off from any means of support. The host of the Dolphin saved me from starving. He invited me to help him at the inn, not exactly to fill Joan's place but to free others for her work by performing tasks for which I myself was better suited. The house had extensive stables, and a good hiring business was done there. I was able to turn my love of horses to practical effect, exercising, feeding and grooming them. There is truth in the taunt which has been directed at me by my enemies, that I once worked as an ostler; but I see no reason to regard it as a disgrace or as evidence of any lack of learning.

Several months passed like this when a messenger came asking me to call on the Master of Jesus. I was astonished and greatly puzzled. Ever since my resignation I had avoided the college and never spoken to my friends there, fearing that it might embarrass them. There was no reason that I could imagine why the Master should want to see me now. The message arrived when I was in the stables. I told the boy working with me to finish bedding out the stall on which I was engaged, then I hurried indoors, changed my clothes, washed, and set out on my errand.

The Master received me with great kindness and made haste to relieve my curiosity by explaining why he had sent for me. But I could scarcely believe as I listened that I heard him rightly.

He told me that a resolution had been carried at a fellows' meeting to the effect that, as I was no longer a married man debarred by the rules of the college, I should be reinstated in my fellowship and allowed to enjoy the emoluments at once as a supernumerary till the next vacancy occurred. I know of no precedent to the tolerance shown by the fellows of Jesus to a delinquent. If they were guilty of irregularity they erred from an excess of charity which deserves my everlasting gratitude.

It was strange to return to the old pattern of life almost as if my marriage had never been. Instead of teaching elementary Latin as a common reader at Buckingham, or rubbing down horses in the stables at the Dolphin, I was a fellow of my college again lecturing in theology and studying myself for a doctor's degree. I felt as a man might who has been lost in a storm and finds himself suddenly transported into warmth and shelter. That is not to say that I forgot Joan or ceased to care for her. If she had lived I should have been well content with the life that we planned to share. But she was not alive. In the disaster of her death I had reason to be thankful to God and my friends for the benevolence which intervened to save me.

Hitherto, even before I fell in love, I always shrank from taking holy orders. I disapprove of compulsory celibacy, and this was no conditional rule like that of the college imposed only while the contract endured; it was a solemn obligation, any breach of which incurred the heavy penalties of the law. In my changed circumstances however there was less to deter me. I was a widower, and Joan's memory was too fresh for me to conceive it possible that I should ever marry again. If I wished to advance in my profession it was folly to remain a layman.

So I was ordained a priest. A vow was no longer demanded; it had become too often an occasion for perjury, brought into contempt by the notorious unchastity of the clergy. But when I review my subsequent conduct I cannot allow the absence of an oath to weigh in my favour. I accepted the state of celibacy at my ordination in plain and irrevocable language. My word was given before God just as much as if I had called on His name. Yet I broke it, and I was right to do so. Of that I am sure. God does not hold a man to a promise that ought never to have been made. If it is wrong to take holy orders on a condition that conflicts with the divine purpose, it cannot undo but only aggravates the wrong to persist in error.

A storm was breaking over the Church at the time of my ordination. It had been brooding for many years. Arguments like those carried on at the White Horse Inn at Cambridge were common wherever the new learning flourished. But now the accumulated dissatisfaction came to a head as if embodied in a single figure, that of the German monk Martin Luther whose fame was already spreading through Christendom. At first his attack was limited to abuses such as the sale of indulgences, which many even of the most orthodox deplored, so scandalously practice diverged from the original principle. The right of the Church to grant an indulgence resembles that of a secular court to commute severer punishment into a fine. Harm only began when the indulgence overstepped the field of ecclesiastical jurisdiction, claiming to remit the sentence for souls in purgatory. There was no limit to the price that the credulous could be persuaded to pay, no danger of their finding out in time whether the benefit was effective.

I never met Luther and only know him by repute, which gave the impression of a man of violent temperament. It is clear however that in his early struggles his mistakes were small in comparison with those of his opponents. He still professed fidelity to the Church and challenged no fundamental doctrine. Pope Leo X was most unwise, when news of the reforming movement in Saxony reached him, to reject the pacific advice of the Elector's own diplomatic agent in Rome and enforce instead the high-handed policy of the Dominicans. His unyielding attitude revealed how profitable the malpractices were, and how much the Church depended on the income that accrued. Luther's attack on indulgences became a threat to the whole authority of the Roman See.

Opinion at Cambridge was sharply divided on the issue, and as the advocates of reform grew more turbulent less willingness was shown to tolerate them. Although Papal claims and financial exactions were unpopular in England, and many Kings in the past had tried to assert independence, there was little inclination at first to follow German leadership. King Henry VIII had public opinion behind him when he wrote his treatise defending the seven sacraments and denouncing Luther, which earned from the Pope the title of Defender of the Faith. I was present myself on the occasion when Luther's works were burnt in public on Cardinal Wolsey's orders in front of St. Mary's Church. It was a magnificent bonfire fed, I suspect, to keep up the blaze with many books that had nothing to do with Luther or even with theology, and ale and other refreshments were served to the crowd at the expense of the university. All greatly enjoyed themselves except the zealots from the White Horse. When I think of the burnings that were to follow in later years my heart softens towards Wolsey, the author of that scene of innocent merrymaking. He preferred to burn books, not men.

I did my best at this time to stand aloof from the controversy. More than ever I wished to see my way clearly before taking sides. The question at issue was that of the source and extent of the authority of the Church, and I was unwilling when so much hung on the decision to accept an answer at second hand. I had to find it out for myself and the first place in which to look seemed to be the Bible, the next the works of the early Fathers who developed the Christian tradition. Till I had studied them thoroughly I felt that I was incompetent to judge. The thought occurred to me which events in later years were to ripen, that the English monarchy is as well fitted as any Italian bishop to maintain and govern the Church. Authority succeeds best in the hands of men who are in contact with local conditions, able to adapt their work to immediate needs, and religion can only be strengthened by enlisting in its support the ancient tradition of obedience owed to the Crown. In spite of the bitterness and cruelty which have been the outcome in my lifetime I still believe that this is no fundamental schism, only a redistribution of temporal functions, and that peace will be restored when men's eyes are opened to see themselves joined as closely as ever in a common faith.

Luther tried to obtain the reform of abuses within the existing organisation of the Church, and it was only when he failed that the attack was turned on the Papacy. It is a wicked error to teach that God's forgiveness can be bought for money, and it was in revolt against this that he put forward his doctrine of justification by faith. Much of the misunderstanding that has arisen about this teaching is the fault of its own advocates, some of whom talk as if faith were a possession already within their reach. They confuse it with works. A pilgrimage is performed, a mass is said, and the merits if any accruing from them is attained; but the faith that transfigures is a vision beckoning from beyond the horizon. A man's whole life is too short a time to spend on the quest.

Nearly ten years slipped quietly by in reading and learning when an event occurred which, however abortive in itself, seems now when I look back at it to have been the presage of graver distractions. The Master came up to me one morning as we were leaving chapel after the service, and he walked across with me towards my rooms.

"I've been seeing the Lord Cardinal," he told me. "He wants a few Cambridge scholars to smarten his new college at Oxford."

Dr. Capon, the Master, had been Cardinal Wolsey's chaplain, and he remained, as I knew, a close friend of his former patron. I was sure that he would be anxious to do his best to carry out the commission entrusted to him, and when he went on to suggest that I myself should be one of the chosen scholars it gratified me to think that he had a sufficiently good opinion of me. Taken by surprise and unwilling to disappoint him I accepted, but as soon as he left me and I was indoors I regretted the impulse. I was thirty-six years old, entering middle age, and my affection had struck deep roots at Cambridge. I thought of the friends whom I might never see again, of the interruption to my work, to the whole way of life to which I was accustomed. What had Oxford to offer in return for what I lost? The chance, presumably, of catching Wolsey's eye and being promoted to high office. But the prospect of office had no attraction for me, least of all under a prelate to much of whose policy I was fundamentally opposed. Wolsey embodied the attitude which seemed to me chiefly responsible for the corruption of the spirit of the Church, that which valued ecclesiastical preferment as a path to worldly success.

Yet I had gone too far in my interview with the Master to

escape with clear conscience from the undertaking. After all the kindness that he had shown me I felt that I should be guilty of the basest ingratitude. So I ordered my horse to be saddled and set out for Oxford to visit Cardinal's College to make arrangements. The way out of town was that which I trod so often in the days when I was the Buckingham reader and Joan was living at the Dolphin. As I crossed the bridge my mind was carried back into the past to a decision equally difficult which had confronted me there, and I was scarcely even surprised to see Edmund, as if my thoughts had evoked him, standing by the parapet and waving to me to stop. I reined in to the side of the road to hear what he had to say.

He told me that my friends at Jesus had been talking to him and were much disturbed at the thought of losing me. They felt that I was deserting my old college to further my ambition at Oxford. Edmund has understanding; he was well aware, I am sure, of the reluctance with which I accepted the Master's offer, and his purpose was to enable me to follow my true inclination by representing it as my duty. His tact made it easy for me to yield, convincing me as I wished to be convinced. I did nothing to resist when he took my horse by the bridle and turned its head, then walked beside me back into the town. I returned happily to my familiar rooms, settled habits, peace.

The scholars whom Dr. Capon sent earned the Cardinal's College—Christ Church, as it was called after Wolsey's fall—an alarming reputation for heresy. I do not know whether I should have followed their example if I had been among them, shared their fame while it lasted and the disgrace which many of them suffered when the climate of opinion changed. Edmund diverted me from what seemed at the time the road to advancement, and I was grateful to him, believing that my choice committed me irrevocably to a quiet backwater. So I believed too on the earlier occasion when he was a messenger tempting me with a prospect of rural obscurity with Joan at Aslockton. Events deprived me of that opportunity. They were about to intervene no less harshly again to thwart my intentions. When I turned my back on Oxford and rode home to my rooms in Jesus the direction which I took led to the see of Canterbury.

5

Rumours began to reach Cambridge of what came to be known as the King's great matter. Concern about the succession had been growing for a long time as the Queen's children died one after the other in infancy or were born dead, and the only survivor to carry on the Royal line was a daughter, the Princess Mary. No Queen had reigned in England in her own right for four hundred years, not since Matilda, daughter of King Henry I, and there was no peace in the realm while she occupied or tried to occupy the throne. The nearest parallel in recent times was equally discouraging, that of Queen Margaret's attempt to govern in the name of her poor mad husband, King Henry VI. The civil war that she provoked still rankled in people's memory. It was not surprising that they were anxious for King Henry VIII to beget a healthy son, but till now they had assumed that the mother would be Queen Catherine.

The first hint of a change in the King's attitude was a crop of stories linking the Queen's failure in childbirth with the irregularity of her marriage, when she accepted as husband a man who was already her brother-in-law. I was appalled when I heard them, amazed that the authorities did not intervene to punish those who propagated superstition defaming not only the King but also God himself. Whether or not the Royal marriage was valid, it was damnable heresy to suggest that God whose love all Christianity teaches would avenge the flaw in the ceremony by laying a curse on the woman and her innocent children. Here was a matter on which there could be no doubt, and I spoke my mind without hesitation when anyone put forward such opinions.

My disapproval was reserved for the superstitious conclusions that were drawn. I neither could nor wished to restrain the mounting flood of discussion arguing whether the Queen was lawfully the King's wife. It was plain that the issue would never have attained such publicity if uncertainty had not arisen in the King's own mind. When one examined the arguments they showed that the objection to the marriage was not without weight. In the year 1501 Princess Catherine, as she then was, came to England from Spain to marry Arthur, Prince of Wales, the eldest son of King Henry VII and heir to the throne. The wedding duly took place, and the young couple went as man and wife to live at Ludlow in their own principality of Wales. Six months later the prince died of the plague. He was only fifteen years old, and his widow sixteen.

No one can feel anything but compassion for the princess left a widow so young in a strange land. She begged her father to let her come home, but she was caught in the cruel web of international politics. Her father-in-law, the King of England, was unwilling to give back the part of her dowry that had already been paid; her father, the King of Spain, still hankered after the English alliance. The two Kings adjusted their interests at her expense by agreeing that she should marry her husband's brother, Henry, the new heir to the English Crown, a boy nearly six years younger than herself. As the proposed alliance fell of course within the degrees prohibited to matrimony a dispensation was sought and obtained from Pope Julius II, on the ground that this was the only way to avert a war between Spain and England. There is no evidence that any danger of such a war existed.

No immediate marriage followed the betrothal. Prince Henry was too young at the time, and later, as has since been revealed, he himself protested against the match chosen for him. It was not till after his father's death and his own accession that he and Princess Catherine were married. I do not know what made him change his mind about her. Perhaps she won his affection and confidence as he met her in the daily routine of the court while he was growing up. Perhaps there was a political motive also, the hope that the Spanish King, becoming his father-in-law, would help him to realise his dream of reconquering the Plantagenet heritage in France. I have heard him say himself that when he was crowned at the age of eighteen his head was full of the exploits of the Black Prince and King Henry V, whom he longed to emulate. He used to add that he owed gratitude to King Ferdinand of Spain whose treachery shattered his illusions and taught him wisdom.

The marriage had lasted for eighteen years, and the King was now thirty-six years old, the Queen forty-two. Ill-informed opinion has assumed the cause of their estrangement to be simply that the King grew tired of an ageing and ailing wife, and that a younger face attracted him. I myself believe this assumption to be false. King Henry VIII had his full share of human weakness, but he was not inconstant in his affections. When one considers how searching is the light that shines on the doings of Kings it is remarkable that up to this time only a single Royal mistress is known, the Lady Tailbois whom he met on a short visit to Calais and who became the mother of his illegitimate son, the Duke of Richmond. It is true of course that when he was persuaded of the invalidity of his marriage he fell in love with Lady Anne Boleyn; but on this as on subsequent occasions his behaviour was that of a man to whom marriage is a binding sacrament, and who enters it always with the hope unshaken by disappointment that at last its blessing will be fulfilled.

I point this out not to excuse his motives but to clarify them, so that the course of events may be understood. I am sure that, whatever he may have thought, said and done later in the bitterness of controversy, he spoke nothing but the truth when he assured me of his attachment to Queen Catherine and his willingness, if she were truly his wife, to remain married to her till death. He disliked change, clung to settled habits and to the woman who was associated with them; but the dominant emotion in his nature, to which everything else had to yield, was pride in the dynasty that his father founded. However mixed this passion might be with vanity and personal ambition, it drew inspiration also from a true regard for the welfare of his people, to whom the dynasty gave order and peace. When Queen Catherine failed to provide a male heir, and it was unlikely that she could ever do so, he was wounded in the most sensitive part of his soul, and fear combined with conscience to remind him of the words of the Book of Leviticus:

"If a man shall take his brother's wife it is an unclean thing; he hath uncovered his brother's nakedness, they shall be childless."

They were words shortly to echo through the courts of Europe. I am afraid that King Henry was impressed not only by their undoubted bearing on canon law but also by the superstitious construction which appealed to his sense of guilt.

Once the validity of the King's marriage was called in question it could not be left in suspense; the interests of the whole nation were too closely affected. The French envoys, it was learnt, expressed doubts of the little Princess Mary's legitimacy during the negotiations for her betrothal to their King Francis or to one of his sons. The news provoked indignation, but it also sharpened anxiety that an issue so productive of embarrassment should be quickly settled. Queen Catherine herself was well enough liked in England. Sincere sympathy was expressed for her, but it was taken for granted that if the marriage were annulled she would accept the decision and retire gracefully.

I listened to many discussions of this question in hall at Jesus and in my friends' rooms, and I tried to think it out for myself; but my attention was rather fully occupied at the time with private duties which I had taken on in addition to my ordinary work. An old acquaintance John Cressy, related to our family by marriage, lived at Waltham in Essex. I did not see him often as his home was so far off, and I was surprised when he called on me one day at Cambridge bringing two boys whom he introduced as his sons. He explained that as there was only a year and a half between them he was sending them up together to the university and had entered them both at Jesus, and he asked me to take them under my care and give them private tuition. I was not very eager, having little leisure to spare; but I did not like to disappoint Cressy, who was after all a kinsman, and his sons made a favourable impression, intelligent-looking and well-behaved.

My hopes were confirmed when they began work with me. They were admirable pupils, and I took pleasure in applying the ideas on education fermenting in my mind, sown there originally by my revolt against Friar Tuck.

Their studies in which they were making good progress were interrupted in the spring by a severe outbreak of plague, which spread so alarmingly in Cambridge that I sent word to their father advising him to remove them till the danger of infection abated. He came in person in answer to my message to take them back with him to Waltham, and he begged me to accompany them myself to continue my tuition there. I cannot pretend that I was sorry to have an excuse to escape from Cambridge in such circumstances, and the college gave me leave without difficulty; so many had fled already that the lecture room was all but emptied. Nonetheless I was ashamed of my flight, feeling sure that Bilney would be staying to visit and comfort the sick.

In spite of misgivings I enjoyed the journey to Essex. It was a lovely morning in early May when we set out, and riding hard we covered the forty-five miles or so before the last glow died out of the clear sky. The two boys were in high spirits at the thought of going home, and Cressy's own demeanour betrayed overwhelming relief. He confessed to me that on his way to Cambridge he imagined them both already in their graves.

We have a word in the country to describe a day of unseasonably fine weather; we call it a "weather-breeder," believing that it is the presage of a storm. I look back on the peaceful happiness of that day when I rode with Cressy and the boys from Cambridge to Waltham as on a weather-breeder in the emotional sense. It stands out the more vividly in my memory by contrast with the blizzard of worldly agitation in which I was shortly to be caught.

Yet the first few months at Waltham were quiet enough. Cressy's house was in a square called Romeland (the rents, I believe, were charged with the payment of Papal dues), facing the main gate of the Abbey. I had never lived at close quarters before with a great religious house, and I was surprised to find it so much the hub of society and commerce. In addition to the crowds of servants and tradesmen hurrying to and fro on errands between the Abbey and the town there were frequent visitors, merchants, knights, nobles, arriving at all hours of the day with the retinue appropriate to their rank to do business or seek hospitality.

A day came when greater multitudes even than usual filled the street below us, and there were soldiers, armed bowmen, mixed with the citizens. The rumour spread that the King himself was on his way here to stay at the Abbey, as he had been known to do before on hunting expeditions in Epping forest. When the news reached my pupils nothing could hold them to Latin literature, not even Orpheus calling in the underworld to his lost Eurydice. At last I gave up the effort and closed the book. We crowded into the bay of the window, all three of us, and leant out to watch.

No one in Waltham can have enjoyed a better view of the procession which rode by directly under our eyes. Although I had never seen the King before I knew at once that it was he. It was not only because of the magnificence of his dress, the scarlet doublet beneath the open hunting cloak, the chain of gold round his neck, or even because his face so closely resembled the descriptions given me, square and heavy but still fresh-complexioned in his late thirties, framed in the golden-red beard whose colour all fashionable society strove to imitate. The unmistakable sign proclaiming his identity was revealed in his bearing, that mixture of geniality and assured, at times arrogant dignity with which I was to grow familiar.

He engaged so much of my attention that I had little to spare for his companions, whether ecclesiastics or secular nobility; but my eye was caught and my curiosity aroused by the girl riding at his side, whom I guessed to be Lady Anne Boleyn herself. Her face was hidden by the King's broad shoulders, but I had a glimpse of dark brown hair under the brim of her high-crowned hat and of her figure erect and shapely in her close-fitting green riding habit. She and the King seemed to be engrossed in each other, talking in low tones, but as she passed under my window she laughed suddenly and I heard her say: "Witches die young." Her voice was deep and melodious, yet there was something in her laughter from which I shrank, an echo of the wilds as of the wind and the rain in its gaiety. I do not know how the King replied. Already they were out of earshot, and in another moment they disappeared from my sight beneath the arched gateway of the Abbey.

The long cavalcade streamed slowly after them till only the onlookers remained in the street. My pupils feeling that there was no more to see, but much to hear, jumped up and ran out of doors; but downstairs they received news which sent them hurrying back, anxious to be the first to inform me. A messenger had come from the Abbey, they announced, to seek hospitality for two of the King's secretaries, as the Abbot had more guests than he could accommodate and wished to lodge the remainder in the town in houses of good standing. It was a compliment to Cressy to be chosen, and there could be no doubt of his willing consent. For the rest of the day I could hear the bustle of the maids getting the rooms ready, but it was not till supper that I met our visitors or learnt who they were.

They were already sitting at the table as I came into the room, and Cressy introduced me; but the ceremony was unnecessary. I recognised them at once as old acquaintances from Cambridge, Edward Fox and Stephen Gardiner. Fox was several years younger, Gardiner a little older than myself; but both had risen to the headship of their respective colleges—Fox at King's, Gardiner at Trinity Hall—and both had been promoted by Cardinal Wolsey to responsible positions in his service, from which they passed into positions of still greater importance under the King. I had not seen either for a long time and was doubtful at first what they would make of me. However content one may be to do without worldly success, it is difficult to avoid a feeling of embarrassment in the company of the more successful. My fears however were groundless. Edward Fox was the most tactful of men, and he put me at my ease at once while he asked after mutual friends at Cambridge. I did not know him very well in those days, but later in our lives we became better acquainted when as Bishop of Hereford he was my colleague to carry out the King's policy in the Church. Beneath his suave manner I found a keen intellect and practical ability, qualities which I valued the more in him because his ideas were developing in the same direction as mine. His death at the early age of forty-two was a grave loss to the cause of religious reform.

To do justice to Gardiner, he was equally amiable at that supper party. He could be excellent company when he was in a good humour, and his amusing tongue kept both Cressy and me entertained. If I seem half-hearted in his praise it is because he lived to become my most formidable opponent when he occupied the see of Winchester, and I of Canterbury. Active disagreement tends to blind one to a man's virtues. Yet Gardiner and I were at one on a fundamental principle, the need of authority to provide shelter for human values to thrive. Where we differed was that he feared any change as a threat to stability, while my own view is that authority becomes more stable by adapting itself to changed conditions.

It is true that he accepted the King's supremacy in the Church and was as outspoken as any of us in denouncing the claims of the Pope, supporting his arguments with precedents going back to the Norman Conquest. It is not to sneer at him that I add that any other attitude would have been incompatible with a successful career. He was a sincere and conscientious man, but on an issue where the scales were nearly balanced he convinced himself that they veered in the direction most convenient to his ambition.

It would indeed have been a shame for his ambition to lack fulfilment, so outstanding was his ability both in diplomacy and in administration. Those who describe him as a masterful politician with a choleric temper speak the truth, but there was another side also to his character. The relentless enemy of heresy was the most merciful of judges to the heretic. He would implore the prisoner with tears in his eyes to recant and save his life, and when all efforts failed against the obduracy of the other's conviction he still sought and often found excuses to let the man go free. He drew his bow not against the hinds and fawns but against the "head deer," among whom, in later years, he regarded me as the stag.

This lay far in the future when young Stephen Gardiner, the King's rising secretary, greeted me at Cressy's supper table. The conversation turned inevitably, as in almost every company at the time, to the King's great matter, the progress of his negotiations for annulment of his marriage. About a year before this the efforts of the English emissaries had at last persuaded Pope

Clement VII to appoint a commission to sit in England to examine the validity of the dispensation given by his predecessor Julius II to enable Prince Henry to marry his sister-in-law. Cardinal Wolsey was one member of the commission and the Italian Cardinal Campeggio the other. They set up their court at Black-friars; but the proceedings dragged on and on, until the Pope recalled the case to Rome, and withdrew the authority of the commission. Gardiner told us of the King's indignation when the news reached him. He described the outburst of rage so vividly that I trembled in sympathy with the messenger. It was to seek distraction, to soothe disappointment, that the Royal party set out on this hunting expedition.

I knew enough of the circumstances to understand the feelings of all concerned. The King was aggrieved with the Pope for with-holding a favour granted to so many others often on the flimsiest grounds. The Pope however dared not offend the Emperor Charles V, whose army had only recently stormed and sacked the city of Rome, holding the Papal court prisoner. Queen Catherine was the Emperor's aunt. If I seem to disregard Queen Catherine's own feelings it is not from any lack of compassion, but the King had convinced himself that he was living with her in sin, and even if I had known him as well then as I came to do later I should have been helpless against the strength of his obsession. The breach between husband and wife was past healing.

Legally the King's case seems to me and always has seemed unanswerable. All that he asked the Pope was to enforce the law as it had been accepted for centuries throughout Christendom. A Papal dispensation can set aside a rule of the Church, but it has no power to authorise disobedience to the word of God re-vealed and defined in the Bible. In my own mind I have grave doubts increasing as I grow older of the divine inspiration of the ancient law of the Jews; but no such line of escape was open to the Roman lawyers (they would have condemned it of course as heresy) when they mustered their arguments against King Henry. On their own terms of reference the text which I have quoted from the Book of Leviticus is sacrosanct. It was their task to show that it did not apply to the marriage of Henry and Catherine.

The best support that they could find is drawn from the Book of Deuteronomy, the passage familiar from the use made of it by the Pharisees on a well-known occasion in the New Testament:

"If brethren dwell together, and one of them die and have no child, the wife of the dead shall not marry without unto a stranger: her husband's brother shall go in unto her and take her to him to wife."

The prohibition is absolute in the Book of Leviticus; but it can be argued with reason that the words are modified by those of Deuteronomy, and that a clearly defined exception is made there to the rule. The conditions to be fulfilled are that the brothers have been living together in a single household, and that the firstborn child of the marriage "shall succeed in the name of his brother which is dead, that his name be not put out of Israel." They are conditions appropriate to a family whose members living in community are anxious each to perpetuate his own line. Nothing resembling such a custom exists in England, least of all in the Royal House. If the principle of Deuteronomy had been applied Princess Mary should have been regarded as daughter of Prince Arthur, becoming Queen in place of King Henry VIII.

Gardiner, who had a keen mind for legal subtleties, showed great interest when I put these arguments to him. Nevertheless I had the impression that he was displeased, deliberately looking for a flaw. His attitude disconcerted me at the time and sapped my confidence; only later when I got to know him better I understood the cause of it. Nothing was ever to his liking unless he was the author of it himself. Edward Fox seemed to perceive my disappointment. He went out of his way to express his agreement with me in the most flattering terms. While I was grateful for his praise I attributed it to an amiable desire to comfort me; but I misjudged him as I was soon to find out. It was his habit to clothe whatever he said in suavity, but it was not his habit to say what he did not believe.

Our conversation turned from the arguments themselves to their chance of prevailing. We all agreed that an impartial hearing was unlikely from a court held at Rome, still cowed by the memory of the outrages committed by the Emperor's army. I asked why the King did not seek a decision on his case from the principal universities of Europe. Although the Pope was not obliged to follow their judgment, it would be embarrassing for him too openly to ignore voices traditionally regarded as the source of authoritative learning. Gardiner replied that this had already been considered, but that in his own view nothing would come of it as the universities would echo whatever their secular rulers commanded. His cynicism rather offended me. I may have been too naïve in my faith in the integrity of theologians, yet I knew from my own experience how much scholarship becomes a habit to those absorbed in it, so that they are almost as unable to depart from its findings as a machine to refuse to obey its own laws of motion. Fox supported me readily. He seemed indeed to be as much drawn to the idea as I was, and he insisted that it ought to be given fair trial. As we discussed it our eagerness increased. We both thought that with a sufficient number of favourable and influential answers the King might even act on the verdict without waiting for the Pope.

Next morning recalling what I had said I was afraid that I had been presumptuous, thrusting my views on men much better versed than I was in affairs of state; but the day's routine claimed my attention, the boys had to have their lessons, and I put the matter out of my mind. We were already at our books when a servant came to the door to tell me that I was wanted downstairs. An officer of the King's bodyguard was waiting in the hall, with an escort of archers outside. I accompanied them in a state of mingled fear and bewilderment, unable to think what I could have done to provoke the summons.

They led me across the street and under the gateway into the Abbey. The courtyard was full of people, mainly on horseback, waiting to set forth on the hunt. Even dressed as they were for sport and exercise the great lords were easy to distinguish by the magnificence of their jewels and bright colours. If I had been less concerned about my own destination I should have taken a delighted interest in observing at close quarters so many of the most notable men in the land. They themselves eyed us with curiosity, but they made way for us to pass in deference to the Royal arms worn by the soldiers. We reached the entrance of the Abbot's house, the officer signed to the escort to wait, and he and I went in alone.

Although the month was August the morning was dull and cold, and a bright fire burnt in the room into which I was shown. A man sat there in a scarlet doublet. His cloak was thrown over a chair, his riding switch with gold-embossed handle lay on the table. He was booted and spurred ready for hunting. I recognised the King and dropped to my knees in homage.

He waited to speak till he had dismissed the officer and we were alone. Then he told me to rise, and his voice was pleasant and easy, almost conversational, as if he took his dignity for granted and had no need to insist on it. That was his habit as long as I knew him, and it never failed to evoke my affection. He liked to talk as man to man, mind to mind, not as monarch to subject. I need hardly add that, if anyone presumed on this familiarity to a degree inconsistent with respect, he learnt quickly and to his cost that he was in the presence of the King of England. No one could be more affable than King Henry when he wished, no one more formidable in his anger.

He told me that he had heard from Edward Fox of our conversation at supper and that he was greatly interested in my arguments, particularly my construction of the text from the Book of Deuteronomy. To my surprise (I had yet to learn that he was an excellent scholar) he quoted the passage in full, as if turning it over in his mind. Then he asked me whether I really thought that his marriage would have satisfied the injunction if on the birth of a child to the Queen he had acknowledged it by legal fiction as his brother Arthur's, and if so whether the duty applied to the firstborn alone. I told him that as the purpose was to ensure his brother's line the duty persisted till a child survived. He laughed at this and replied that what I said strengthened the ground on which he claimed annulment. Who believed that when he married his sister-in-law he was willing to yield his place for a daughter to sit on the throne?

At this point a young woman joined us from an inner room.

She also was dressed for riding, the same who rode beside him when I watched the procession through the town, Lady Anne Boleyn.

"They're all waiting for us, sir," she told him.

I noticed how his face lit with pleasure as he glanced at her, but his voice was grave, almost reproving:

"Let them wait, sweetheart. This man's words are worth more than a day's hunting. He has the sow by the right ear."

Her eyes rested on me with interest, black eyes extraordinarily bright as if her soul gleamed naked in every change of their expression. I have heard men speak disparagingly of her beauty, denying either symmetry to her features or delicacy to her complexion. Whether they judged rightly I do not know. In her presence I was conscious of nothing but the spirit now mocking, now brooding, reflected in the brilliance of her eyes and in the curve of her wide lips when she smiled. If it was not beauty it was certainly enchantment.

She said nothing to me at that first meeting, yet I felt that her impression was favourable and that if need arose she was my friend. Such feelings come without either reason or volition. I did not really expect ever to meet her again, not even when the King rose suddenly to his feet and turned to me, grasping his cloak and whip:

"No," he exclaimed. "What's the hurry? Rome wasn't built in a day. Go away now, and I'll send for you when I get back to Greenwich."

He moved towards the inner door, and I knelt as they both left the room. Then I waited uncertainly for someone to show me out, but as no one came I went at last by myself and found my own way through the house and out of doors. The courtyard was full of movement and bustle, and I guessed that the King had mounted. The procession was already streaming out under the gateway. I stood on the steps of the Abbot's house and watched them. When all had gone I followed them into the street.

Cressy was anxious to know on my return why I had been summoned to the Abbey, but I told him no more than that it was for further discussion of our evening's argument. He assumed, as

I intended, that I had visited one of the secretaries, some colleague whose interest Fox or Gardiner had aroused. I did not
tell anyone that I had spoken to the King. I tried to forget it
too, but I did not succeed. Lady Anne's eyes persisted undimmed
in my memory.

6

When the message reached me from the King summoning me to his palace at Greenwich I was at Aslockton for my mother's funeral. Her last years had been spent in our old home with John and his wife Joan looking after her. She was very unwilling at first to be dependent on them, and for some time after Alice's departure for Stixwould Priory she insisted on living alone; but the new agent appointed from Welbeck in my place wanted the house, and she had to give it up. When the change was made she accepted it with her habitual composure.

The whole family attended the funeral, but most of them left to return home immediately afterwards. Only Alice and I stayed on for a few days, I to help John over legal business arising from our mother's death, Alice for no other reason, I believe, than to keep me company. She seemed to be given as much freedom as she wished by her prioress, evidence of the regard in which she was held, although her position was only that of sacristan in charge of the vestments and other utensils of worship. She and I had been for my favourite walk to the old earthwork with the view of Aslockton on one side and of Whatton on the other across the little river. As I looked towards Aslockton I saw a horseman galloping along the road, and my heart sank in premonition. I seemed to know whom he was seeking and what he wanted.

I had grounds for my apprehension. During the last few months much had happened to warn me that my visit to Waltham Abbey was destined to bear fruit. Soon after my return to Cambridge a formal discussion was ordered by the university (acting of course on higher orders still) between twelve doctors of divinity, six from Cambridge and six from Oxford, who were asked to examine the validity of the Royal marriage. It was a step that followed so closely the lines of my conversation with the King that I could not doubt its connection, and I was told in fact that my name was among those chosen to take part. Unfortunately when the time came for the hearing I was ill and unable to be present. A decision was given finding the marriage valid. I was much distressed when I learnt this, as I felt that many arguments which I could have put forward had either been ignored altogether or inadequately explained. The Oxford members of the panel had already left, but I visited each of the Cambridge men in turn to bring them round to my point of view. With five of them I was successful; they acknowledged that their judgment had been wrong, and they were so honest in their regret that they signed a joint letter to the King's council announcing their change of mind.

Naturally I was glad to have persuaded them. Not only was my success likely, as I hoped, to be a useful service to the King, it was also, I must admit, gratifying to my vanity. Yet a nagging fear haunted me, that of being drawn into affairs of State incompatible with the academic quiet which I cherished. The danger might seem remote in view of the obscurity in which I lived; but I remembered how the King had said that he would send for me to Greenwich, and I was no longer as convinced as before that he spoke lightly.

I was right in divining the messenger's errand. He brought an order from the King summoning me at once to Greenwich Palace. Alone with Alice I gave free expression to the fears which the news aroused in me. I explained to her how happy I was at Cambridge and how much I longed to spend the rest of my life there. She listened to my complaints with patience, but when I finished she spoke with a bluntness that reminded me of our mother. It was cowardice, she told me, fear of action and decision that made me shrink from playing my part in the world. If I sincerely believed that my arguments could be useful to the King I was untrue to both mind and soul in seeking to be excused. I was the more impressed by the honesty of her advice because I knew that her own inclination prejudiced her in favour of Queen Catherine.

That interview with the King was the beginning of the political

career from which I shrank so obstinately. Yet it has always remained a happy memory. I saw him alone, and he was as genial as
he had been at Waltham but less hurried. We went over the whole
ground on which he sought annulment of his marriage, and he
showed particular interest in the arguments with which I converted the divines who decided against him at Cambridge. It
was on this occasion that he spoke to me of his love and respect
for Queen Catherine, and I believed and still believe that he
was sincere. Many have scoffed at me for this belief, quoting
examples of his callous behaviour to her, the enforced separation
from her daughter, the banishment from the house of her choice.
I neither deny the charges nor defend the actions. There were
two men in King Henry or perhaps I should say a man and a
beast, and when the beast took control the man was powerless.
Afterwards when the man prevailed again he wanted to forget
what he had done, and was surprised and offended to find that
the victims, those who survived, held it against him.

My affection for him could never have lasted as it did if I had
not been aware of the two sides to his character, recognising his
true self in the one, an obsessive demon in the other. If one were
unable to distinguish a man from his faults one would never like
anybody. His salient quality in my eyes, impressing me the more
the longer I knew him, was his passionate desire for creative
achievement. This was not only the means of self-aggrandisement,
there was present also a genuine impulse to devote his life to a
cause greater than himself. Stephen Gardiner was a shrewd judge
when he advised the Imperial ambassador that the way to entice
King Henry into an alliance was to persuade him that the effect
would be to cure the ills of Christendom.

Many of the dreams which the King cherished in his youth
faded with age and experience; but there was one which he never
abandoned, that of completing the work begun by his father, the
establishment of secure peace and prosperity in England under the
Tudor dynasty. It was the purpose that lay nearest his heart, and
his conviction of its beneficence made him the more ruthless when
it was frustrated by the Queen's failure to give him a male heir.
The setback not only disappointed, it also frightened him. He at-

tributed his plight for the reason that I have explained to divine anger. There was a perpetual conflict in his mind between the rational and the superstitious. I have often thought that the theological argument in which he excelled chiefly attracted him because its dry logic hid the terrors looming for him in the gulf beneath.

In spite of his strength of will he was a man who needed reassurance, and incongruous as it may seem I believe that I was able however inadequately to supply it, so that he found relief in my company. The feeling that I could help him drew me to him and enabled me to sympathise in his troubles, even those of his own making. His designs had a nobility and magnanimity which not even the violence of his self-will could entirely eliminate.

In addition he had great personal charm when he was in a mood to exert it. The effect of that interview at Greenwich was to reconcile me more than I should have thought possible to the prospect of working in his service. He wished me to write a book setting out his case for the annulment of his marriage, so that the arguments could be submitted in convenient form to the universities for their verdict (the debate which had already taken place at Cambridge was only, so to speak, a rehearsal, not intended to be a final expression of academic opinion). As he was in a hurry for the book to be ready it was arranged that I should write it in London, with no other duties to distract me and easy access to his presence if I needed to consult him. I must admit that it greatly helped to banish my reluctance that I was to live and work at Durham House, the London home of the Boleyn family. I hoped that opportunity would be afforded not only for ecclesiastical research but also to become better acquainted with Lady Anne.

At first however my hopes were disappointed. She was too busy at court to come often to visit her father and stepmother, and as I myself spent most of my time working in my room I was unlikely to meet her if she happened to call in. The few occasions when chance was favourable, when for instance she stayed to dinner, gave me all the greater joy for their unexpectedness. Later I was to see more of her, but my feelings towards her never changed. She had the gift of transfiguring any gathering of people in which she was present, rather as the colours of a landscape spring to life when the sun touches them.

Durham House stands with gardens running down to the Thames on the north bank about halfway between Westminster and the Temple. This whole reach of the river is fringed with great houses; but behind them lies open country well stocked with game. My own room faced south, and I was able in the intervals of work to watch the stream of boats passing to and fro beneath me.

On fine afternoons I used to walk down to the shore to enjoy a closer view, and often my host came to join me. He was a man in the early fifties, holding high office in the State; a few weeks after my arrival he was created Earl of Wiltshire, a title that had become extinct in his mother's family and was revived for his benefit. Since his death his reputation has suffered from the malice of his enemies, who attribute his promotion to his daughter's influence with the King. There is enough truth in this to injure him, enough untruth to do him grave injustice. His career began in the reign of the old King Henry VII when he fought at his father's side against the Cornish rebels. After that his talents won swift recognition, and although he derived no immediate advantage from his marriage to Lady Elizabeth Howard, as her family was in disgrace having chosen the losing side at the battle of Bosworth, he shared the good fortune that followed the Royal pardon granted later to the head of the house and the restoration of its titles. It could not fail to help Thomas Boleyn, an impecunious second son, when his father-in-law was reinstated as Earl of Surrey, then as Duke of Norfolk in reward for his victory over the Scots at Flodden.

But if he owed much to his wife's relations, he owed still more to his own ability, to his agile intelligence with its sure grasp of detail and the liveliness and variety of his interests. I have seen a letter in which Erasmus describes him as "almost the only man of learning among the nobility, with a mind trained in philosophy," and as I stood with him talking by the river I could understand what it was that drew Erasmus to him and confirmed their friendship. His conversation was always well informed, and he enjoyed discussing matters of weight; but he had the art of presenting his ideas in an entertaining manner.

When we were together the subject often turned to foreign affairs about which he had intimate knowledge. He spoke French fluently and for that reason was commonly chosen to lead any mission sent abroad. The arrangements were in his hands on the famous occasion known as the Field of the Cloth of Gold when the English and French Kings celebrated their reconciliation at a meeting outside Calais, and shortly afterwards he accompanied King Henry to a less public conference with France's rival, the Emperor Charles. His account of these events which lost nothing in the telling transported me into a world as remote from Aslockton and Cambridge as if it had lain on the farther shore of the ocean like the fabulous empire of Montezuma recently discovered by the Spaniards. Since then I have visited many of the places which he described and taken part myself in their life. The experience, as was to be expected, brought disenchantment. Yet in memory I still recapture the mood of wonder and delight with which I listened to his stories. He had the gift shared by his daughter of investing what he said and did with a mysterious fascination.

I am too conscious of my own very different sins to condemn Lord Wiltshire for his ambition. What I regretted much more, if only because of the harm that it did him, was his habit of reckless jubilation when things were going well, an overweening confidence unable to believe that the sun would ever stop shining. This quality also his daughter inherited. There was nothing cold in their arrogance, they were never disdainful to their friends; but their triumph often offended good taste and earned them many enemies by its exuberance. I am afraid that the story is true that on the night after Wolsey's death the French ambassador was entertained at Durham House to a dramatic performance, a farce describing the reception of the fallen Cardinal in hell. It is no excuse to add that Wolsey did great disservice in his lifetime to the Boleyns.

Lord Wiltshire's first wife died before I met him, and I cannot say whether he married her for her rank; but no suspicion of the sort could attach to his second marriage. Everyone was very silent about Lady Wiltshire's parentage, but it was obvious when she spoke in her broad Norfolk accent that she came from a humbler level of society than her husband. She was a great deal younger than he was, a tall fair large-boned woman still retaining much of the comeliness which she must have possessed as a girl. Her usual temper was placid and amiable, and she was on the best of terms with her elder stepdaughter, Anne, whom she admired with disarming simplicity and who showed her much affection in return. She was also very popular with the King, whom she amused by her racy sense of humour.

The only member of the family with whom she had difficulty was her younger stepdaughter, Mary, a widow left almost penniless with two small children since the death of her husband, William Carey, in the epidemic of plague the year before. Lady Wiltshire had opposed the marriage from the outset as Carey had little means beyond what he drew from his office at court. Mary however had her full share of the impulsiveness that ran in the family. She defied her stepmother and maintained her independence for eight years as Carey's wife. I do not know to what period the gossip refers which accuses her of becoming the King's mistress. No evidence has ever been offered, as far as I am aware, that seriously disparages her virtue, and my own opinion is that the whole is a baseless calumny. I am convinced in any case that, even if there is a shred of truth in it, the affair took place while she was unmarried and was of short duration. She was devoted to Carey and utterly forlorn at his death.

Her sorrow was sharpened by anxiety for herself and her children. Having asserted her freedom so boldly she shrank from the humiliation of returning home to beg for shelter. I had the story from her own mouth, and she said little about the attitude taken by her father and stepmother, but my impression was that they were less willing than she hoped to forgive and forget. Her sister however stood by her and spoke about it to the King, asking him to help; it was the result of his intervention that Mary was received back at Durham House. She was given a suite of rooms there for herself and her children but seemed to spend most of her time with the family, fully restored to favour with her father if not with her stepmother.

Mary Carey had none of her sister's force of personality, but she was probably the better-looking of the two. They were indeed sharply contrasted; Mary's hair was very fair, almost corn-coloured, her eyes were blue, and her face with its soft curves and clear complexion had an endearing but rather helpless gentleness. Perhaps their very difference drew them together.

I wish that I could say their affection remained unbroken to the end, but the truth is that soon after Anne became Queen an event occurred which caused a bitter estrangement. Mary fell in love with William Stafford, an officer of the garrison at Calais, and knowing that everyone would regard the match as unsuitable she did just what she had done before, left home suddenly without a word and married him. Her offence was aggravated on this occasion by the fact that she was the Queen's sister and her marriage needed the King's consent as well as her father's. She and her husband incurred deep disgrace, and he was in danger of being stripped of his rank and commission. In her extremity she appealed to Cromwell to intercede for her with the King and Queen. I have seen the letter that she wrote. She expresses great penitence and humility, but there is a sentence about her husband in which her natural spirit asserts itself, so that I can almost hear the tone of her voice:

"If I might choose, I assure you, Master Secretary, I had rather beg my bread with him than be the greatest Queen christened."

There was an indomitable quality in Mary, and however erratic her escapades I could not help secretly admiring her for them.

Stafford escaped punishment, and if the Queen had had time I hope and believe from what I know of her that her anger with her sister would have melted. It grieves me to think that when that last morning of her life broke in desolation and terror they were still unreconciled.

The only member of the family of whom I have said nothing so far is her brother, older by a year or so, George Lord Rochford. I was to see a great deal of him later and enjoy his friendship, but on this first visit of mine to Durham House we did not meet as he had gone to take up his appointment as ambassador to the King of France. The envious grumbled at the choice of so young a man for a responsible post; but he spoke excellent French, was intelligent, lively and accomplished. There were good reasons more-over at this time for England to be represented in Paris by a man who was wholeheartedly in sympathy with King Henry's policy. Al-though Wolsey had fallen from power and was in disgrace he had not given up hope of regaining Royal favour, and as he was a stubborn enemy of the Boleyns his restoration was likely to be at their expense. Many of his intrigues had their centre in France, where his agents were bargaining to obtain French support for the dismissal of Queen Catherine on condition that her place was taken by the French King's unmarried sister-in-law, Catherine Renée, daughter of Louis XII. I feel sure myself that King Henry was too much in love with Lady Anne to agree to such a proposal, apart from the fact that the French princess was distressingly plain. It was a relief nonetheless to know that Lord Rochford was on the spot to watch and frustrate the design.

Perhaps I judge Wolsey's motives too harshly. For twenty years he had ruled without a rival as chief minister of the Crown. It was a cruel experience for a man as ambitious as he was to be overthrown and see his work undone by a girl. The aim of his policy had been to use the wealth amassed by the King's father to hold the balance of power and establish England as the decisive influence in Europe. This was the sort of diplomatic chess game in which he excelled, where Kings and Queens, castles, bishops, knights and pawns moved in obedience to a master plan. He would not have shrunk from dissolving a Royal marriage if the new pair-ing to emerge offered the advantage of a useful exchange of al-liances; but he had no place on his board for a King who fell in love with one of his own subjects, a girl fitting nowhere into the pattern of international relations. The arrogance with which he op-posed her shows that he lost both his temper and his skill. The game became too difficult to play when the pieces turned to flesh and blood.

Yet even without him the game still had to be played to save the nation whose treasury his wars had emptied from a situation of mounting danger. The continental powers from whose divisions England had profited were drawing together, and the most formida-ble was emerging predominant, the Emperor Charles, who was

Queen Catherine's nephew and the champion of her rights. He made peace on favourable terms with the French at Cambrai in the summer, and the Pope so far forgave the sack of Rome as to agree to officiate at the ceremony of crowning him Holy Roman Emperor in the new year, belated confirmation of a title which he had already borne for a decade. It was not a happy prospect for the inexperienced ministers who served King Henry in Wolsey's place. They appointed a roving ambassador to attend the coronation and try to patch up an agreement, but in any case to go on afterwards to Rome and Paris to encourage resistance to Imperial ambitions. This was a task demanding fluency in foreign languages no less than tact and discretion. Lord Wiltshire to whom it was given was well qualified at least in the first respect.

My book on which I had been working for two months was finished, and the King was kind enough to express his satisfaction; but when I asked if I might go back to Cambridge he demurred. He told me that he wished me to accompany Lord Wiltshire on his mission, so that I might bring the views expressed in the book to the notice of the foreign universities to whose decision the question would shortly be referred. When I heard this I was willing enough to prolong my absence from Cambridge. I was forty years old and had never yet been out of the kingdom. The prospect of the journey delighted me, the more so as I was to travel in the company of a nobleman whom I so much liked and admired. Not even the responsibility laid on me, the gravity of the issues awaiting us abroad, could diminish the eagerness with which I looked forward to our departure.

7

My opportunities to observe and explore were restricted at first by the ceremony in which we travelled. Lord Wiltshire was accompanied by a number of prominent colleagues, and in France the party received added weight from the arrival of John Stokesley, soon to be Bishop of London, a pillar of ecclesiastical orthodoxy already advanced in years and almost as ponderous in his movements as in his doctrine. We went forward at a leisurely pace with a huge retinue, sumptuously entertained in great abbeys and by noblemen in their castles. When we were approaching a night's lodging where our host was of sufficient distinction it was our custom to halt at some convenient spot a mile or so short of it, usually a wayside farm or inn. The month was January, and although the weather was mild for the time of year it was not of a sort to encourage much lingering out of doors. The cavalcade drew up, carts were uncovered, bags opened and servants unpacked their masters' fine clothes. Then we changed our muddy travelling coats for velvet and adorned ourselves with jewels and other suitable trinkets, while the horses and mules were groomed and resaddled, with crimson trappings and stirrups of polished copper, gold for Lord Wiltshire himself. Thus transformed we rode up to the abbey or castle with a magnificence worthy of an embassy from the King of England.

At the speed at which we were moving it began to seem unlikely that we should reach Bologna, our destination, in time for the coronation which was fixed for the last week in February; but Lord Wiltshire was not greatly disturbed as he expected the Emperor to stay on for several weeks afterwards, and his business with him would be conducted more easily when the festivities were over. It was a disagreeable shock therefore, when we reached Roanne on the upper waters of the Loire, to receive the news that the Emperor had changed his plans and would be leaving Bologna as soon as the Pope did. We had covered little more than half the distance in three weeks and had a fortnight at most for the remainder.

Lord Wiltshire was in dismay. However small his own hopes might be of a successful outcome to the negotiations, he did not relish the idea of telling King Henry that he had arrived too late to negotiate at all. We were spending the night with the Lord of Roanne in his castle. I had been round to look at the stables and noticed the excellent condition of the horses kept there, so now I proposed to him that we should borrow a few of the best of these, enough to mount him and me and one or two active servants, and that we should press on ahead to Bologna, leaving Stokesley and the others to follow at their leisure with the baggage. At first he was rather taken aback and could only think of objections; but when I asked him if similar difficulties would have deterred him in his youth on his Cornish campaign I could see that I touched his pride. He accepted the challenge with a laugh and yielded.

We set off early the next morning before our companions were awake. It was a joy to be free of the crowd, to feel a spirited horse beneath me and be able to give it its head. My contentment lasted as we trotted briskly over the uplands between the Loire and the Saône. Our purpose was to reach Lyon before night. It was a distance of more than fifty miles, but our horses were fit enough to carry us there. All day we kept up a steady pace, stopping only once or twice for a hasty bite of food provided by the servants from their saddlebags and eaten without dismounting. Dusk was closing in however when we looked down at last from a wooded crest on the Saône, with Lyon still far away beneath us at the confluence where Saône and Rhone meet. I pointed it out to Lord Wiltshire and he replied with a laconic nod. He had been very silent for some hours, and now remembering how much older a man he was, I began to feel anxious about him. His face was pale and drawn, and his body sagged; but I dared not show my concern, knowing that it would annoy him, and it was too late in any case to turn back.

It was nearly midnight when we entered Lyon. We were directed to the house of a leading citizen, a merchant prominent in the silk trade who had commercial relations with England. He and his wife received us hospitably, and when they perceived Lord Wiltshire's exhaustion they cut short all tiring formalities and insisted on his going straight to bed, where hot water, food and other comforts were brought him. I myself stayed up and talked to my host, enjoying both the excellent supper provided to satisfy my hunger and the wide range of his conversation. When I explained that we were in a hurry to catch the Emperor at Bologna he told me that we fretted without need, that the Emperor himself would take care to wait for us, having reasons of his own to desire a meeting.

As we talked I heard much to correct my ideas of the Emperor's power. It was true that he ruled an empire greater than any known in Christendom since the time of Charlemagne; but it was an untidy agglomeration lacking tradition or common sympathies and split in two by a hostile wedge, the kingdom of France. Although he had emerged victorious from his latest war against the French, had asserted his will in Italy and forced even the Pope to submit, he remained vulnerable in too many places to be able to count on the subjection of his recent enemies.

The conclusion which my host drew from this account was that the Emperor had every reason to avoid offending the English and would do all that he could to meet us and reach agreement. I asked whether he was likely to change his attitude towards King Henry's marriage, and I added that I had myself written a book to clarify the argument and was hoping that the Emperor would accept a copy and perhaps allow me to explain the points to him. But my host shook his head and smiled:

"If he agrees that his aunt commits incest, what becomes of his cousin Mary? She is wasted as a bastard when she might be so useful as a Queen."

His view of the Emperor's motives was cynical. He insisted that there was no love between nephew and aunt. If King Henry's wish to annul his marriage remained an obstacle to reconciliation with England the reason sprang from grounds of politics alone, the dynastic ambitions of the house of Habsburg.

When we parted to go to our beds any lingering doubts of the rightness of the English cause had been dissipated. I saw the issue clearly as a struggle between the law on which King Henry founded his claim and the covetous power of the Emperor seeking a foothold in England, using a wretched girl as his instrument.

Much abuse has been heaped since then on King Henry and Queen Anne. Their behaviour is made to seem the more heartless in contrast with the devotion shown by Queen Catherine's nephew, her faithful champion. I learnt too much from my host at Lyon ever to be deceived by that hypocrisy.

Lord Wiltshire awoke very stiff the next morning, but determined to continue on his journey. When I told him what I had heard, that the Emperor was anxious to meet us, he yielded with a good grace, deciding to wait at Lyon for his retinue, then proceed with them quietly in comfort.

Having succeeded so far I ventured to broach another idea that I had in my head. I pointed out that there was little for me to do in Bologna, where diplomatic bargaining would be more appropriate than academic discussion of the canon law. So I asked to be allowed to ride on alone to Rome. The very fact that the Pope was away, still attending the Emperor, would be to my advantage, enabling me to explore the ground before taking an active part in events. These arguments were true, and I put them forward sincerely; but I must admit that I was eager for the adventure of travelling in Italy by myself.

Except for a polite expression of regret Lord Wiltshire made no effort to detain me; but he warned me that a great part of my way lay through country devastated by war where little respect was paid to law and order, and he advised me to take a capable servant as my companion. I chose one with whom I had talked on our ride from Roanne, attracted by his South Nottinghamshire accent. He was a burly giant of a man likely to be useful in any violent emergency. I called him Little John for the same reason as his prototype bore the name in the legend of Robin Hood.

Our road over the high passes from France into Italy was intimidating enough for a lowlander like myself. The valley up which we climbed narrowed to a gorge winding beneath towering cliffs, and as the way grew steeper winter met us again. Our horses were soon wading through snow, floundering in it at times up to the hocks. If it had not been for the footprints of travellers who had gone before us I should have given up in despair and turned back. I nearly did so in any case in the blizzards that seared my face till I scarcely dared to open my eyes. When night fell there was no hospitable abbey or castle to receive us; we were lucky if we found as much as a ruined hut, often our only shelter was the nook of an overhanging crag. Without my servant's vigour and resourcefulness I could not have survived.

One evening we had just settled down to sleep in an old watchtower on which we came by chance, and which offered the unaccustomed luxury of a roof more or less proof against the weather. Dry brushwood was stacked inside, and we used it to build a fire that glowed cheerfully on the walls around us, and also no doubt through their abundant holes so as to be seen by anyone approaching. We only became aware that we were watched when intruders burst in on us through the doorway. They spoke in a language unknown to me, but it was very clear that the words were unfriendly. I drew my sword, and if my first intention had been fulfilled I should have been guilty as a priest of shedding the blood of wretches distraught by hunger and injustice.

But Little John gave them no chance to come near me. He rushed at them like a veritable Behemoth, felling them to the ground with his enormous fists, seizing others by the waist and hurling them across the room. Although they greatly outnumbered us they were weakened in body and spirit by privation. Their ferocity quickly subsided in the presence of a victim so well able to defend himself, and they fled in panic, jostling and fighting each other to escape. I was immensely relieved to see them go, glad too that they went suffering nothing worse than bruises.

After that we were allowed to travel in peace except for occasional volleys of stones from an outpost high above us among the rocks. Even these ceased when we replied to them with arrows. Our appearance was not of a sort to encourage the belief that we carried anything worth plundering, and their recent experience had taught the robbers that the effort was likely to be costly. Nevertheless we were lucky to complete the journey with so little disturbance. When we came down into Italy we were told alarming stories of earlier travellers, some found murdered in their tracks, others carried off into the mountains to be held for ransom.

Down in the plain of northern Italy the scars of war were even more evident than in the mountains. The greater fertility of the land seemed to aggravate the crime of the destruction committed there. To us however the change of scene was a pleasant relief. We were able to travel in comfort and safety; roads became easier, villages more frequent, and when night fell we could count on a roof to shelter us. Any suspicion that greeted our arrival disappeared quickly when we explained that we were English, not French or German or Spaniards. The Italians had no grudge against England. Although I speak the language poorly I could generally make myself understood by relying in any difficulty on Latin.

I had heard so much of the atrocities committed by the Imperial troops who sacked Rome that I almost expected to find the city a ruin, and I stared in surprise on my arrival at the magnificence of the buildings, the busy crowds unconcerned in the streets. Nearly three years had passed since the disaster, and most of the scars had healed. Occasionally as I walked about in the next few days I caught sight of a broken window, a door battered in that hung loose not yet repaired, or a mutilated image in one of the churches, victim either of greed that coveted its precious metals or of the fanaticism of the Lutheran mercenaries enrolled in the Emperor's army.

Such traces however were rare. The Romans have great powers of recovery and short memories. When I visited the cathedral of St. Peter begun a quarter of a century before under Pope Julius II and still incomplete (not even completed yet as I write these words) the masons and artists were back on their scaffoldings, and it was as though the work had never been interrupted.

The Pope lingered on after the coronation at Bologna with the Emperor, and news reached me soon that Lord Wiltshire had joined them there and that the Emperor would receive him. Meanwhile I had time to look round and talk to anyone who could be useful. The King's case which, as I have said, the Pope had recalled to Rome was due to be heard shortly in the Court of Rota, the supreme tribunal for civil affairs, and I hoped that the hearing

might be arranged when I was present so that I could myself put
the arguments favouring annulment of the marriage. I still believed
that if these were explained clearly they must prevail, and many
Romans to whom I had letters of introduction encouraged me,
hinting that the Pope himself would be glad of a decision in the
highest court of Christendom which provoked difficulties for the
Emperor without directly involving the Holy See.

I had been several weeks in Rome when at last Lord Wiltshire
arrived to join me, much upset by his treatment at Bologna. That
he was too late for the coronation was a small matter; the Emperor stayed on, as we had hoped, to wait for him, and negotiations began at once on the questions covered by King Henry's
instructions. Beyond that however there was no comfort in events.
Whether the Emperor had changed his mind about the value of
improved relations with England, or whether he trusted in intimi-
dation as the best means of attaining his end, he adopted the
tone of a conqueror triumphant everywhere in Europe and offered
no concession with which King Henry was likely to be satisfied.

A still worse shock was added. Lord Wiltshire was informed
that King Henry had been summoned by the Pope to appear in
person to plead his case before the Court of Rota, and that till he
obeyed the order his ambassador would be held under arrest as
his proxy. Although the detention was enforced with civility and
all due regard for dignity and comfort the hard fact remained
that Lord Wiltshire was a prisoner in Bologna. Only when the
Pope himself left was he allowed to come on to Rome, travelling
under Papal escort, and even so he was warned that it was merely
a temporary reprieve, that his position would be reconsidered in
six weeks' time.

It was not in his nature however to remain dejected for long,
and he was soon making plans to recover from the setback, congratulating himself that at least he had escaped from the Emperor's clutches:

"I can deal with the Pope," he declared confidently, "when
I get him alone."

He sought and obtained an audience at the Vatican, and when
the time came he invited me to go with him. He told me that

the Pope expressed regret not to have met me at Bologna, having had a letter from King Henry recommending me to him in the kindest terms as *"un merveilleux et sérieux sage homme."* The description flattered my vanity, but I was nervous of my ability to live up to it. I looked forward nevertheless with curiosity to a meeting with the holder of St. Peter's keys.

Our visit to the Vatican has suffered unjust notoriety from an accretion of legend. The true facts are of no discredit either to Lord Wiltshire or to the Pope. Some blame for the incident that disturbed the gravity of the proceedings lies with the chamberlain responsible for the arrangements, who should have warned the Pope that in the delicate state of relations between the King of England and the Holy See any overt symbol of homage was likely to provoke embarrassment. The real offender however was Amanda, Lord Wiltshire's spaniel bitch. She was a black-and-white roan cocker, little more than a puppy, and Lord Wiltshire was very fond of her so that she accompanied him wherever he went. She and I made friends at Durham House where she used to come and lie by the fire in my room while I was writing, and on our long journey across France, where she travelled in one of the carts, I was glad of the excuse that she needed exercise to take her for an evening walk. An official visit paid to the Vatican on business of state was not of course an occasion to be chosen for exercising her; but she followed us without our knowledge, and when we noticed her we were already crossing the bridge over the Tiber and it was too late to send her back. The audience was to be a private ceremony and we were only a small party, Lord Wiltshire, Stokesley and myself with four or five servants. One of these had a piece of cord which he tied to her collar, and she was put in his charge.

This was the first time that I had been inside the Papal apartments, and as we were led through them I was fascinated by the colours of the mosaic pavements on which we walked and the scenes from Scripture and legend painted on the walls a generation ago, as fresh as if the paint had not yet dried, by Bernardino di Betto whom the Italians call Pinturicchio. The magnificence of the decoration was in odd contrast to the scantiness and shabbiness of the furniture. In many rooms the floor was quite bare, in others an occasional bench of rough wood had evidently been put there for temporary use for lack of anything better. I had observed similar signs of penury in other Roman houses; but here in the Vatican itself they made a greater impression, reminding me of the ruthlessness with which the Imperial troops carried off everything of value that could be removed without difficulty. Even the room in which the Pope waited to receive us had a derelict appearance, except for the pictures. As I knelt with the rest of the party before the Pope sitting on his throne, my eyes were fixed on a remarkably charming St. Catherine (modelled, they say, on Lucrezia Borgia, daughter of Pope Alexander VI) reasoning on the wall behind him with the heathen Emperor Maximinus. I thought to myself how much better it would have been for Christianity if it had always been propagated by advocates as decorative.

I was recalled abruptly to the present by a sense of embarrassment around me. The Pope's foot was propped on a well-worn cushion of purple silk; his sandal left his toes bare, and I remembered what for the moment I had forgotten, that it is customary to kiss the Pope's toe as an act of homage. I do not suppose that Lord Wiltshire also had forgotten, but he probably assumed that in the circumstances the formality would not be demanded. Now as I glanced at him I saw him dismayed and uncertain, and I understood his hesitation. He had protested in the strongest terms against his detention at Bologna, denying the right of the Court of Rota to summon the King of England, even by proxy. It would look too like retractation to comply meekly here in public with the Roman custom.

We remained kneeling, waiting for the Pope to invite us to rise; but he himself was waiting for Lord Wiltshire to bend forward and give the traditional salute. Both men looked equally embarrassed. The secretaries and other clerics grouped on either side of the throne glared at us in indignation. Then the hush was interrupted by a noise of scuffling, and my heart sank in sudden foreboding. I looked round, and my worst fears were confirmed. Amanda had broken loose from the servant at the back of the room and was racing triumphantly towards us, trailing the cord after her. She saw me and bounded up to me, almost knocking me off my knees in the ebullience of her delight. I tried to grab her leash, but already she was rushing on to find her master, choosing the most conspicuous way round the front of the throne. The obstacle diverted her, aroused her curiosity, and before anyone could stop her she had raised her head to sniff the cushion and was licking the Pope's toe with an assiduity unsurpassed by the devoutest of pilgrims.

There was a gasp of horror from the Italian clerics, an angry mutter of "Anathema maranatha." But the Pope checked them; he stooped to the dog and fondled her neck, and she transferred her tongue from his toe to his fingers. He was smiling as he turned to Lord Wiltshire, speaking in Italian, and the relief in his voice was unmistakable:

"Such devotion, your Excellency, is worthy of a plenary indulgence."

He signed to us to rise to our feet, and I made haste to pick up the end of Amanda's cord, keeping tight hold of her till the interview was over. She lay down and gave no more trouble, and from time to time the Pope's eyes rested on her benevolently. I feel sure that he was sincerely grateful to her for her timely intrusion.

My first impression of Pope Clement VII was favourable, and I have never ceased to regard him with sympathy and respect, so that even now when I must recant so much to accept the claims of the Roman See I believe that I could do so without scruple if he were still alive to occupy it. He was a middle-aged man of spare build with clear-cut, regular features, better-looking than most Italians except for a cast in his right eye which gave something evasive to his expression. The qualities which his appearance suggested, and which fuller acquaintance confirmed, were those of a man both intelligent and sensitive whose good intentions were likely to be frustrated by lack of resolution. I had been looking forward with some apprehension to this confrontation, but the gentleness of his manners at once reassured me. When Lord Wiltshire introduced me he greeted me with the utmost kindness, declaring that he had read my book with interest. He was careful however to refrain from commenting on the arguments.

The conversation that followed was friendly but unfruitful. Taking courage from his affability I asked to be allowed to argue in the Court of Rota myself on the King's behalf; but he shook his head regretfully, explaining that it was the rule for those who sought a decision to appear in person, and the summons had already been issued inviting King Henry's attendance. He did his best to soften the rebuff by the courtesy of his language, assuring us that it was for King Henry's own good that he had recalled the case to Rome to be heard before the most exalted tribunal in Christendom. Where could an opinion be obtained better able to resolve conscientious scruples, the King's fear of incurring guilt of incest by consorting with his brother's widow? The only answer, if we had been frank, was that by this time the King had made up his mind and no longer wanted the Pope's opinion but his approval. I was sorry for the Pope, sympathising with him in his vain efforts to find a compromise. He was, in one of his favourite phrases, between the hammer and the anvil, anxious to conciliate King Henry without offending the Emperor.

No compliments however could hide the fact that the Roman court had summoned the King of England, and that Lord Wiltshire would be held personally forfeit if he were still in Rome when the six weeks' grace expired. I suspect that he himself was not sorry to have such an excuse to return home. He was in an invidious position as it was his daughter who would become Queen if the marriage were annulled, and I know that in many moods he wished heartily that she and the King had never met.

I myself stayed on after he had gone. Although I was refused permission to plead the King's cause in the Court of Rota I could still be of use supervising the deliberations of the universities of Europe, which had been invited to pronounce on the issue. Someone was needed here in Rome to advise and elucidate, to stir up the dilatory, and to see that when the replies were put in evidence they were presented in the most favourable light. These duties, as I learnt very soon, were exercised not only in the fields of theology and canon law. My confidence in the integrity of scholarship suffered a disillusioning shock when I found that money was more necessary than argument in shaping academic opinion. It was my first lesson in the conduct of public affairs, to which all my life I have been slow in adapting myself. On this occasion I accepted the standards of those around me. Whether the English bribed or not the Emperor's agents still would do so, and our refusal to soil our own hands would ensure that the wrong prevailed.

During these six months in Rome I saw a great deal of the Pope, who, anxious perhaps to make amends for my disappointment, offered me the post of English Penitentiary, an officer of the Curia who deals with requests for dispensations and other matters of conscience emanating from his country of origin. The duties were not onerous, and the appointment gave me access to the Vatican for which I soon had reason to be thankful. Replies had already come in from the English and two of the French universities condemning the validity of King Henry's marriage, and the Emperor's agents afraid that the example would be followed in Italy complained to the Pope of the methods by which English and French influence was extended there. The Pope of course was well aware that they were guilty of similar practices themselves, but he shrank from rebuking the Emperor. He saved his face with a brief forbidding any discussion of the subject in Italian universities while it remained *sub judice* at Rome. This was a grave threat to the success of our plans, and the task fell on me to persuade him to revoke or moderate the prohibition.

My difficulty in the many interviews that I had with him was that I understood his point of view too clearly to be able to oppose it with conviction. If the legal issue had stood alone he would have granted the annulment as readily as his predecessors did in similar circumstances. He hesitated solely on political grounds, but these were of a sort that filled him with alarm. He knew too well what it meant to quarrel with the Emperor and was determined not to invite a repetition of the sack of Rome. If he had yielded to his natural timidity he would not have listened to me at all; but he cherished the independence of the Papacy and fought for it with the only weapon available to him, that of tortuous diplomacy, which he used with all the aptitude of a Florentine of the house of Medici. The more clearly I understood his difficulties the more I was encouraged to believe that the Church had lost too much already to be willing to estrange the Defender of the Faith.

It seemed that my instinct was right when I heard that the brief against which I protested was going to be withdrawn and freedom of discussion restored to the Italian universities. The Pope confirmed the news himself at our next meeting; he added with a cynical smile that he had imposed the condition on both sides to refrain from bribery. I am afraid that I smiled too when he said this. What good was it to pretend that the condition would be observed, or to affect a rectitude which neither of us practised? I put it to his credit that he was not a hypocrite. Yet it was clear from his sincere piety, the Christian simplicity of his manner of living that he was far from being a cynic at heart. I am sure that he truly believed that God's kingdom on earth depended on a universal Church ruled by the successor of St. Peter. The trouble was that its interests too often became confused in his mind with those of family loyalty, his devotion admirable in the man but inconvenient in a Pope to his Medici relations in Florence. International problems were hard enough to solve without the intrusion of the domestic politics of Tuscany.

The renewal of debate in the Italian universities was of course only a small victory in our struggle to obtain Papal approval of King Henry's plans for the succession to the English Crown. Many difficulties remained to be overcome, of which the greatest was the insistence laid on the King's appearing in person before the court. If he refused, as he almost certainly would, what chance had we to submit the academic evidence which we were collecting so industriously? If I was not left altogether despondent the reason lay in the character of the Pope himself. I felt that he was a man open to reason, free from either the obstinacy or the vanity which regards concession as defeat.

We differed on many issues of importance. A time came when he prepared, but did not publish, a bull excommunicating me.

Yet I felt in conversation with him, as with few of the reformers whom I met later, that we shared the same values, that details of organisation meant less to him than Christian unity. He died at the height of the controversy following Queen Anne's coronation. I still believe that if he had lived he would have found means of averting the rupture, and that England would have remained in communion with the Roman See.

8

King Henry sent for me to return to England before the last of the replies from the universities was received, and I had to leave the work in the hands of an Italian friar, Brother Dionysius, who was in sympathy with our cause and succeeded me as English Penitentiary at Rome. The flattering reason was given for my recall that the King had appointed me a Royal chaplain, but I rather think that he chiefly wished to see me to hear my report on the doings of the English agents in Italy, some of whom were in difficulties that caused him anxiety. An especially embarrassing setback had occurred at Bologna, where our agent was an old acquaintance of mine, Richard Croke, formerly public orator at Cambridge. He was a brilliant Greek scholar and had even taught the King, but he was plainly out of his depths in international diplomacy. Old Stokesley tried to help him when he was there, but only succeeded in making matters worse, distributing "retainers," as they were politely called, on such a scale that the Papal governor, Cardinal de Gambara, was obliged to take notice and intervened to suspend the decision of the university.

On my arrival in Bologna I went as soon as I could to see Cardinal de Gambara. He received me with much kindness, for which no doubt I owed thanks to the letter of introduction given me by the Pope, and when I apologised for the irregularities of which the English agents had been guilty, and explained that they were inexperienced men who erred in ignorance, he accepted the excuse with good grace and his suspending order was withdrawn. The university at once published its decision declaring that the King's marriage fell within the prohibited degrees, although it was careful to refrain from pronouncing on the Pope's dispensing power.

On my return to England, I found the King in difficulties with the conscience of Sir Thomas More, the new chancellor who succeeded Wolsey just before I went abroad. More was one of the most charming of men, learned, sagacious and humane with a witty tongue that illuminated his conversation. The King delighted in his company and probably thought when he chose him for high office that business of state would become a perpetual round of entertainment. But there was another side to More which he overlooked. The merry humanist was a man of strict and high principle, who at one time seriously considered taking monastic vows. More's faith had an unbending integrity that deserves respect however regrettable many of the actions to which it led him. As chancellor he was much harsher than Wolsey had been in enforcing religious orthodoxy; but he is one of the few such zealots of whom I can believe that he really cared for his victim's welfare, that he sentenced a heretic to death in the honest conviction that the punishment was the only means of preserving the soul to life eternal. When the time came he was as hard on himself as on others.

I liked and admired the man, much as I detested his doctrine. When his steadfast belief in the sanctity of Papal authority brought him into conflict with the King on the issue of the Royal marriage I was sent with others of the King's chaplains to argue with him, and I was greatly impressed by the courtesy that he showed us. He reminded us however that he was a layman, no theologian, and that it was for the Pope to decide whether or not the marriage was valid, and that he must wait for and accept the ruling of the Vatican. The King was unwilling to press him. If the Court of Rota gave a verdict in our favour, as we still hoped that it would, everything could be settled amicably and the chancellor's lack of cooperation forgotten or ignored. I am sure that this was what the King intended. He was fond of More and very ready to make concessions to their friendship, provided that these did not interfere with his own cherished desires; but in the following year, when the conflict became insoluble, he accepted his resignation with only perfunctory expressions of sorrow.

There were moods occurring frequently at this time when he spoke regretfully of Wolsey, whose virtues shone brighter in retrospect than ever in real life. But Wolsey had gone beyond recall, far beyond even his province of York to which he was banished in disgrace soon after I left England, and from which he was brought back under arrest within a week or two of my return. He never completed the journey to learn what fate awaited him in London. He was taken ill in Lord Shrewsbury's house at Sheffield, and although he was able to travel on a few more stages the sickness returned with greater violence and he died in the abbey at Leicester. I never met or even saw him; but he had dominated the political scene since my early youth, and his death was like the end of an epoch.

The circumstances in which I heard the news added to the shock. I was living again at Durham House and was in the garden with Lord Wiltshire and Lady Anne talking of French poetry, of which father and daughter alike were passionate admirers. Lady Anne was singing at our request her favourite of the ballads of Villon. I well remember the deep melody of her voice in the stillness of the November afternoon, the lapping undertone of the river beneath us strewn with autumn leaves:

> Et Jeanne, la bonne Lorraine,
> Qu'Anglois bruslèrent à Rouen;
> Où sont elles, Vierge souvraine?
> Mais où sont les neiges d'antan?

As she finished the refrain a secretary came towards us across the grass, and she broke off in evident surprise and curiosity. He went up to Lord Wiltshire and spoke to him in a voice too low for me to catch, but we were not left long in ignorance. Lord Wiltshire's face lit up with pleasure, he turned to us and exclaimed loudly and exultantly:

"Wolsey's dead. The only pity is, he's cheated the hangman."

The conversation that followed is one that I do not care to recall. The change in Lady Anne's voice shocked me as she burst into a peal of jubilant laughter. I have known no one else able to veer so suddenly from extreme to extreme, capable of such delicacy of understanding at one moment, of such reckless abandonment to coarse emotion at another. They were soon busy planning their triumph, the entertainment to which they would invite the French ambassador, Wolsey's enemy, the farce that they would exhibit to mock the dead. It was useless for me to remonstrate; they did not listen, did not even seem to hear me. Already they were composing ribald verses for the performance, and they went off together in high spirits to find Lord Rochford to help them with his literary skill. He was back at home from his mission in France.

When the evening came I was among the guests. I stayed as long as I could so as not to put my host to shame; but the whole business was in such glaringly bad taste that at last I could endure it no longer, and I left my seat before the farce was over. The family bore me no ill-will for my disapproval. They were much too pleased with themselves to care, and as I could not persuade them that there was anything wrong in their behaviour I ceased in time to let it trouble me. This would be a loveless world for all of us were it only possible to love the faultless.

There was good reason for Lady Anne's dislike of Wolsey even if it did not excuse her for exulting over his death. She told me the story herself one evening when she came up to my room to put in an hour or so before going on to a ball at York House, the former residence of the Archbishops of York which Wolsey handed over to the King before his fall. She was dressed ready for the occasion, an incongruous goddess among my piles of papers and books. Her green silk bodice and skirt caught in tightly at the waist had a damask sheen, a pattern of nymphs and satyrs that danced in the firelight. A double string of emeralds clasped her bare neck. But what I admired most of all was her hair which she wore loose in the French style, so long that she sat on it when I brought a chair for her. It hung almost straight over her shoulders, dark brown against the flush of her skin, brushed to such gloss that the jewels fastened in it seemed to glisten with reflected brightness. This was the first time that I had seen her in court dress, and I could sympathise with the King's infatuation. Her presence transfigured the room as she sat by the fire talking to me, fending off Amanda's paws vigorously from her lap but leaving her undisturbed to lick her ankles and lie curled asleep over her feet.

Our conversation began on ground remote from troublesome issues. She asked for news of France through which I had recently passed, and went on to recall her memories of the years which she spent there as a young girl, attending the "White Queen" during her brief marriage to King Louis XII and staying on at Paris after his death in the care of his daughter Queen Claude, the wife of his successor, King Francis. I encouraged these reminiscences which were as interesting to me as they were evidently soothing to herself. I was pleasantly surprised to hear how kindly she spoke of the old King, telling me that the French people greatly loved him and called him "Louis the Good," and praising his indomitable spirit in insisting, in spite of his failing health, on gaieties suited to his young wife till the strain killed him.

Her manner changed however, and she reverted to a tone more usual to her of lighthearted mockery, when she passed to King Francis. She could be very amusing, and I am afraid that I laughed more than I should at her malicious description of his pursuit of the girls, often little more than children, who attended his court. Queen Claude was too young, too gentle, too self-effacing to restrain him; she had a plain face, an ungainly figure (a deformed leg caused her to limp when she walked), and suffered much neglect as soon as her father was no longer there to care for her. Lady Anne spoke of her with pity; but I suspected that she herself contributed to the Queen's anxiety, that she was not unwilling to play the nymph to the Royal satyr. It seems to have been at the Queen's request that she was transferred to the household of the King's sister, the Duchess of Alençon. There was greater gaiety there, but there was also more competent guidance. The duchess, better known today as the Queen of Navarre, was even at that time renowned for distinction of mind, corresponding on equal terms with scholars and writing verse which has a lasting place in French literature. Her enlightened character made an ineffaceable impression on the girl placed in her charge. The glow tinting Lady Anne's memories of the French court owed much of its enchantment to the influence of Marguerite d'Alençon.

At last however even this theme became exhausted. I had the feeling that she was not giving full attention to what she said, that her thoughts were elsewhere. I waited in patience to learn the true purpose of the interview, and we seemed to be approaching it when, with an abrupt transition, she began to talk of Queen Catherine, to whom she was appointed a maid-of-honour on her return to England. Her words came more slowly, and her face was grave, preoccupied.

Suddenly she broke off and exclaimed:

"If you knew how much the Lord Cardinal was to blame, you wouldn't perhaps think me so heartless."

I was uncertain whether she referred to her behaviour in jeering at Wolsey's death or in depriving the Queen of her husband, but she plunged into her story without waiting for me to reply. The King and Queen were at Greenwich, she said, and she was with them with the other maids-of-honour, when she first met Sir Henry Percy, heir to the Earl of Northumberland. She was about twenty years old at the time and had been brought home from France to marry an unknown cousin from the Irish side of her father's family, in the hope that the marriage would resolve conflicting claims to the titles and estates. Sir Henry too had a partner already chosen for him, Lord Shrewsbury's daughter, to whom he was plighted as a boy; but it was plain that when he saw Lady Anne Boleyn he felt no more bound than she did by a contract imposed under duress without regard for personal affection. They were both of them sanguine and impulsive, refusing to believe that any insuperable barrier could part them when, even on worldly grounds, there was so much to be said for the match.

He held an appointment at the time in Wolsey's household and accompanied him on his frequent visits to court, where it was easy while the great were in conference to slip away to enjoy the society of the maids-of-honour, and of one in particular. The intensity of feeling in her voice gripped me as she spoke of the pleasure with which she looked forward to his coming, and of her disappointment when, as sometimes happened, he was ill and had to stay behind. He had been delicate from a child, liable to recurrent feverish attacks which left him shivering as if he could never be warm again; but she made haste to assure me that between them he was as active as most young men, an excellent horseman and a fair shot with both longbow and crossbow. In any case, if he fell short of his redoubtable ancestors in physique, he surpassed most of them in intellect, was fond of art and literature, a friend and disciple of the poet Skelton, so that he and she had many interests in common.

She was careful not to admit that they had formally plighted troth to each other, and I asked no questions, perceiving how dangerous in the changed circumstances the admission could be. But it was perfectly clear from the way in which she talked that they counted on becoming husband and wife, and she even told me where they planned to spend their honeymoon. There was a small manor on his father's estates in Yorkshire of which he was particularly fond; he often used to stay there in his childhood, and he came to regard it as his own. Kildale Castle stood in a valley in the moors within two hours' ride of the coast, but there was nothing bleak or forbidding in the description that he gave her. A wooded ridge sheltered it from the north, great beech trees surrounded the knoll on which it was built, and the stream winding beneath was dammed into a miniature lake. With its grey stone walls and roof of red pantiles it was a building worthy in her imagination to compare with the enchanted hiding place of Cupid and Psyche. As I listened to her I could not help smiling at the thought of the lively Lady Anne presiding as chatelaine over this Arcadian fastness. But she was very much in love with Henry Percy and would probably have enjoyed Kildale for a time.

Although they kept their intention to themselves as long as they could she had too much experience of the sharpness of eyes and activity of tongues at court to be surprised when her father asked her what the stories meant that were going round about Henry Percy and herself. When she told him, imploring him to release her from her engagement to the Irish cousin, he looked very grave and replied that he could do nothing without the consent of the King, who had given authority to the family arrangement. Even so she was not greatly disturbed. Since her introduction to the King when she was appointed a maid-of-honour he had gone out of his way to be kind to her, and in her innocence she could not believe that he would deny her this favour. As for her father she knew how easily she could cajole him.

It was all the more of a shock therefore when her lover came to her in agitation and described an interview with Wolsey at York Place. He had been summoned into the great gallery, and in the presence of all the servants assembled there Wolsey lashed him with his tongue as if he had been a schoolboy, accusing him of disloyalty both to his father and to the King who had plighted him to Lady Mary Talbot, Lord Shrewsbury's daughter, and speaking in the most insulting terms of the Boleyn family.

She flushed as she told me this, and added earnestly: "But he stood up to the Lord Cardinal. He swore that he and I were in love, and he'd given me his word and would keep it."

Defiance however provoked retribution. A message was sent to his father, the Earl of Northumberland, who rode down at once from the north to call his son to order. The account which I had of their meeting may have been prejudiced, coming from Lady Anne who was herself repeating what her lover told her; but I have since heard it confirmed in the main by one of Wolsey's closest retainers. When the Earl arrived Wolsey received him in the gallery, and the two old men sat in conclave over their wine conversing in tones too low to reach those in attendance—among whom was the boy himself, compelled to watch without understanding the preparations for his discomfiture. At last the Earl rose to leave and was escorted to the door at the farther end, where the usual crowd waited seeking audience. Instead of going out he sat down on the bench provided there, and called his son to him.

Then in front of everyone, more shamefully even than Wolsey had done, he shouted and ranted, denouncing him as wastrel, libertine, spendthrift. The last of these sneers rankled especially as the old man himself was addicted to the most ostentatious extravagance, piling up debts which his son had to pay off at heavy cost to the estate after his death. No chance however was given to interrupt the stream of vituperation and reproach. The publicity which overwhelmed the son added zest to the father, who called the onlookers to bear witness that unless the boy mended his ways and accepted the wife allotted he would disinherit him.

Whether the threat of disinheritance had effect, or the humiliation put on him was too much for her lover, Lady Anne did not say; but the outcome was that he yielded and married Lady Mary Talbot.

"They were miserable together," she told me. "She's got a face like sour milk. She left him almost at once and ran off home to her prayers and needlework."

The pity is that if he had held out a little longer the disaster could have been avoided. His father died barely three years afterwards, and he himself became Earl of Northumberland.

I noticed that in telling this story Lady Anne laid the blame on Wolsey and was careful not to suggest that the King had any part in it. I myself am convinced that both Wolsey and the old Earl behaved as they did at the King's command; but whatever she herself may have suspected she bore resentment against Wolsey as long as he lived, a persistence most unusual in her, quite out of keeping with her character whose habit was to forget quarrels as quickly as she took them up. It is no evidence of reconciliation that she wrote letters to him, which I have seen, addressing him in the most cordial terms. I am afraid that the feeling expressed was wholly insincere, but it would be unjust to convict her of duplicity. She knew that he was not deceived, and as their daily lives brought them into frequent contact it was more comfortable for both that they should meet without friction, maintain the pretense of civility and outward truce.

I am the more inclined to condone it because I knew her at heart to be almost too impetuously honest. It puzzled me for a time, and she herself of course did not enlighten me, how she was persuaded, devoted as she had been to Henry Percy, to accept in his place the King who was the author of her misfortunes. Even if she was unaware at first she must surely have guessed the part that he played, as his passionate feelings for her became apparent. By then however she had fallen under the spell of his personality, the great charm which he was so well able to exert. She was the less likely to resist it when Percy was already married to someone else.

Without doubt her decision was affected by the knowledge that if she married the King he would make her Queen of England. No girl in her position could fail to be attracted by the prospect. But I am certain that the glitter of the throne was not her only or even her main reason for accepting him. Stray words that she dropped revealed the extent to which he had inspired her with his own purpose, how ardently she hoped to bear a son to establish the dynasty. She spoke mysteriously at times of a compact between them; but when I tried to elicit what she meant her mouth curved in a secret smile, and she changed the subject.

Oddly enough, it was she who taught me compassion for Queen Catherine whom I tended to regard less as a living woman than as an obstacle hindering the King's plans for the succession to the Crown. It is so easy to forget that people whom one has never met are human beings. My conscience was not greatly troubled till Lady Anne's misgivings aroused my own. She never put them directly into words; but after our conversation about Henry Percy she often used to come up to my room to talk, and the subject had a way of veering towards her early days at court. It was as though something compelled her to utter her thoughts of Queen Catherine the more she shrank from them. The portrait that she drew was in many respects very favourable, that of a woman of great honesty of character, simple in her manners and considerate to her subordinates. Yet it was easy to see that the two had not been congenial to each other, that there was incompatibility of temperament even before the King's behaviour widened the breach. The fault really lay with neither of them. Queen Catherine, rigidly devoted to the ideas inculcated at home in Spain, was incapable of understanding a girl of a younger generation brought up in the modern spirit of free inquiry. Both intellectually and emotionally they were opposed, and Queen Catherine had too little tact or too strict principles to avert friction.

For Queen Catherine with all her virtues was masterful and heavy-handed. That was plain from her dealings not only with her maid-of-honour but also with the King himself. Her message to him after the battle of Flodden is of course only a single example, but I doubt if it would have been held against her so long if the attitude had not been typical. The King was fighting in France at the time of the Scottish invasion, and the Queen as regent had to make arrangements for the defence of the realm. The victory won by her army happened to coincide with a lesser one against the French, the Battle of the Spurs, and the King not yet aware of events in England sent her the Duc de Longueville as a prisoner, a trophy of his success. Her reply was to send him three Scotsmen in chains, with a note pinned to them:

"*What a man does well, a woman can do three times better.*"

Justly or not, for a variety of reasons, he was seeking means of annulment, when he first set eyes on Lady Anne Boleyn on her return from France. She supplanted a wife from whom he was already estranged.

I stayed on at Durham House all through that summer of the year 1531 and look back on it now as an interlude of cloudless sunshine. The family took so much care to make me feel at home that I forgot that I was a stranger, seemed to settle down as a permanent member of the household. My duties as a Royal chaplain were not onerous, consisting chiefly of written work. Reginald Pole, the King's cousin—a name meaning little to me then, but now so full of menace—sent a letter to the King from abroad pleading with great ability against the annulment of the marriage, and it was my task to examine his arguments and refute them. This left me plenty of time to enjoy the company in which I lived, including that of Lady Anne, of whom I saw much more than on my earlier visit. In spite of attendance on the King at Greenwich and Hampton Court she was continually in and out of her father's house.

A motive to attract her was the return of her brother, Lord Rochford. Having completed his mission in France he remained for the time being at home, lodged by his father while his wife was in the country. He stood in high favour with the King, higher than ever since the success of his work in Paris. I heard the beginning of the story the year before from Stokesley. It seems that difficulty arose when an opinion on King Henry's marriage was sought from the university at Paris, the Sorbonne. Stokesley complained that when he pleaded his case they shouted him down. When he was called away to accompany Lord Wiltshire to Rome, Rochford adopted tactics better suited to his own temperament. He had his horse saddled and galloped across country to the Loire where King Francis was supervising the alterations of his castle at Chambord. I do not know whether Rochford's arguments prevailed or whether he owed success to the appeal of his fiery impulsiveness, reminding King Francis of his own youth. The result however was that the doctors of the Sorbonne received a Royal command, in obedience to which they declared that the Pope has no power to dispense with the sin of incest, to allow a man to marry his brother's wife. I was myself at Durham House when a copy of the judgment reached England, and I was caught up in the gale of exhilaration with which the family greeted the news. Rochford resembled the others in lack of moderation. When he was pleased with himself his pleasure knew no restraint.

No one understood the true Rochford better than his sister Anne. They were very near in age, there was little more than eighteen months between them, and from childhood they were accustomed to share all their interests and ideas. They seemed to find a peculiar release in each other's company, as if there alone they were free to behave truly as themselves. I noticed the quick change in their manner when anyone unattuned to this intimacy joined them, even their stepmother with whom they were both on excellent terms. On her arrival it was as though a curtain were unobtrusively drawn. Already they were talking about something entirely different, and very soon Rochford was entertaining her with a racy titbit of gossip from the court.

I met his wife when she returned to town. They were an ill-matched pair, and it was said that he neglected her; but they lived together in outward amity. I never got to know her well. The occasions when she was present at Durham House were usually of a sort to which many were invited. She was an amiable, garrulous young woman, not very intelligent or discreet, who concerned herself with more relish than was wise in other people's amorous in-

trigues. There was a lack of stability in her character, indicating
even then a danger of nervous collapse under too severe a strain.

The literary and artistic interests which Lord Wiltshire shared
with his son and daughter drew a stream of like-minded visitors to
Durham House. Among those who attended these gatherings I was
especially impressed by Sir Thomas Wyatt. I still read his poems
with enjoyment. He was an old friend of Lady Anne's, having
known her even before she met the King. It was said indeed, not
without ground, that he and the King were rivals for her favour.

I have no doubt that she flirted with Wyatt and continued to do
so, but I am sure that the charges brought against them later were
malicious slander. If they had given the King real ground of complaint he would not have remained as he did on terms of close
friendship with Wyatt. It was indiscreet of her perhaps to see so
much of her old admirer; but indiscretion was natural to her, unfaithfulness and disloyalty were not. I am equally unwilling to believe that Wyatt himself was capable of treachery, of deceiving
one who was both his friend and his King. He loved Lady Anne
Boleyn as long as she lived, and in the terrible days at the end of her
life he was among the few who had the courage to stand by her.

Tears fill my eyes as I recall the faces associated with that summer at Durham House. I cannot bear to think how many of those
companions, most of them younger than myself, I have outlived,
how many suffered violent death. The future was mercifully hidden from us.

A day came which heralded the end of this chapter in my life.
I was sitting a little apart from the others, content to watch and
listen, when Rochford approached accompanied by a short heavily
built man, tight-lipped, with an unexpressive face, whom he introduced as Thomas Cromwell. This was my first meeting with the
King's new secretary, formerly in Wolsey's service, who was already attracting attention by his ability, his influence on public
affairs. He greeted me with a few words of perfunctory civility,
then beckoned me to stroll with him away from the others into
the rose garden. When we were alone he announced abruptly that
the King judged me worthy of preferment and wished to appoint
me Archdeacon of Taunton. I was taken aback, never having been

to Taunton or indeed anywhere in the western counties in my life. When I explained this to Cromwell he laughed gruffly, glancing at me out of the corner of his eye, and an expression flickered there, shrewd, sly and amused. It was as if a mask lifted from his face.

"Your road to Taunton," he told me, "leads through Nuremberg."

Then he lowered his voice, and I understood why he desired seclusion for our conversation. He revealed that Sir Thomas Elyot, resident ambassador at the Imperial court, was showing a suspicious lack of zeal, that letters had been intercepted between him and opponents of the King's policy at home. This was especially deplorable at a time when conditions were more favourable than they had ever been to bring pressure on the Emperor. The Turks sweeping across Hungary to invade the Empire already threatened Vienna, and the Emperor himself was on his way to Nuremberg to meet the leaders of the Lutheran party among the German princes, to obtain their help against the common danger. He was in no mood to reject overtures from England.

"So Elyot has been recalled," Cromwell concluded, "and you go to Germany in his place."

My new title, it seemed, was only to lend dignity to my position.

When he left me I remained in the rose garden, pacing to and fro. My mind was too bewildered, my feelings were too mixed for me to rejoin the others without betraying my agitation. The prospect of Nuremberg attracted me, a much more fascinating destination than Taunton, and it pleased me that the King had such confidence in me to entrust me with the mission. On the other hand I was alarmed by the responsibility, appalled by my own lack of experience. I shrank from the inexorable fate urging me into a public career.

9

Nuremberg was the first of the free cities of the Empire to support Luther's demands for reform of the Church; but as it is such a wealthy place, the busiest market in Europe, it dared not quarrel openly with the Emperor who controlled the communications on which its trade depends. So at the time when his growing intransigence provoked violent protest in Germany, and those who protested (they took the name of Protestants from the incident) met at the little town of Schmalkalde to league themselves against him, Nuremberg abstained and played no part in the military operations that followed. Its uncommitted attitude made it a convenient scene now for negotiations when he sought reconciliation with his defiant vassals.

I myself was thinking more of its intellectual and artistic reputation as I approached the city with a small body of old retainers chosen by Lord Wiltshire, including Little John, the faithful giant who served me so well in the Alps. My heart leapt as I told myself that this at last was Nuremberg, the birthplace of German enlightenment, home of the painter Albrecht Dürer, of the mastersinger Hans Sachs.

On arrival however I received disconcerting news. The Emperor would not be coming till later; meanwhile he held court at Regensburg on the Danube, where I was to join him. I do not know what made him change his plans. The reason given was that his gout troubled him, and he was taking a cure at the sulphur springs at Abbach, a little watering place above Regensburg in the hills. As far as it went the story was true, but I do not suppose that it was the whole truth. In any case I saw no need to press on in a hurry. I wanted to explore Nuremberg, to spend a few days there first.

I had an introduction from friends in England to Andreas Osiander, a leader of the reforming party and preacher in one of the principal churches in the town. His house stood behind the marketplace with its back to the castle rock, and when I called there he received me with great courtesy and insisted that I should stay as his guest. The visit introduced me to surroundings which I came to regard as a home from home before I left Germany. Yet at first I did not feel altogether at ease with Osiander. There was something in his bearing that overawed me, a dominance hard to resist, although I myself was the elder by nine years. He was a man above normal height with black hair and beard and a swarthy complexion more Oriental than German. His nose was like a great beak, and under his bushy brows a fire smouldered in his eyes kindling fiercely into a blaze when he was angry. His looks were well suited to his eminence in Hebrew scholarship; he himself might have stepped out of the Old Testament, the prophet Isaiah in the flesh. He had in fact, as he told me, Jewish ancestry, but the family had been Christian for at least two generations. The name Osiander—coined from the Greek and meaning "holy man"—was assumed by his grandfather, who was probably translating an ancestral title from the Hebrew; but as it is the fashion among the learned in Germany to turn native names into Greek most people believed that it disguised a familiar Heiligmann, and Osiander himself wisely refrained from correcting them, unwilling to incur the hostility shown by many to the Jews.

As I came to understand his character its formidable surface no longer disturbed me. I had great respect for his judgment and learning, all the more so when he told me how he trained himself, studying as a boy for the priesthood while he helped his father in the smithy. He was proud to reveal that he was a blacksmith's son.

The burning issue at Nuremberg at the time was that of the league of Protestant princes and cities against the Emperor. Osiander fiercely condemned the timidity shown by his fellow citizens in refusing to join. When I asked how he reconciled himself to armed conflict with the Imperial troops, and reminded him of the misery produced in Germany only seven years before by the peasants' revolt, he replied that the purpose of the league was to prevent anarchy, that unless the Protestants were united the Emperor would destroy them singly, leaving chaos in their place.

I stayed no more than a few days in Nuremberg, then pressed on across the wooded hills to Regensburg. There was no snow here. Trees were breaking into leaf, and as I rode through them down into the valley their opening buds scented the sun-flecked tunnel with spring. I was glad that I had left my escort to follow and was accompanied by Little John alone, so that I could enjoy my impressions undisturbed. There was a wonderful moment when I came out into the fields of a small farm perched on a grassy shelf, and Regensburg lay below me bestriding the Danube with a bridge of sixteen arches.

At Regensburg I learnt that the Emperor was still at Abbach taking the cure. His gout was no figment of diplomatic imagination. Till he rejoined the court I had to be content to discuss my business with his minister Nicholas de Granvelle, a lawyer from the French-speaking border of the Netherlands whose excellent command of Latin made up for my own lack of proficiency in his native tongue. He received me with patience and civility, except for a sharp retort now and then when his temper was aroused; but our negotiations made little progress, forever hampered by his extreme caution, his unwillingness to commit himself. Whenever a decision was needed he insisted that he must wait to consult the Emperor. I reflected with some annoyance that I was wasting my time in his room, when I might have been out in the open air, enjoying the beauty of the scene, strolling on the bank of the Danube.

A small success afforded me more gratification than I deserved. Among the duties with which I was charged was that of concluding a treaty with the Emperor to protect and extend our trade with the Flemish ports. It is a weakness of the English economy that our wool, which is the main source of our wealth, depends for outlet on the Flemish merchants who convert it into textiles. Whenever the King allied himself with France or other enemy of the Empire his policy was unpopular in the country, for fear that it would interrupt this vital trade. There was in fact little ground for the anxiety aroused. If the English grazier cannot afford to lose the Flemish market, the Flemish looms are left idle without English wool, so the dependence is mutual. Granvelle as usual put up obstacles, telling me that the question would have to be referred to the Emperor's sister, the former Queen of Hungary, to whom he had recently entrusted the regency of the Netherlands. Nevertheless he gave me to understand that her decision was likely to be favourable. No eloquence was needed to persuade; the issue turned on self-interest.

At last the Emperor arrived, and I was summoned to an audience; but I found him in no mood to be troubled with English problems, whether they had to do with our sheep or his aunt. All his attention was occupied by the Turks, whose designs were indeed the talk of everyone whom I met in Regensburg. They were in control of territory almost up to the frontier of the Empire, had already once advanced across it and besieged Vienna, from which the sturdy resistance of the citizens forced them to retreat. Now the Sultan was trying again; his forces were already in action, advancing up the Danube. The Emperor in urgent need sought allies to repel the attack.

As he had been so long a name to me I looked forward to the meeting with curiosity. I had been warned of his appearance, the grotesque chin, the exaggerated jaw protruding almost to deformity, the leaden pallor of his complexion, so that to see him in the flesh was no shock. He himself used to say that he was grateful to the painters whose portraits made him look so hideous, because when people met him they were often quite pleasantly surprised. There was indeed much that pleased in his face, especially in his wide brow and steady eyes. I had the impression of a man sincere in his ideals, stubbornly attached to them, but lacking the strength to put them into effect. The impassivity, the detachment of his expression seemed to be a defensive armour covering a fundamental timidity that shrank from the effort of decision.

His reticence was such that it suggested, however misleadingly, inherent coldness of heart. I never felt at ease in his company, never enjoyed the entertainment to which I was invited. His table was loaded with good food, for which he had an insatiable appetite; but his presence cast a gloom, his banquets were as prim and constrained as those at the English court were free and gay.

He listened frigidly while I dilated on the advantages of an English alliance, and when I had done he was silent for a time,

then asked what King Henry offered in terms of men and money.
My instructions did not equip me for detailed haggling, and vague
promises failed to satisfy him. It was difficult to make them sound
convincing when I suspected at the back of my mind that when
it came to the point King Henry intended to send nothing at all.
He was left with a treasury too heavily depleted by Wolsey's wars.

The pity was that in his desperate straits the Emperor was in a
mood for concessions if the reward were sufficiently worth his while.
It was no secret that, when he met the Protestant leaders at the
diet which he had summoned at Nuremberg, he would propose
important measures of religious toleration in return for their armed
support against the Turks.

The leaders were already gathering at Nuremberg to await him
there, and when I heard that the Elector John of Saxony, Luther's
old friend and champion, who carried greatest influence in the
league, had joined them I decided to visit him and discuss the
matter, to draw up plans before the diet began. A succession of
visits proved to be necessary, so that for some time I was continually
travelling to and fro. I was as unobtrusive as possible, avoiding
ceremony, and as I always stayed at Osiander's house in Nuremberg
my known friendship with him helped to cover the purpose of my
journey.

The course of negotiations however was less smooth than I
hoped. Many of the princes to whom I spoke, including the Elector John himself, shared the Emperor's view rather than ours of
King Henry's behaviour. The Elector was an enormously fat
man; but if his figure was that of a pig he had the heart of a
lion. He was impatient to challenge the Turks who threatened Germany, and it was hard to get him to talk of anything else. I took no
pride in the part that I was playing.

An interview stands out in my memory because of the events
that followed. Usually on my visits to Nuremberg I found Osiander
and his wife alone, except for the children; but on this occasion he
announced as he greeted me that he was expecting a guest, his
wife's niece from Ingolstadt on the Danube. I paid no great attention, and his words soon slipped from my mind as I climbed up
to the castle to call on the Elector.

The conversation was unsatisfactory from the start. He was in an irritable mood and taunted King Henry for hanging back when Christendom was fighting for its life. He went on to comment severely on the disruption of a marriage that had lasted so many years, and he expressed his sympathy for Queen Catherine. I was accustomed to lectures of this sort from Granvelle and the Emperor himself, on whose lips they were sheer hypocrisy. From the Elector however the words had a different sound, commanded belief. One could not be long in his presence without respecting his massive integrity, and I valued his good opinion both for my King and for myself. I spoke nothing but the truth when I retorted: "I'm very sorry for her too. Everyone is, the King most of all."

It was an unwise remark perhaps, and I had trouble to explain it on my return to England. Yet there was no disloyalty in it, no inconsistency. One can be genuinely sorry for a person on whom one inflicts inevitable misfortune. Malice of course corrupted and distorted what I said, and by that time the Elector himself was dead. King Henry alone took my meaning correctly, declaring that he retained great affection for his former wife, was much fonder of her than her nephew Charles had ever been.

I left the castle in an unhappy frame of mind, disturbed in my conscience and ashamed. It was still only the middle of the morning. I had more than an hour to spare before dinner, and I craved for solitude and exercise, a healing mixture that seldom fails to restore equanimity. When I came to the turning that led to Osiander's house I kept on past it to the river, and went for a long walk by myself upstream through the water meadows.

It was high summer, and the buttercups were so thick in the grass that I seemed to wade in a sea of gold. Under a cloudless sky the splendour was dazzling, and I was glad when I saw a large wood ahead stretching to the river bank. As I reached the fringe and stepped out of the glare into the shade, the sudden change to coolness and green twilight was as if I entered a many-storeyed cathedral built by God himself. The trees were almost entirely beech, many of great size a hundred and fifty or even two hundred years old. In the middle of the wood they grew straight and tall with glisten-ing sun-flecked boles rising often for more than forty feet without an offset.

I sat down to rest beneath on a carpet of mast. The channel of the river was narrow where an island split the stream, and across the water I could smell the elderblossom clustered on the farther shore. The air around me was heavy with the fragrance, sweet and drowsy. It was like a spell soothing, lulling me. I fell asleep.

I slept so soundly that when I awoke I had forgotten where I was, and it seemed as I stared across at the island that I was still in a dream or transported into a legendary Arcady, the fairyland of the ancient poets. Among the leaves of the thicket of elder a face was peeping, framed in smooth wet skeins of very fair hair. It was a face that belonged less perhaps to a Greek nymph than to a German nixie; the full mouth impudent and mirthful contrasted with the simple gravity, the honesty of the widely set grey eyes. Those eyes at the moment were carefully scanning the opposite bank upstream and downstream, but it was evident that she did not see me behind the screen of the great beech. She parted the bushes, climbed out on to the turf, then turned away and knelt down to pick a bunch of yellow flags in the ditch behind. "*Tibi candida Nais*," I muttered under my breath. She was a goddess incarnate, naked.

If the feeling of enchantment had been less strong I should not have pried on her. It was shocking to behave like the two unworthy priests in the story of Susannah, and my only excuse is that I forgot who I was, ceased even to be myself, under the bewildering spell of the elderblossom and the vision. I was not aware that I stirred. It may have been the breeze that shook the branches hiding me. Something in the sound, a warning tingle of her skin made her glance round quickly over her shoulder, and our eyes met. I could not see her blush, I was too conscious of my own. When I looked again the bushes had closed over her. Only the flowers scattered in the water where she had dropped them remained as evidence that the island was haunted by a goddess.

I was still dazed as I walked back to the town; but approaching Osiander's house I remembered that I was very late for dinner and was appalled by my bad manners. As soon as I met him I began my apology, not noticing that there was a stranger in the room; then I saw her and broke off abruptly, my voice failed me. Osiander glanced at me in surprise, and his wife introduced her niece. I tried to pull myself together, to persuade myself that I had never seen the girl before. As I hesitated she came towards me. I was about to make a formal bow, but she bent forward and gave me a smacking kiss on either cheek.

"Margaret," her aunt cried reproachfully. "You impudent minx." Then she turned to me with an embarrassed smile and explained: "I was telling her of your English custom, and she took it too much in earnest. She wants to make you feel at home."

It was indeed the custom in England, although it is dying out now, that a guest arriving was greeted by the women of the house with a kiss. I remember how it charmed Erasmus, even making up to him for the climate, for our ale which he refused to drink, and for the dirt and discomfort of which he complained in our dwellings.

During the next few weeks I saw more of Margaret than of the Elector. We went for walks by the river, rode together in the woods. She was of active habit and a proficient horsewoman; she was also an amusing and intelligent companion, well-read in classical literature and as pleased to discuss it as to tell me lively and witty stories of events in her native Ingolstadt. Her father owned a fleet of barges there, trading down the Danube to Regensburg and Passau. He was an early convert to Luther's views, so that Osiander coming to the town to complete his studies made his acquaintance and eventually married his sister. Margaret spoke much of her father for whom she had great admiration. He was indeed a remarkable man, not only in giving his daughter a good education, engaging teachers for her of sound learning, but also in the steadfastness with which he clung to his religious principles in a town where university and intellectual life were dominated by Johann Eck, Luther's relentless opponent, the foremost champion of the Papacy. I knew Eck of course by reputation as a scholar and theologian; but Margaret added details to the portrait which surprised me in a man so renowned for the severity of his rule. She described his assiduous pursuit of the local girls, the influence used to compel those whom he failed to attract, the tricks by which they thwarted his lust and held him up to ridicule. His behaviour shocked me, but her description made me laugh.

In the middle of this pleasant interlude the Emperor arrived at Nuremberg with his court, and the diet sat attended by the Protestant leaders. In return for their armed support he offered far-reaching concessions, on the understanding that these were provisional, depending on ratification by a general council of the Church. It was his long-cherished hope that a council would be convened, affording means to increase the power of the Empire at the expense of the Papacy; but the Pope for that reason was stubbornly opposed to the plan, and the Protestants knew that they had little to fear in the condition limiting the measures of toleration. They were all too much elated by the Emperor's conciliatory words, too eager to fight the Turks, to have any thought to spare for King Henry's troubles, even the few of them who believed in the justice of our cause. There was nothing for the present that I could usefully say or do.

I was glad that I could turn with an easy conscience to my private affairs. A decision lay before me of surpassing importance to the whole direction of my life. I came to see how much Margaret meant to me, and was appalled by the thought of living without her. Sixteen years had passed since Joan's death, and I had changed, grown up in the interval. I could not believe that there was any disloyalty to her memory in marrying again, in choosing a wife as unlike her as I was at the age of forty-three to the callow scholar whom she knew at Cambridge. A graver objection arose from the rule of celibacy which I accepted on taking holy orders. I was thankful to have sworn no oath; nevertheless it grieved me to think that many whose good opinion I valued would disapprove of a married priest. The outlook would have troubled me more if I had been in England; but here in Germany I had the example of the Lutherans to support me, among whom the celibate commanded no respect. Osiander himself was a priest, and he had a wife.

My hesitation was swept away when, on the very island in the Pegnitz where she first appeared to me, I told Margaret that I loved her and learnt that my love was returned. To her the rule of the priesthood presented no obstacle; she had been brought up to believe it an error and saw nothing in my calling at which there was reason to demur. As for the practical difficulties, she laughed at them. For the present none would arise, and it would be time enough to think when I was recalled to England. Little as she and Joan resembled each other, they had in common a cheerful trust in the benevolence of the future or an unwillingness to worry about it.

I was in no mood myself to let forethought spoil the happiness of the moment, and when we went back to her uncle and aunt and told them what we intended they expressed satisfaction in words so friendly that their sincerity could not be doubted. They did not understand how far England lagged behind Germany in clerical reform, and I felt no need to enlighten them, trusting that things would be different when Lady Anne became Queen. We were married by Osiander in St. Sebald's Church.

It is odd how patterns tend to repeat themselves in one's life. In little more than a month from our wedding circumstances arose to part us, putting me at a greater distance from Margaret than Cambridge ever put me from Joan. The diet came to an end, agreement was reached and a truce declared, and the champions of Christendom, Protestant and Catholic alike, allied themselves under the Emperor's leadership against the common enemy. There was a great bustle of departure in the town as the company broke up and princes rode off to their domains to collect their forces. The Emperor left too with a huge and magnificent retinue, announcing that he intended to accompany the army on active service. He added to my dismay that he expected all the foreign ambassadors accredited to his court to follow him. Our destination was country ravaged by Turkish invasion. It was quite clear that I should have to leave Margaret behind.

A respite however was offered when I learnt that the first stage of our journey was only to Regensburg, where we were to wait till the army was equipped. There was no reason why she should not travel so far with me, then go on up the river to Ingolstadt in one of her father's boats. As things turned out we remained at Regensburg for several weeks, greatly to my satisfaction. The time spent there would have been even more precious to me if I had known how long it would be before we were able to live together again openly as man and wife.

At Regensburg there was no need of concealment. Protestants were in high favour, the Emperor's allies in a crusade to save Christendom from the infidel, all Germany from massacre and devastation. When I called on friends and acquaintances I could introduce my wife without embarrassment.

Even so staunch an upholder of ecclesiastical tradition as old Dantiscus, the Polish ambassador, accepted my marriage with no more than a jesting reproach. He was a bishop of the strictest orthodoxy on whom no arguments of mine made any impression when I tried to win him over to King Henry's cause; but he was also one of the kindest of men, and if he had any scruples about receiving Margaret they melted at once when he looked at her. He behaved to her so charmingly that we were sorry that he was himself on the point of departure, having been recalled to Poland.

When he left we both accompanied him to the quay to see him off on the boat, and he surprised me by beckoning to a boy of about Margaret's age or a little younger, who was among his Polish attendants, and introducing him to me.

"I've a favour to ask," he told me. "This young man wants to be educated in England. Will you take him into your service and give him the chance?"

The request was so unexpected that I was at a loss to reply. I did not want to disoblige my old friend, but I had responsibilities enough already. I pointed out that I was unlikely to return to England for some time, and that when I did it would be as Archdeacon of Taunton without influence or establishment. But Dantiscus made light of my objections; he seemed to be convinced that I could do more than I said, and rather than offend him I agreed to keep the boy in my service while I was ambassador abroad, and take him back with me to England when I was recalled. It was a charge that I undertook reluctantly, but I had reason later to be grateful to Dantiscus for his insistence.

A sadder leave-taking awaited me a day or two afterwards when it was Margaret's turn to be seen off at the quay. We did not know when we should meet again, so much depended on the Emperor's plans and the course of events. As the crew poled the barge out from the shore, and hoisted sail to catch the fresh breeze blowing upstream, she knelt on the sacks of corn piled in the stern and leant forward to shout to me:

"Don't forget that you've promised to take Little John."

I remembered her kneeling to pick flowers on the island in the Pegnitz, and my eyes filled with tears.

Little John, the giant from Nottinghamshire, was indeed an indispensable escort, and for much of the way my only companion, on the journey on which I set out on the Emperor's heels. As I advanced into country recently evacuated by the Turks the destruction exceeded anything seen in Italy two years before. There was a place where a great battle had been fought, and I still revisit it in nightmare, see not only the charred ruins of the farms and the ripe wheat trampled in the fields, but also more horribly the bodies lying unburied, scattered by the side of the road for more than two miles. I rode by as quickly as I could and was told when I overtook Granvelle's headquarters in the evening that an entire Turkish army had been wiped out there; but when I repeated this to Little John he expressed contempt for foreign exaggeration, declaring that he counted the dead and the total barely reached two thousand, of whom at least half were Christians. Even so, it is an appalling number of souls to be cut off in their prime.

It was true that the Turks were in full retreat. The enormous army collected by the Emperor saw in fact little fighting as the Sultan alarmed by its size slipped back across the Hungarian border. We pursued without haste, as if content to be rid of the enemy and not anxious to inflict further punishment. Many found fault with the Emperor for his failure to press the victory home, to avenge his sister's misfortunes and restore her to the throne of Hungary; but he shrank from becoming involved in a campaign so far beyond his eastern frontier out of reach of the supplies on which he depended from Spain. He suffered already from shortage of money, and his army clamoured in vain for pay.

There was bitter disappointment among the soldiers who had been hoping to reimburse themselves from plunder as soon as they crossed into Turkish territory. Their indignation bordered on mutiny when he began to disband them without payment of the arrears which he owed. The effect was to let loose on the country a rabble of desperate vagrants, whose behaviour was scarcely less destructive than that of the Turks.

Not unnaturally the inhabitants retorted with violence of their own, hiding in the mountains and pouncing on any small party of soldiers or courtiers that they were able to cut off. Danger of brigands was the least however of the worries that oppressed me. The Emperor was making for Italy, and I learnt that his ultimate destination was Spain, where I should have to accompany him. How was Margaret to get there, and what would be her reception in a country which clung so fanatically to traditional ideas? On reaching Innsbruck I sent her a message by a merchant travelling back into Germany. I told her to ask her father to send her by barge down to Passau, where a captain to whom I spoke agreed to call for her and bring her up the Inn. She must wait at Innsbruck till I could come and fetch her.

While I lingered to make these arrangements the Emperor and his court pushed on over the Brenner pass into Italy, and I had to hurry to overtake them. Little John and I were alone again, as the rest of my servants went ahead with the Emperor's retinue. We made good speed and in three days' riding were coming down from the hills and could see Lake Garda beneath us. We found a ruined cottage in which to spend the night, with hay and corn left by the owners when they fled, and straw to serve as bedding for both man and beast.

I was comfortable enough on the straw, but I could not sleep. I lay awake brooding over my troubles, longing to have Margaret with me again and yet fearing the difficulties in which our marriage involved us. At last I could endure them no longer and got up and stepped out of doors.

It wanted at least two hours to dawn, but at first glance I thought that time had deceived me, the sky was so bright in the east. Then as I stared in amazement I saw that this was no glow of sunrise; its source was a star brighter than Hesperus or a planet, which rose over the shoulder of the hill, shining *luce maligna*, with a white radiance. A fine beam of light was reflected from it across the sky, pointing up towards the zenith. I recognised it from the description in Seneca's *Natural Questions* as a comet, one of those wandering stars that appear fitfully at intervals of many years, regarded in every age as a presage of disaster.

We were on horseback again early and reached Mantua the same day at a late hour of the evening. The Emperor was making a protracted stay there, and lodgings had been assigned to me. When I rode up my servants told me that Nicholas Hawkins, Archdeacon of Ely, was waiting for me. I went in to greet him and was surprised when he announced that he came both to take my place and to congratulate me. King Henry ordered me to return to England as quickly as possible. Archbishop Warham was dead, and I was chosen to succeed him as Archbishop of Canterbury, Primate of all England.

10

Spain might have been uncomfortable for a married Archdeacon of Taunton, but life would be incomparably more dangerous in England for a married Archbishop of Canterbury. When I recovered from my stupefaction at the news which Hawkins brought, and the consequences became clear to me, I was overwhelmed with dismay. I ought of course to have been grateful to King Henry for so remarkable a token of his favour, for promoting me so suddenly to the highest office in the Church over the heads of my ecclesiastical superiors. I was indeed anxious to justify the good opinion which he expressed of my abilities, but for the moment I had little thought for anything in my mind beyond the difficulties which my promotion created. There had been great changes recently in the Church of England, and I hoped for more when Lady Anne became Queen; but I could not believe even in my most sanguine moments that either the King himself or public opinion would accept a girl sitting as hostess at Lambeth Palace.

The first problem was to get her there; it would be time enough when she arrived to think what I was to do with her. A girl could not travel across Europe alone, with a sea passage to arrange at the end of her journey and a strange country to receive her of whose language she spoke only a few words. Still less could she travel in the company of the Archbishop designate of Canterbury, setting tongues wagging in every town through which we passed. I longed desperately for the tolerant atmosphere of Regensburg, where even Dantiscus was persuaded to condone my offence. Dantiscus. As I recalled his benevolence a chord was struck in my memory, from which inspiration flowed. I promised Hawkins to hasten my departure, telling him that I needed only a small escort of servants and adding casually that these would include a Polish boy left in my charge by the Bishop of Chelm. He showed little interest, was concerned only to see me off without delay, spoke anxiously of the King's impatience for my investiture.

I had been unable to pay attention to the Polish boy on the journey, had indeed almost forgotten his existence. When I summoned him now I was pleased to find him both intelligent and obliging. I had to take him into my confidence, but he never betrayed, never even presumed on it. He cannot be blamed if there was a trace of amusement in his attitude towards the adventure. My predicament appealed to his sense of humour.

The plan which I made with him was for Margaret to borrow his identity. They bore no resemblance to each other, but we were unlikely to meet anyone who knew him, who would reveal the imposture. If she carried his papers which identified him, and the difference of sex were well enough disguised, there was little danger. His clothes, I thought, would fit her, and her voice which was low and melodious might easily be taken for a boy's that was late in breaking. No one would be aware that the accent of her halting English was that of a German and not of a Pole. When I went to take leave of the Emperor I was careful to spread the news round the court that I was travelling with a Polish companion. The better the story became known of the duty imposed on me by Dantiscus, the safer my page would be from inconvenient questions.

I wound up my affairs at Mantua as quickly as I could, so quickly that my inventory of stores delivered to Hawkins was found after my departure to be inaccurate (the error was luckily to my disadvantage, not his), then I set forth with my escort on the journey to England. Hawkins courteously accompanied me for a mile or so along the road; but as soon as we were rid of him and he was out of sight our party split up. The servants rode on to Milan, where I told them to wait for me. The boy and I took a turning which would lead us over the mountains to Innsbruck.

The distance is the best part of a hundred and fifty miles. We rode scarcely pausing for food or sleep, spending all day and often most of the night in the saddle, changing horses when we could at an inn or farm. There was urgent need of haste, of secrecy. This was where the danger was greatest, where a mishap could defeat my whole plan. How could I explain if I were recognised what I was doing on the road to Innsbruck, when I left Mantua bound for England?

We rode for the most part in silence. Conversation carried on in Latin, eked out by the boy with a smattering of German and unintelligible Polish, was too much effort in the circumstances. But his companionship sustained me, his ardour was infectious. He had the high spirits, the generosity of youth, a willingness to share the excitement of another's hopes as if they were his own. He had also untiring energy of body, a resilience surviving the most gruelling exertion.

Late on the fourth evening we rode into Innsbruck, where I learnt that my friendly captain had returned from Passau and was to be found on his barge at the moorings a few miles downstream, the limit of navigation. We wasted no time in the town but pressed on at once through the darkness.

Light glowed from the barge, beckoning to us out of the night as we approached. At last I was in sight of the goal, but my mind ached with suspense, with nagging fears. What if Margaret was not on board, had been unable or unwilling to make the journey, and the captain waiting for her in vain had come back without her? I spurred my horse to a gallop. The wharf was plainly revealed now, lit by the radiance pouring from door and windows. A figure knelt in the bows of the ship, leaning out and waving to me. It was as if she knew in her heart the time of my coming. I sprang from my horse, tied it to a mooring post, and strode over the gunwale on to the deck.

A task still lay ahead from which I shrank. As soon as I could I broke the news to her of my promotion. She was less disturbed however than I expected. It even pleased her to see herself as an Archbishop's wife. Her education accustomed her to the idea of a married prelate, and she could not understand what a shock it would be to English convention, or how cruelly the disapproving might behave. I tried to explain the facts bluntly, neither hiding nor mitigating their harshness. I was determined that she should be fully warned, not led into danger in ignorance; but even while I spoke to deter her I dreaded to hear her say that she would prefer to stay behind in Germany.

She said nothing of the kind, and when I told her of my plan for her to impersonate the Polish boy she accepted it with delight. In my eagerness to meet her I had left him standing on the quay; but now I called to him to join us and introduced him, and we all sat down in the cabin to a good meal. Margaret and the boy laughed and talked together, and I was sadly aware of my own sober age as I watched their gaiety. The inadequacy of his German was no obstacle, and she even got him to teach her some Polish words to support her disguise if need arose. Afterwards he pulled from his pack a smart doublet and hose made to his measure for the purpose in Mantua, and she went out and tried them on. She returned smiling, pleased with the novelty of her appearance, and when the boy laughed she scolded him hotly. The clothes fitted her indeed as well as could be expected, although the doublet was rather too short, the hose too tight in the seat.

We parted from the boy the following morning. I gave him ample money for his journey and detailed instructions to guide him, telling him to go down the Inn, up the Danube, then by any transport that he could find to Nuremberg, where Osiander would receive him, put him in charge of one of the merchants trading between the Hanseatic ports and the Steelyard in London. There was no reason to fear for his safety, and I had confidence in his discretion, his ability to travel without attracting attention. His journey went in fact smoothly enough, and he reached England soon after my own return. I sent him to my brother Edmund who took care of his education at Cambridge, and when he himself was transferred on my recommendation to be Archdeacon of Canterbury he brought the boy with him. We had reason to be proud of the rapid progress made by our scholar, even if he owed as much to native aptitude as to the teaching which we procured for him.

All this lay many years ahead when I set out from Innsbruck to cross back over the Alps with my Polish page. I was tormented by anxiety, doubtful both of the effectiveness of her disguise and of her ability to bear the strain of the journey. She was a capable horsewoman, but this was such a distance as she had never travelled in the saddle before, and I dared not loiter.

In the event her endurance amazed me. She seemed to be untiring or refused to betray that she was tired, and as the weather remained favourable we covered the rough ground in the mountains at a pace little less brisk than that which I set with the boy. I refused however to let her ride through the night, and when darkness fell we put up at an inn. Sometimes as we dismounted I caught inquisitive glances, and it was easy to guess the thought that lay behind the sly leer; but I could only pretend that I had not noticed, and trust that she had not either. I was thankful at least to escape active annoyance, even if the indulgence that we enjoyed sprang from a moral laxity of which no Archbishop should approve. It occurred to no one that Margaret was my wife.

When we came down into the plain we turned west, skirting the shore of Lake Garda, and I showed her the peninsula of Sirmio of which the Latin poet Catullus was so fond. In spite of our haste and my anxiety those days spent riding alone with her held great happiness, whose flavour clings unfading in my memory. I had a feeling even at the time that I must make the most of them, a premonition that I should never again travel abroad.

At Milan we picked up the servants. They were of course aware of our secret and received my new page without surprise. We followed in reverse direction the road by which I first entered Italy on my way to Rome. Our troubles began when we climbed into the mountains to cross the pass into France. The weather changed suddenly. Without warning we plunged into winter, plodding through snowdrifts and slipping and stumbling on the ice where the path was blown clear by the gale. We took comfort from the hope that these conditions were local to the high ground on the watershed, and that they would improve as we came down on the other side.

We were disappointed. Even when we left the hills altogether the going remained abominable. The whole of France was gripped by freezing cold, a winter unparalleled in living memory. I am accustomed myself to riding on icy roads, but for Margaret's sake we had to slacken speed. It was a terrible experience for her. When all our attention was needed to keep our horses from falling a blizzard would strike us, cutting our faces and blinding us with driven hail. We seldom covered more than fifteen miles in a day.

As we approached Lyon, moving at this desperately slow pace, I was astonished to meet Stephen Vaughan, a friend of Cromwell's and partner in his commercial enterprises, who told me that my delay was causing concern at court and that he was sent to hurry me up. His message and his company were equally disturbing. It was not that I had anything against him. He was a man of open mind and cheerful warmth with whom I had much in common, an outspoken admirer of Tindale's controversial translation of the Bible. When I knew him better I learnt to respect him for the loyalty of his friendship for Cromwell. But he could hardly have chosen a more inconvenient moment to arrive.

As he joined us to escort us home my heart sank, foreseeing that for the rest of the journey we should not only have to contend with the weather but also guard our behaviour so as not to betray Margaret's disguise. The only comfort was that he himself had as much struggle as we to ride through the snow and ice, and he was fully occupied with fears for his safety. He told me that he had already suffered one bad fall, nearly breaking his leg as he rode south, and he was anxious not to repeat it.

Our chief danger of discovery was when we stopped for the night at an inn. At first he seemed to take it for granted that my page spoke only Polish, but when he overheard her one evening talking to me in German, a language in which he was proficient, he began to draw her into the conversation, to pay more attention. He showed an embarrassing interest in Polish customs, asking her many questions about her supposed fatherland. Her answers reflected credit on her power of imagination, but I observed his eyebrows lift sometimes in incredulous surprise. There was too much of Nuremberg in her Poland, with decorations borrowed from German romance, from Von Eschenbach's Castle of the Grail.

If his suspicions were aroused he kept them to himself on the journey, and with one exception he divulged them to nobody on our arrival in England. The exception, I am sure, was Cromwell. When I called on him at last in London, and expatiated on the obstacles that delayed me, there was a glint of mockery in the sidelong glance with which he replied:

"I congratulate you. Like Aeneas you enjoy the protection of the goddess. I hope that to spare your blushes Venus wore breeches."

I smiled as politely as I could, and said nothing. By then the Polish boy had vanished, not to reappear till he landed unobtrusively at the Steelyard. Margaret, transformed back into a girl, was safe with Alice at Stixwould, where I sent her in the care of a trusted woman, a servant from Durham House. On principle Alice disapproved of the marriage of priests, even more of Archbishops: but I knew that she would behave with loving kindness to anyone of whom I was fond, and I left Margaret there with an easy mind till I had a house of my own to shelter her. When at last I saw her again I asked her what she thought of the nuns of Stixwould, and she pouted expressively; but in a moment she added with a smile:

"Your sister was a great comfort."

At my interview with Cromwell he told me to go on at once to Hampton Court to the King. I went in some foreboding; it was already the middle of January, and I was expected before Christmas. The urgency of the summons puzzled me, I could not guess the reason. It is the usual custom when a prelate dies to leave an interval of at least a year before installing his successor, so that the King's treasury may enjoy the vacant revenues of the see. Six months had not passed since Warham's death. Why was the King so impatient then for my investiture? It seemed to me that mystery was piled on mystery. The preferment of a mere archdeacon to the see of Canterbury was odd enough in itself, without all this haste to complete it.

At Hampton Court I found the King watching a bear baiting. It is a sport that I detest, my sympathies are all with the bear; but I was glad of it on this occasion as it put the King in a genial humour. He was content to chaff me on my horsemanship, without probing too inquisitively into the causes of the delay. He went on almost at once to talk of his own affairs. His voice dropped, and it was not easy to hear him through the shouting of men and barking of dogs; but I caught the name of the Marchioness of Pembroke, and I knew that he spoke of Lady Anne. News of the title granted to her, raising her to the peerage in her own right, reached me while I was in Germany. It was an honour without precedent in English history.

At last he himself became aware of the impossibility of conversation in such a din, and he drew me away into an alley between hedges of box. As we paced to and fro he opened his mind, inveighing bitterly against the deferment of hope as the interminable proceedings dragged on at Rome. I had the feeling not only of impatience but also of anxiety prompting his resentment, and I wondered if Lady Anne was the source, if she was losing enthusiasm for a match so long withheld. His agitation was distressing to watch, the more so as there seemed to be nothing that I could do to help him. Suddenly he broke off, was silent for a moment, then declared in a tone that held appeal as well as authority:

"This is why I sent for you. I rely on my Archbishop for the justice which the Pope denies."

I learnt that my first duty on taking office would be to set up a court of my own to pronounce judgment on the validity of his marriage.

Lord Wiltshire, whose hospitality I again enjoyed, filled in details of what had been happening while I was out of the country. He himself was less pleased by his daughter's new title than I expected. People were saying, he complained, that it was compensation paid to a paramour whom the King no longer wished to marry. Little as I believed this to be true, I saw clearly how vulnerable to slander the uncertainty left her. Her father described with feeling the humiliation to which she was exposed in the autumn when she wanted to accompany the King to Boulogne to meet the King of France. No lady of rank at the French court could be persuaded to attend to receive her. Queen Eleanor was our Queen Catherine's niece, so she had reason for her scruples. There was no such excuse for the others.

The blow that hurt Lady Anne most was the conveniently timed illness pleaded by her own dear Duchess of Alençon, now Queen of Navarre, the presiding genius of her girlhood in Paris. I remembered how her voice warmed when she spoke of her, the golden glow lighting her reminiscences, and could imagine what she felt when her idol let her down. The Queen of Navarre however was devoted to her brother, King Francis, and would never oppose his will.

It was impossible of course for Lady Anne to visit a court where the womenfolk took such pains to avoid her, and King Henry had to leave her at Calais when he rode out to be entertained at Boulogne. All the same, she got her own back in the end. King Francis escorted his English guests back to Calais, and a masked ball was held in his honour in which she joined unrecognised. When she lifted her mask and revealed herself he was dancing with her, and for the rest of the evening he behaved to her with courtesy, even with gallantry, charmed by her gaiety, intelligence and fluent command of French.

Her father blamed her both for inviting rebuff and for the boldness with which she defeated its purpose, but I could not find it in my heart to condemn her.

I began to look at my coming elevation in a new and more favourable light, now that I knew for what service I was chosen and how great was the need. Little as I was qualified in other respects for the office, I had given more thought probably than anyone else in the country to the law governing this issue of the King's marriage, and where the happiness of those whom I loved, the peace and security of the realm itself were at stake I did not shrink from defying the Pope, or even from usurping his authority. The organisation of the Church exists to help, not to hinder the good intentions of secular government.

For the very reason that controversial action was intended the King was anxious for my appointment to conform with established rules, and he applied to the Pope for the bulls needed to authorise my consecration. They were issued promptly, without demur. Thanks were due for this no doubt to French influence, a fruit of King Henry's negotiations at Boulogne, perhaps even of the impression made on King Francis by Lady Anne herself at Calais. The voice of France carried weight with the Pope, who was trying to arrange a marriage between his niece Catherine de Medici and the French King's second son. All the same, I like to think that in granting me the bulls he bore in mind our pleasant acquaintance when I was in Rome, and that his readiness to agree was at least partly a gesture of personal goodwill.

Was I guilty of treachery in accepting the favour, intending to use it in defiance of his jurisdiction? I take comfort from my firm conviction that he was not deceived, that he knew very well that I was appointed as an instrument to promote the King's policy. It is true that he did not expect me to go so far as to pronounce judgment on my own annulling the marriage, and I have heard that he expressed sharp irritation when the news reached him. One can distinguish however between words uttered in heat when a man is annoyed and the considered aims which he pursues guided by his reason. To Pope Clement no aunt of the Emperor's was worth a schism in the Church. He earnestly desired reconciliation with England, no matter whom King Henry chose for wife.

Another source of difficulty to my conscience was the oath which I had to take to the Pope at my consecration. My predecessors at Canterbury accepted it without scruple, although it was plainly incompatible with loyalty to the King under the Statute of Praemunire. The words stuck in my throat however when the first official duty demanded of me was to override Papal authority in the matter of the King's marriage. I asked the King whether the oath could not be omitted, but he replied that this would precipitate the schism which he was as anxious as the Pope himself to avoid. We still hoped that if we stood fast on the issue the Pope would give way, and that independence could be won for the Church in England without disrupting Christian unity.

The compromise which I adopted has provoked much recrimination from my enemies; but I believe that it was an honest expedient, the only way in which the conflict of duties could be resolved. When I went to Westminster for the ceremony I carried a copy of a declaration that I had composed, and I read it aloud in the chapter house before a select company including lawyers assembled there. I declared that the words of the oath which I was about to swear bore meaning only in so far as they were consistent with the law of God and my allegiance to the King, and with my professed intention to reform the Church in England and strengthen its government. I repeated this at the ceremony itself, reading it from the steps of the altar immediately after taking the oath. The Papal legate was present in the congregation, and even at that stage he could have protested if he wished. He said nothing.

I was consecrated and took office in March. There were heavy expenses to be met, a sum far beyond my resources; but the difficulty was solved for me by the King, who lent me the money from the Royal treasury. I was grateful to him for his kindness, but he had pressing reasons which disinclined him to wait till I was in a position to pay for myself. At the end of January he was secretly married to Lady Anne Boleyn, Marchioness of Pembroke, at York Place in an attic in one of the turrets. I knew nothing about it at the time, or indeed for many weeks afterwards. At first when rumours leaked out I dismissed them with incredulity; but as the stories grew more circumstantial, the evidence on which they were founded more worthy of belief, I could no longer banish my suspicions. I observed that Lord Wiltshire had lost his worried frown and recovered all his old cheerfulness and buoyancy.

If I had seen more of Lady Anne herself I should probably have known the truth sooner. She was too indiscreet to keep a secret from anyone long in her company. In the end it was an incident arising from her behaviour that opened my eyes. I was at court at Greenwich when she came out of the King's room biting an apple and crossed the hall where a group of people stood, Wyatt among them. She went up to him and spoke in a tone that no one could help overhearing. Her voice was low in pitch, but it carried:

"I've such a craving for apples I can't stop eating. The King says I must be pregnant."

Then she laughed suddenly, partly in embarrassment, but there was exhilaration too. We could still hear her laughing as she walked on down the passage.

Wyatt himself moved away, paying no attention to the chatter that broke out as soon as her back was turned. I followed his example. I was uncertain even whether she had seen me there at all; but on the next day when we met again she drew me aside, and there was contrition in her manner. She told me that the King and she were married, and asked me to pray for their child to be a son. If I had known all that she herself staked on the birth of an heir I should have been even readier than I was to forgive her, to make allowances for any mood of rash flippancy flaunted to mask the strain.

She offered no excuse for the concealment of her marriage, and I cannot deny that my feelings were hurt by it. Their failure to take me into their confidence seemed to be a slight not only to my office but also to my friendship. Yet when I had time to think it over I came to understand and approve of the King's reasons. It would have been embarrassing for me as Archbishop to celebrate a second marriage when I had not yet given judgment on the annulment of the first. The proceedings at York Place were in fact extremely irregular. I suppose that they can be defended on the ground that, if the King's first marriage was void *ab initio*, he remained unmarried and free to take a bride even without a verdict formally recorded. It is not an argument that I should press with any conviction, and I am thankful that I was not asked for my opinion.

The busy gossip of court had the effect very soon that everyone was talking of the King's marriage behind his back, and as Easter approached I advised him to take the opportunity for a public announcement, formally acknowledge his wife and proclaim her Queen. She was already pregnant, and it was of vital importance that no shadow of legal impediment should threaten the heir when he was born. There were too many people in the country ready to dispute the succession if a possible flaw could be found. This argument made the impression that I expected, and on Easter Eve a ceremony was held to which all the courtiers were summoned and invited to pay homage to Queen Anne. I wish that I could say that all paid it willingly. Many of the men were enemies of her family, most of the women jealous of her looks. A few objected on principle, adherents of the former Queen Catherine, henceforward to be known as the Princess Dowager.

It was high time that doubts were removed, that a clear judgment was given pronouncing the nullity of the marriage contracted between the King and his brother's wife. As she was living at Ampthill Castle in Bedfordshire I arranged to hold my court at the priory at Dunstable to suit her convenience. I must confess that I was glad of the excuse to be as far as possible from London, where opponents of the King's policy whipped up popular feeling, and there had already been demonstrations of ill-will. These were noisy and disagreeable, but they proceeded rather from the desperate efforts of a few troublemakers than from any widespread disloyalty to the King. Men regarded him as a bulwark against anarchy; they remembered that he had kept peace and order at home during a reign already of a quarter of a century, and they were more interested in his continuing ability to fill the part than in his choice of a wife. In so far as his new marriage helped to ensure the survival of the dynasty they approved of his behaviour.

When I presided at the court at Dunstable I had been Archbishop for only two months, and had no experience of high office or judicial functions to guide me. It was a daunting prospect to play the leading part in an issue of such importance, watched by all Christendom. There can be few cases if any before in which the King was suitor, his own subject the judge, and it cost me hours of painful thought to find appropriate phrases for the writ summoning the parties to a hearing. When I showed my draft to the King he altered it in one or two places to make it more deferential. He understood better than I how careful a balance was needed to prevent misinterpretation, to assert the authority of the judgment which determined his suit without impairing that of the Crown for whose sake it was pronounced. In submitting to be judged by his Archbishop he sought to establish Royal supremacy over the Church.

The writ served on the Princess Dowager involved me in less difficulty as she paid no attention to it. Ampthill might have been a hundred miles from Dunstable, for any willingness that she showed to take part in the proceedings. I was greatly relieved by her refusal to appear, having heard that if she came she intended to dispute the jurisdiction of the court and appeal to the Pope, and as that would be an offence against Praemunire it would put me in the embarrassing position of having to order her arrest. Her absence had the further advantage that it enabled me to pronounce judgment with less delay. Time was running short. It was already the middle of May, and Queen Anne's coronation was fixed for Whitsunday, June 1st.

My memory of Dunstable is of a torment of anxiety and impatience. We seemed to be dogged by petty misfortunes. At the first session indispensable witnesses were not available, and nearly a week was wasted before the oversight was made good. Then came the three Rogation days followed by Ascension Day, when the court could not sit. I was dismayed when I thought of the narrow margin of time left me to fulfil my task. I wished with all my heart that King Henry had chosen someone more capable for the work.

There was not even congenial entertainment to take my mind off my cares. Except for Stephen Gardiner who led the counsel for the Crown my colleagues were strangers, men known to me only as distinguished names when I was at Cambridge, inhabitants of a remote Olympus. I was ill at ease among them, suspecting arrogance and disdain often probably without cause. It was not really a consolation even to have Gardiner's company. He could be very amusing when he wished, and I admired his brilliant ability; but I knew that he was jealous of my promotion, had himself aspired to my place. I was discouraged from seeking his advice when it was so plainly to his advantage that I should fail.

There was an excellent library at the priory, but I was in no mood to settle down to a book. A relaxation that I preferred when I had the opportunity was to escape out of doors and ride or walk alone on the downs. The Chilterns rise behind Dunstable in a steep escarpment of bare turf scarred in places with gleaming outcrop of chalk. Such hills have a clarity of outline, a grave serenity that allures as if all the wonder of eternity lay waiting just over the brow. I found a healing quiet there.

I gave judgment on May 23rd with nine days to spare before the date of the coronation, but there was still a matter needing my attention before all was in order. I hurried back to Lambeth to confirm the validity of the marriage celebrated secretly between the King and Queen in January. It was in keeping with the breathless pace of events that I was still occupied with legal prerequisites when the Queen set out from Greenwich to be crowned, travelling in state up the river to the Tower of London. To my great regret I missed the spectacle.

On the next day I made up for my disappointment, riding behind her in procession from the Tower to Westminster. I do not usually enjoy ceremonial occasions, but this had a flavour of its own which carried me out of myself. The sudden relief from effort and anxiety was an intoxication, and I lived under its spell. At last the obstacles yielded; our policy bore fruit, and I shared the triumph. If there was a reckoning to be paid when the news reached the Emperor and the Vatican we were in no mood to worry about it till the festivities were over. No forebodings indeed could survive in the sunshine of the Queen's progress. Two white ponies led by footmen supported her litter; she was dressed all in silver, and her head was bare except for a golden circlet set with rubies. Her dark hair fell over her shoulders and reached to her hips so that she sat on it. She was transformed by the scene, by the radiance of her eyes into a goddess, a Queen of the Night, Diana supreme in the underworld.

I had this glimpse of her before we started, but thereafter her litter was hidden by the carriages containing the great ladies of the court who followed her. My own place was behind them in the van of the horsemen, where I rode beside the French ambassador. London was barely recognisable as we passed through. Cornhill was hung with crimson, Cheapside with cloth of gold, conduits flowed with wine, and for the whole distance from the Tower to Temple Bar the road was strewn with fine gravel and bordered with railings to protect the crowd from the horses. Even so the children climbed over or crept under, and we had to ride with care not to hurt them.

In later years, when the opinion was likely to find favour, it has been said that the crowd watched the festivities with apathy, even with sullen hostility to the Queen. This is very far from my impression of the events in which I took part. The English love pageantry, and they flocked into the streets as the procession went by. The town rang with spontaneous merrymaking, singing and dancing. If there were enemies at work stirring up mischief they had no success.

The King himself took part neither in the procession nor in the service that followed on the Sunday in the Abbey church. He wanted the Queen to enjoy undivided glory, not only for her own sake but also in the hope that this unprecedented honour would reinforce the legitimacy of the child whom she carried in her womb. She was already midway through her pregnancy. Good reason existed for the urgency to fix the date of the coronation while she was still able to bear the strain. I felt anxiety when I placed the crown of St. Edward on her head, for it is very heavy, and I made haste as soon as the ritual allowed to replace it with the smaller crown brought for her use. Yet she betrayed no fatigue at any time during the proceedings. It was as if her spirit took charge of her body, transfigured it with power. She moved and spoke in a dream which we shared with her, alive and responsive to each other within its enchantment, but remote from the limitations of the accustomed world.

When the service was over and she sat down to dine in Westminster Hall, presiding over the banquet with the greatest peers of the realm to wait on her, I admired not only her animation but also the grace, charm and sweetness that adorned it. At first a fear nagged me that she would blunder, would let the wild imp prevail in her and outrage decorum. But when I saw how she rose to the occasion, as she always did when it was great enough, I was reassured. I was in a good position to watch her as I was given a place at her table, a privilege that I enjoyed as Archbishop while the other lords served or stood.

Dreams end in waking up. The repercussions provoked abroad by the coronation were more violent even than we feared. Far from acquiescing in the annulment and remarriage as an accomplished fact, the Pope—in the first shock of the news—was bitterly offended and pressed on with his own investigation in the Court of Rota. His temper was not improved when King Henry sent a chaplain, Edmund Bonner, to explain our views. Later events have brought me so often into conflict with Bonner that my opinion of him possibly is warped; but even in those days I disliked his hectoring manner which despised conciliation as weakness, and I myself was inclined to despise him in turn for his likeness to a little strutting cock-pigeon, paunchy and pompous. He certainly made a deplorable impression on the Pope, who threatened in exasperation to have him boiled in a tub of molten lead. On his return home Bonner never tired of repeating the story, flinging up his hands in horror to inveigh against Papal barbarity, preening himself on the courage with which he defied it. I am afraid that I chuckled as I listened, very sure that the lead would be stone-cold before Pope Clement made up his mind.

Elsewhere in Europe also opinion hardened against us. Even King Francis was incensed, complaining that he was not given proper warning and that our precipitancy thwarted his careful plans. Alarming reports reached the council from the Duke of Norfolk, the Queen's uncle, who had been sent as ambassador to France. These spoke of the hostility aroused everywhere by English policy, of reprisals contemplated by the Emperor, the Pope and the French King acting in concert. There was danger of an embargo imposed on our Flemish trade, even of military invasion. King Henry prepared to raise levies to man the defences on the coast.

Cromwell alone was unperturbed:

"The Duke," he told me, "reports what he'd like to be true."

There was certainly a note of relish in the insistence with which the Duke prophesied disaster. He resented the influence of the King's advisers, that of Cromwell especially, whom he suspected not without reason of sending him to France to keep him out of the way.

Nothing was said about these anxieties to the Queen. Everyone was careful to shelter her, to spare her any agitation. So much depended on the safe delivery of her child. The birth of an heir apparent would disarm opposition at home, extinguishing the claims of the Princess Dowager and Princess Mary. Abroad too the result was likely to be decisive; the Pope had good reason to desire the secure establishment of a dynasty in England to counteract the dangerous predominance of France and Spain, and I was sure that he would soon become reconciled to its origin. Even the Emperor would abandon the feud when he saw that his aunt's cause was hopeless.

For the next few months the nation waited in suspense. The King consulted astrologers and crystal-gazers, who assured him without hesitation that the baby would be a boy, a healthy prince. Earnest prayers were offered in the churches in the belief, scarcely less superstitious, that God will determine the laws of nature to suit human will.

On Sunday, September 7th, the Queen gave birth to a girl, who received the name of Elizabeth after her grandmother, the heiress of the Plantagenets.

11

Knole was my favourite of the houses available to me in the country, belonging to the see of Canterbury. It stands far enough away from London to offer seclusion and rest, near enough, within a day's ride, to keep in touch with public affairs. It is a pleasant house in which to live, largely rebuilt at the end of the last century by a predecessor, Archbishop Bourchier, to bring it up to modern standards of comfort. In the ample grounds which surround it I could indulge my taste for walking unrebuked and unobserved, and as the park lies on a shelf of the hills delectable views rewarded me, looking out across the Weald of Kent to the distant glimpse of the downs on the skyline, the last rampart of the kingdom bounding the sea. It was a great grief to me some years later when the King proposed an exchange of lands under which I had to give up Knole to him. I tried to get him to take Otford instead as it is in the same neighbourhood, an enormous palace much too big for me, on which old Warham spent tens of thousands of pounds. The glowing terms in which I praised Otford to tempt the King were disingenuous, and I deserved the outcome. The exchange was made to cover both houses, Knole and Otford too.

I should have been false to my principles if I had opposed an exchange desired by the King, even that of a house as dear to me as Knole. The revenues of the Church are provided to help it to reveal and propagate the love of God on earth. They are necessary for the purpose, but by a paradox that cannot be escaped they also defeat it. They become poison to the spirit when rights of property are claimed. The antidote is to regard them as a gift limited by conditions, which the secular authority can vary at will.

For the first few years however Knole was mine, and I made a home there for Margaret when I brought her south from Stixwould. Few places could be more suitable for a refuge. Within the ring-fence of the park we could forget the dangers besetting our marriage and live together naturally as husband and wife. We had complete trust in the loyalty of our servants, both men and women, and events proved that it was not misplaced. As the new policy took shape in the Church it made many enemies, and the disaffected lost no opportunity to throw discredit on the King's advisers, among whom I myself as Archbishop was an obvious target. They raked up every scandal against me that they could find, ranging from my work as an ostler in the Dolphin stables at Cambridge to charges of equivocation in my consecration oath. Among all this calumny no one even hinted at the most damaging fact of all, the plain truth that I was married. Margaret remained hidden from the nation, undefiled by prurient tongues till the time came when I could acknowledge her in public as my wife. I have never forgotten what gratitude I owe my servants for their discretion.

She herself deserves praise for the patience with which she endured concealment. Although she was fond of Knole and glad to be safe there she was young and adventurous, eager to know what England was like, and the restrictions imposed on her movements were peculiarly irksome to her. When she began to make plans, to suggest ways in which she could accompany me unremarked I had not the heart to reprove her. I discussed them at first without serious intention; but her spirits rose so irrepressibly as we talked, her cheeks glowed and her eyes lit with such animation, that she infected me with her own recklessness, my reluctance melted.

The difficulty was to choose her a suitable disguise. There were few places in my retinue that a young woman could fill without comment. On the first occasion that I ventured to take her with me to Lambeth I arranged for some of the kitchen staff at Knole to come too, and she travelled among them as Cinderella. This was not a success. The Lambeth cooks were affronted, asking why I needed to bring women from Kent to prepare my food, and Margaret whose accent, pretty as it sounded, was still unmistakably foreign, attracted unwelcome curiosity. Even as entertainment for her the expedition was scarcely worthwhile, affording too circumscribed a view of the world when she was tied to the kitchen. On our return to Knole she declared firmly:

"I'm sure I'm better as a Polish boy than a kitchenmaid."

By that time the Polish boy was in England, being educated at Cambridge, and it would be rash to let her impersonate him when she might meet anyone even in London who knew him by sight. Her words however put ideas into my head. As relations with the Pope grew more strained King Henry was increasing his efforts to win support among the German Protestants, and I was encouraged to keep contact with my acquaintances there. It was not implausible that from time to time I should introduce a young man as my guest, son of a remote and unknown, if not fictitious German dignitary. In this way Margaret and I made many pleasant excursions together. She accompanied me on my visitations of the diocese and was present in Canterbury cathedral when I was enthroned. She even came with me to Hampton Court to watch a jousting match.

Stephen Gardiner, without knowing it, created an obstacle that interrupted the custom. A rumour spread round the town that he kept two young men in his household who were really girls. It was probably a groundless calumny. As he was so outspoken in disapproval of married clergy I cannot believe that either was his wife, and I should have thought him too careful both of his principles and of his reputation to indulge in casual unchastity. Nothing in the story concerned me directly, but I listened with growing discomfort as I heard it repeated, gathering salacious detail from mouth to mouth, wherever I went. I reflected how much closer a scrutiny Margaret might now undergo.

She was with me at the time at Lambeth, and if I could I should have taken her straight back to Knole; but I had important business at Canterbury which could not be put off. There was no time to change our plans, we were going to travel by water round the coast to Sandwich. It seemed to me indeed that there could be little danger on the voyage, in the seclusion of the ship. We embarked as quickly as possible, and she went into the cabin and stayed there, screened from public view.

All would have been well if an incompetent steersman had not run us aground on a mudbank at the mouth of the Medway. It was a raw afternoon in February with a blustering wind, and as we came out on deck to see what had happened the river looked peculiarly uninviting, turgid water curling into foam under a leaden sky. The tide was on the ebb, and islands of slime already glistened, left bare among the shoals where we stuck. The captain was seriously alarmed. He told me that he would have to wait for the next tide to float us off, and meanwhile the ship was listing badly and had sprung a leak. There was another within hailing distance, drawing in to sail up to Rochester, and he offered to row me with my party across in the dinghy and transfer us. It was evident that he wanted us out of the way, and I could not very well refuse; but I disliked the thought of spending the night in Rochester, where the bishop, John Fisher, was an active opponent of the King's policy, suspected even of conspiring to overthrow it. In the shadow of his cathedral I should be surrounded by enemies, to whom nothing would give greater pleasure than the chance to discredit me.

My eyes rested doubtfully on Margaret, and panic gripped me. It seemed to me that not even Gardiner's girls could have worn so transparent a disguise, that already I listened to the jeers of the bishop's party in Rochester. In my agitation I acted on an impulse which a saner mood would have rejected.

I told the captain that among my luggage I had a crate of great value, which could not be let out of my sight. He agreed reluctantly to take it with us in the dinghy. At once I drew Margaret apart, and we hurried together into the cabin where I had a large packing case of books. When I flung them out there was just room for her to curl up inside, and I shut the lid and fastened the bolts, taking care to see that there were cracks between the boards wide enough for her to breathe. When all was ready I called to the sailors, and two of them lifted the case out and lowered it into the boat. I myself sat beside it, keeping anxious watch as we crossed rocking in the swell, and again after transshipment as we sailed up the Medway. On arrival at Rochester I hired porters to carry it, telling them to accompany me to the inn, where I gave orders that it should be taken straight to my bedroom.

I was about to follow it upstairs; but the landlord held me in conversation, and it would have been churlish to rebuff him. He told me that he and his family were of the reforming party, that they had been in trouble more than once for their opinions with their orthodox bishop, and that they regarded me as their protector, a champion of enlightenment in the Church. In other circumstances I should have been delighted by what he said; but he was terribly long-winded, and my impatience grew as he talked. I tried to assure myself that there was no need to fret, that the crate would be handled with care, that Margaret could be left for a few more minutes without discomfort. Then while I fidgeted, unable to escape, feet came scuttling down the staircase, and a chambermaid burst into the taproom where I was standing.

"Your Grace, your Grace," she cried. "Your box is bewitched. It's making the oddest noises."

I tore upstairs with the landlord and two potboys on my heels. As soon as I entered the bedroom I understood what had happened. The men had put the crate where I told them; but in their anxiety to leave it tidily in place they hoisted it up on end, the wrong end unluckily with Margaret head downwards. The noise that I heard was a succession of choking gasps.

Most of the staff of the inn seemed to have gathered, but I was too frantic to heed. With their help I laid the crate flat, unbolted and opened it. When I pulled Margaret out she was crimson in the face, speechless, and I thought that she was dying; but as she sat up the posture and a volley of pats on the back from her rescuers soon brought her to life, and she even found her tongue to protest in indignant German at the blows. The cure was completed by the landlord's wife, who came running with a flagon of wine.

My relief was so great that at first I was scarcely aware of a new danger. Margaret had lost her cap, and her hair no longer confined fell in flaxen streams over her shoulders. Her tunic rucked up revealed too much of her figure. No one present could doubt that she was a girl. As I watched the expression on their faces, saw the landlord's confusion and distress, I was appalled by the harm that the misadventure was likely to cause, the shock dealt to their piety. Complete honesty alone could undo the disillusioning effect, restore their faith in me. I told them frankly that Margaret was my wife, that I hid her to defend her from bigots.

Their response showed at once that I judged rightly. Everyone smiled at her, lavishing sympathy and reassurance, whose warmth reflected the relief with which they accepted my explanation, their joy that suspicion was dispelled. As long as we stayed there she was treated with the utmost kindness. The landlord's wife herself waited on her, and one of the chambermaids lent clothes as disguise was no longer necessary. When I obtained a suitable ship they smuggled her on board, and we resumed our journey to Sandwich where I had many friends.

After this experience even Margaret agreed that it was wiser to stay at home at Knole. Two events helped to reconcile her to the prospect. The first was the knowledge, confirmed as the months went by, of the approaching birth of our child; the second was the arrival of Alice, who moved from Stixwould on my recommendation to a Benedictine house on the island of Sheppey. I encouraged her to make the change, knowing that her new prioress was ill and unlikely to recover, and I saw no reason why the nuns should not elect Alice to fill the place. There is no harm in using influence if one's efforts are on behalf of a worthy candidate, and I am sure that the nuns of Sheppey had reason to congratulate themselves on their choice. Alice herself was doubtful at first whether she did right to exchange the Cistercian for the less strict rule of St. Benedict; but her conscience was at rest when she found that, without neglecting her duty at the priory, she could use the freedom available to pay frequent visits to Knole, and how much these contributed to Margaret's happiness.

She approved no more than ever of our marriage; but as it was too late to dissuade us she was determined, as far as lay in her power, that Margaret should feel no regret. When our first child was born, our daughter Margaret, I asked her to be godmother, and she warned me that if she accepted she would teach her goddaughter many doctrines which I myself rejected. I told her that she had my full consent. The child would learn too much good from Alice's example to take any harm from her gentle doses of intellectual error.

In any case doctrinal differences were less wide in these early days than they became later. The King was more concerned to establish his authority in the Church than to reform its teaching.

A decision was still awaited from the Court of Rota at Rome, and if it were favourable a reconciliation could follow provided that the Church in England were not separated too widely in doctrine from the rest of Christendom.

As Archbishop I had the painful task of presiding at inquiries to examine and restrain heretical preachers. My first experience of this sort came very soon after my appointment, and as many have blamed me for my conduct I shall tell the story as fully as possible and let posterity judge. The prisoner, John Frith, was known to me, having come up from Eton to King's while I was at Cambridge; but I lost sight of him when he left to become a junior canon at Wolsey's new college at Oxford. Later he became acquainted with William Tindale, helping him in his work of translating the New Testament and joining him in Germany when he fled there from persecution. When his enemies heard that he was back in the country they were on the alert to catch him, and after many adventures too long to recount they overtook him in Essex ready to board a ship to escape abroad.

He was arrested and imprisoned in the Tower on a charge of heresy; but he had friends able to exert influence so that his trial was continually postponed. It is possible indeed that the case would have been dropped and he himself released, if a treatise which he wrote in prison on the sacrament of the altar had not been shown to More, who, having recently resigned his office of chancellor, had the more time to spare for theological controversy. The answer which More published attracted attention again to Frith. The King ordered me to preside over a commission to examine him at Croydon, out of reach of any protest raised by his friends in London.

I chose two of my most trusted servants to bring him from London to Croydon. They would travel by Brixton causeway which passes through great woods, and I told them to stop on the way and let Frith go off alone into the trees on the pretext of relieving nature. They must be careful to direct him to the left-hand side of the road, so that if he kept on walking he would come out into Kent, which was his native country. They themselves would wait for him an hour or so to give him as much time as possible, then they would go on to Streatham to raise the alarm, declaring that he had escaped from them into the woods.

Everything seemed to be arranged to my satisfaction, and I was in the best of spirits as I entertained the other members of the commission—the Duke of Suffolk, Lord Wiltshire, Sir Thomas Audley, and Gardiner and Stokesley, recently appointed bishops respectively of Winchester and London—who were dining at my house in Croydon. As the hour grew late, and I looked out of the window into the slowly gathering June dusk, I smiled to myself thinking of the fruitless hue and cry still continuing among the thickets between Streatham and Wandsworth. Then my heart sank in dismay. Three men were coming in through the gate, un-recognisable at that distance in the twilight to any one as short-sighted as I am, but there could be no doubt of their number, three not two. They advanced in single file across the courtyard. The front and rear guard wore my livery; between them marched a prisoner, and although I had not seen him for years I knew that it was Frith.

I left my guests abruptly and hurried out of the room, meeting one of my emissaries in the passage as he came to report. He was crestfallen and contrite, and I had not the heart to reproach him. To his surprise and dismay Frith had refused to cooperate, insisting that he must appear before his judges and defend his views.

He spent the night in the porter's lodge where everything possible was done for his comfort, and on the following morning we held court to examine him. Looking back after long experience of trials of this sort, and of the attitude to be expected from the prisoner, I am amazed when I recall how reasonably he argued before us. His voice was quiet and courteous; far from thrusting his opinions on us he listened with grave attention to ours, waiting till we had finished speaking to offer his comments. But on two fundamental tenets he stood firm and nothing could shake him. He refused to believe that the body of Christ is present in the bread on the altar, or that acceptance of the sacrament is indispensable to salvation.

When I consider how closely his opinions correspond with my own today it shames me to remember that I sat as judge to convict him. My only excuse is that I was still groping for certitude, unwilling to abandon accepted doctrines till I had convinced myself that they were wrong. I did my best to bring Frith round to my own position, to get him to admit that there were arguments in favour of the old belief which left the issue in doubt, so that I could acquit him of the charge of denying the Real Presence. But conciliatory in everything else he remained on this one point inflexible.

I was fully prepared to keep the commission sitting all night if the result would lead to an acquittal; but Frith himself cut it short. I was arguing in a circle, repeating myself, and as I paused for his reply he shook his head firmly and sadly:

"Your Grace, we've both said enough. You must do your duty." His tone held great compassion.

The findings which I signed reported that he denied the Real Presence and had not recanted. He was recalled to London and charged with heresy in the bishop's court. Stokesley showed him no mercy. He was burnt at the stake.

Stories of the proceedings at Croydon provoked gossip to an extent that alarmed but ought not to have surprised me. Neither Gardiner nor Stokesley was likely to miss the opportunity to spread an embroidered account of my conduct of the examination. When I heard that it was even being said abroad that the Archbishop of Canterbury was a heretic I feared that, unless the suspicion were removed, English relations with the Emperor and the King of France, to say nothing of the Pope, would become still more dangerously strained than they were already. So I wrote to Archdeacon Hawkins, my successor as ambassador to the Emperor, on the pretext of describing the Queen's coronation, ending the letter with a short paragraph to inform him of Frith's trial and conviction, of which I spoke in the most orthodox language that I could choose. I was sure that the letter would reassure Hawkins and that he would show it to Granvelle, if not to the Emperor himself. It could do no harm to Frith, who was dead.

Although I presided at Croydon on King Henry's orders he made no comment afterwards either to praise or to blame. I could almost believe that none of the stories about me had reached him, if I did not know that little escaped his ears. It was never easy to guess his thoughts. He had a disconcerting habit of retaining a piece of knowledge hidden at the back of his mind, to be produced when one least expected it. At moments indeed I was doubtful whether even Margaret remained a secret from him.

The religious policy of the reign has been denounced as inconsistent because Papist and Protestant suffered under it alike. In justice to King Henry one must remember how difficult was the balance that he had to maintain, how much it needed skill and firmness. He was determined that no one should make him go faster than he wished, and he struck fiercely anyone who tried; but he was equally determined not to yield to the often treasonable opposition of the enemies of reform who put loyalty to the Pope before that owed to the Crown. The vision which he cherished was of a kingdom developing its own genius without either foreign interference or violent change.

Of the dangers besetting him that from the Papists was most to be feared. The Emperor threatened to invade, the Pope to excommunicate, and their agents were busy in England stirring up trouble. They found fruitful ground for discontent among the great nobles, whose sympathies were by training on the side of tradition and who resented the curtailment of their privileges under the Tudor dynasty. They hated Wolsey, hated Cromwell even more, and although I myself got on well enough with them for the time being, probably because my functions seldom brought me into conflict, I knew how quickly their tone would change if events arose in which I stood in their way.

There was grave urgency in Cromwell's voice when he gave me the King's orders to examine and report to him on the activities of Elizabeth Barton, a nun living in the priory of St. Sepulchre in my own metropolis of Canterbury, who was known as the Holy Maid of Kent.

The most remarkable feature of her story is the tolerance shown her over a period of many years, while she made statements in public claiming divine inspiration, denouncing even the King himself. She came originally from the village of Aldington and was employed as a domestic servant on a farm belonging to my pre-

decessor, Archbishop Warham. From what I can gather she was
quite normal till the age of twenty or so, when she succumbed to
a disease like that known to the ancients as *morbus sacer*. The
symptoms were fits in which her face became hideously distorted,
her tongue lolled out and her eyes bulged as if they would leave
their sockets. During these seizures, it was said, a voice spoke from
her belly, revealing events of which she could have no knowledge
so that her hearers were greatly impressed. They were simple people unlikely to apply too rigorous a test to her ravings, especially
when she seasoned them with pious exhortation.

Her fame spread rapidly in the neighbourhood. A priest carried
the news to Warham, who declared at once that the messages were
the work of God. The old man was already in his dotage; even so
I am surprised at his credulity, whose effect of course was firmly
to establish the reputation of the prophetess. She became a person
of consequence, and her employer feeling it wrong to demand service from one acclaimed by the Archbishop as the mouthpiece of
heaven promoted her from the scullery to his own table, where he
treated her as a member of the family. When two monks were sent
from Christ Church at Canterbury to observe her, the character of
her revelations changed. She was no longer content to praise virtue
and denounce vice, the spirit possessing her developed a new interest in abstruse doctrines of theology, those especially which
Luther and other reformers attacked. The voice of God speaking
from the belly of an uneducated servant girl at Aldington affirmed
the efficacy of pilgrimages and confession, of masses for the dead.

A remote village was not the place in which to house so useful
an oracle. The Holy Maid was transferred to Canterbury and
settled as a nun in the priory of St. Sepulchre in a commodious
cell, where the pious could visit her without inconvenience. The
dispute was at its height over the King's first marriage, and the nun
well coached by the monks of the foundation of Christ Church at
Canterbury pronounced vociferously against any annulment.

When the King and Queen (Marchioness of Pembroke as she
was then) spent the night at Canterbury as Warham's guests, the
nun gained admission to their presence, interrupting them at dinner. She knelt to the King and warned him shrilly in a voice
audible to the whole room that unless he took back his former

wife he would not reign a month and would die "a villain's death."
Everyone waited aghast for his explosion of rage, but he merely
ordered the servants to remove her, and she returned to her cell
unpunished.

His leniency under such provocation aroused comment, and
some attributed it to superstitious fear which restrained him from
molesting the prophetess. My own view is that he felt nothing but
a contemptuous pity, regarding her as sick and deluded, a nuisance
too unimportant to resent.

He had to change his mind later when evidence reached him that
she was being used to foment insurrection, to kindle a conflagration
spreading through the kingdom. Nearly a year had passed since she
gave him only a month to reign, and he still sat on the throne; but
she overcame the failure of her prophecy with little loss of credit,
explaining that, like King Saul in the Bible, he reigned only in
appearance when he ceased to be King in God's eyes.

That was a plain invitation to treason. I made haste to Canterbury to investigate her behaviour.

When I told the prior of Christ Church that I wished to see
her he betrayed distress. He was a good man, but simple and im-
pressionable, much under her influence, and he tried to persuade
me to visit her in her cell. I insisted that she should be brought
to my house at Otford, so that we met on my ground not hers. It
was necessary to make it clear from the start that I was not interested in her miraculous sanctity, but in the light which she could
throw on a conspiracy against the Crown.

Plucked from her accustomed setting, from the bric-a-brac of
piety, she was not an impressive figure. It may have been the result
of her illness that she looked older than her twenty-seven years,
but she could never have been comely even in her bloom. Her
face was narrow like a weasel's, her mouth pinched and small, her
eyes set too close together, and her skin had a greasy texture that
enhanced its sallowness. I was sorry for her, spiritual renown made
up to her no doubt for her ill-favoured appearance.

Almost before I could get in a word she burst into a passionate
harangue, declaring that it was her mission to save the Church of
Christ as Joan of Arc, the Maid of Orleans, saved the kingdom of

France. She showed me letters written in characters of gold, given her by St. Mary Magdalene in a vision. The language was Latin, and the saint clumsy in grammar and syntax, but I admired the ornate skill of the lettering, the monkish calligraphy. I was not greatly surprised when later we found stocks of the same gold leaf at St. Augustine's abbey at Canterbury, in a cell occupied by a monk employed to illuminate the Abbot's missal.

Her strength lay in her confidence. She was herself the dupe of her delusions and the better able therefore to delude others. I had a list of questions given me by Cromwell to elicit the names of her confederates, but even if I could get her to betray them I saw little advantage. We had evidence already to incriminate many important people and still hesitated to act on it, desiring rather to nip the plot in the bud without aggravating dissension in the country. The most useful service that I could perform was to deprive the conspirators of their fetish. The plot would die out of its own accord if I stripped the Holy Maid of her sanctity, persuaded her to confess herself a fraud.

No confession could be extracted by bullying, even if I were inclined to try. So I allowed her to talk on and flattered her with my earnest attention. From time to time I asked questions, not aggressively as a judge, but with the docility of a neophyte seeking illumination. She was delighted to instrust me, repeating as long as she could the familiar catchwords of orthodoxy; but as I steered the debate into fields of abstruser doctrine she began to show signs of confusion, hesitating and taking refuge in pious verbiage to avoid the issue. At last she glanced up at me, hesitated, then asked if she could speak to me in private. I agreed willingly, and we withdrew into an inner room.

When we were alone she begged to be allowed to visit the shrine of Our Lady at the hamlet of Court-at-Street near Aldington. This was where her earliest visions were vouchsafed, and she assured me that, if she went back there, the angels would reveal who was chosen to wear the Crown of England. I affected to be suitably impressed, adjourned the examination and assigned two servants to escort her as far as Canterbury, where she would dismiss them and make her own arrangements to travel on. They carried letters from me to my agents in the town, whom I ordered to keep secret watch on her while she was there. My brother Edmund was with me at Otford, and we worked out a plan of action together. He hurried on ahead of the Holy Maid to Court-at-Street.

The report which eventually I received from him afforded ground for the charge on which she herself with five monks of Christ Church, her accomplices, were tried in the autumn at Lambeth. Edmund described the excitement that he found at Aldington, the huge concourse of people among whom rumours spread of a miracle about to be performed. Although the chapel was of good size it was too small to accommodate such numbers. Men and women stood packed together too tightly almost to breathe. Many swarmed up the pillars and the fretted canopies of the stalls or clung to the ledges of the windows, even to the mouldings projecting from the splendidly decorated ceiling. Edmund who has a wiry body and indomitable will edged himself into a corner of the chancel at the altar steps.

The Holy Maid was lying on the altar at the feet of a great image of Our Lady. Her trance had begun, her limbs writhed, her face was contorted. Suddenly a voice as deep and hollow as her own normally was shrill boomed from the pit of her stomach, announcing that King Henry was deposed and that Princess Mary reigned as Queen in the sight of heaven. No sooner were the words uttered than she jerked herself up into a sitting posture, pointed her finger at the image and with a thrice-repeated cry of "Ave Maria" called on the Mother of God to bear her witness.

The congregation waited and watched in a hush of expectation. Already the painted skirt rustled, the wooden feet stirred and parted. Slowly and majestically the great image stepped down from its niche in the reredos and stood with a gesture of benediction over the nun.

Then Edmund acted. He leapt up the steps, and almost before anyone was aware he was climbing on to the altar, grasping the celestial apparition, tugging at the cloak, the hood. The fabric tore as he clung to it; his hands groped for the face, caught it by the nose, and the mask on which the features were drawn crumpled into a pad of linen. Beneath the tattered disguise the Queen of

Heaven was revealed as a middle-aged man in shirt and breeches, the monk Bocking, cellarer at Christ Church priory at Canterbury.

Edmund was lucky to escape with his life. His action provoked a gasp of dismay, then an appalling howl of rage from the clerics indignant at the sacrilege. What saved him was the fact that the men nearest were mostly laity, farmers, tradesmen, labourers. As it became clear to these that the miracle was a fraud their anger turned against the deceivers. The monks threatened Edmund, but a growing number of the congregation began to threaten the monks.

When I sat with Cromwell and Latimer in judgment on them at Lambeth the five monks gave in at once, hoping to save their skins. They confessed that for years they had carried on the imposture, taking advantage of popular superstition to serve treasonable ends. I had more respect for the woman, who insisted to the end that her early visions were genuine, probably with truth if she meant that they were genuinely the effect of disease. But when she heard that her accomplices had betrayed her she no longer denied her part in their designs. She pleaded that she thought it her duty to obey them.

All six were sentenced to stand on the following Sunday at Paul's Cross in London on a platform beside the pulpit, while the preacher read out on their behalf a detailed statement of their crimes. On the Sunday after they repeated the performance at Canterbury. Then they were held in the Tower to await a decision on their fate.

I wrote and published a book to make it known as widely as possible that the Holy Maid's miracles were faked and her claims to sanctity spurious. After that it seemed that she was too thoroughly discredited to be a source of danger any longer to the King's authority, and I hoped that she would be released. I was sorry for her. Much that was wrong in her behaviour could be attributed to bodily affliction, and even if she exulted in her brief triumph as a Sibyl the shame of her exposure was punishment enough. Cromwell agreed with me, and if events had remained quiet I have no doubt that she would have been sent back to her convent. Unfortunately for her the Court of Rota, having delayed so long, chose this moment to pronounce judgment adverse to King Henry, provoking in England a frenzy of indignation and alarm, under whose influence many suspected of disaffection were put on trial. Elizabeth Barton and the five monks were hanged.

The list of victims would have been longer if it had not been for the Queen's intercession. She obtained a Royal pardon for the lesser offenders, including the too credulous prior.

12

Queen Anne hated bloodshed and had the courage to despise rather than to fear her enemies. Eyewitnesses told me that she showed more amusement than annoyance when the Holy Maid interrupted her at dinner with King Henry at Canterbury and chastised her in public with pious invective. The decision of the Papal court was a much more serious rebuff however, and she deserves the more credit for preserving a sense of proportion, refusing to vent her disappointment on the helpless.

She was in fact bitterly disappointed, as we all were, and with better reason than at first appears. In spite of the Pope's outburst of anger, his threat to boil Bonner in molten lead, negotiations were in progress with him which encouraged great hopes.

At Marseilles, where he attended the wedding of his niece, Catherine de Medici, to the young French prince, he admitted in private to King Francis as plainly as he dared that King Henry's cause was just, and hinted that only a formal act of submission was needed to obtain a favourable judgment. King Francis reported the hint to us at once through his ambassador. He himself was anxious to avert an irrevocable breach between England and the Vatican, which would compel him under threat of excommunication to join forces with his great rival, the Emperor. So he sent a special emissary to London to help to smooth out the difficulties, Jean du Bellay, Bishop of Paris, who had known the Queen as a young girl at the French court and was her staunch admirer. It was an agonising race against time, and du Bellay complained bitterly of delay, of King Henry's hesitation.

When at last the King resigned himself to important concessions the messenger carrying his answer to Rome was held up by bad weather in the mountains. The court met on the Monday in Passion week, and as no answer from England had yet arrived the dispensation given by Pope Julius II was upheld, and King Henry's first marriage declared to be valid.

Five days later the messenger from England was in Rome. The Pope tried to reconvene the court to hear fresh evidence. But Rome was packed with the Emperor's supporters, and the verdict stood unchanged.

Could the breach with Rome have been avoided if the messenger had ridden with better speed across the Alps? I have no doubt that King Henry would still have insisted on self-government for the Church in England, on concessions even more radical than those obtained by King Francis for the Church in France. Yet in his dislike of violent change, his delight in compromise, he would gladly, I am sure, have preserved the form without the burden of Papal authority, paid respect to the universal Church to guard it from schism.

Cromwell believed that a clean cut is the least painful, and gladly proceeded with legislation to rid the Church of the Pope. There was nothing insular in his dislike of the Papacy. He himself lived in Italy in his youth and retained many cosmopolitan ideas and acquaintances. He could forgive the Pope for being an Italian, but from the bottom of his heart he distrusted him as an ecclesiastic. If he had had his way he would have manned the Church entirely with laity. It was an inconsistency in him, which I took as a compliment, that he and I remained friends, that his anti-clerical prejudice allowed an exception in my favour.

From now on he and I were much together. He was already the King's chief minister, and in a few months' time when the King assumed the title of supreme head of the Church he appointed Cromwell his vicegerent to direct affairs. In a sense I was passed over; but any resentment that I felt at the King's choice was quickly allayed when I saw how heavy was the responsibility, how thankful I ought to be to escape the task of leading the Church to independence. Cromwell had qualities needed for success which were entirely lacking in myself. He had genius for organisation and enjoyed its exercise; he had the vision to promote farsighted policy and ambition to persevere in spite of discouragement; he had the force of personality to win over or intimidate opposition. Above all he was a layman standing apart from professional jealousies in the Church. He made many enemies in his career, was often the target of calumny; but he could never be accused as Wolsey was of abusing ecclesiastical office, accumulating spiritual honours to attract homage to himself.

While he believed with ardent conviction in the beneficence of his policy, that of strengthening and extending the Royal authority, he seldom missed an opportunity to enrich himself as he pursued it. The elaborate establishment which he built up over the country to keep him informed of the thoughts and doings of the people supplied information not only to preserve peace and order but also to threaten the guilty for his own profit. I had a glimpse of his methods from the way in which he showed me, without ever saying so outright, that he was aware of Margaret's hiding place. He spoke without malice, but I was reminded of the behaviour of a cat which keeps itself in practice, playing with a mouse that it does not mean to kill.

He was in fact the most loyal of friends, but where no personal feelings were concerned he could be hard and unscrupulous.

My relations with him were not always harmonious. I protested when he sent his agents into my diocese without my authority to enforce his policy of dissolving the smaller houses of religion; but I quickly got over my jealousy and supported him willingly in his purpose. In the course of a few years, as the larger houses came to share the fate of the smaller, the whole monastic system was abolished. For good or ill, the result of our work was to transform the appearance and social life of England.

I accepted the decision with the more alacrity thinking of the useful purposes for which the buildings could be used, turned into schools and colleges for the young, almshouses for the poor, hospitals for the sick. If the opportunity had been taken no nation would have equalled the English in enlightenment and happiness. I am convinced that the King shared my hopes and was as disappointed as I was by the outcome. He was the victim of forces beyond his control.

He had urgent need of money. The treasury which his father left full was almost empty as a result of Wolsey's policy of military commitments abroad. Barely enough remained to defend England itself at a time when rumours multiplied of the Emperor's preparations for invasion. Current expenses had first call on the expropriated wealth of the monks, and their movable effects, a very considerable treasure, were sold for this purpose as soon as possible. Meanwhile however the King retained control of the buildings and land, hoping that in time as conditions improved our plans for social welfare could be fulfilled there.

Time passed, and still the work was put off. The buildings were left untenanted and unguarded. Few could resist the temptation to use them as a quarry, robbery went on relentlessly, till the stately house became a ruin unfit for any purpose at all. The end of the story was almost invariably that the King, in financial straits again, sold the site for what it would fetch, and a new owner took possession concerned only to make a profit.

Cromwell expressed no regret for these events, no indignation at the rapacity of those who enriched themselves. He made sure, I suspect, of his own share of the loot, and he was no hypocrite to condemn behaviour in others of which he himself was as guilty. He pointed out that the sale of monastic land was in fact a source of strength to the Crown. The purchasers, great nobles and small yeomen alike, had an interest in preserving the settlement and would oppose any movement to restore the property to the Church. They became allies of the Royal policy, a solid body of opinion on which we could depend to resist subversion.

Cromwell believed sincerely in the benefit of strong government to defend the peace and encourage the prosperity of the nation. For the moment his enemies were thwarted, but they waited only to gather strength again to renew the struggle, conspiring meanwhile with the Emperor and the Pope.

The active spirit of revolt was embodied in the wizened figure of a middle-aged lawyer from Annecy in Savoy, the Imperial ambassador, Eugene Chapuis. In his enthusiasm indeed he outran the instructions of his own government. In official eyes he was the servant of the Empire, but in his heart his allegiance was given to the Princess Dowager. The plots which he fomented on her behalf were a work of love.

Many of the despatches which Chapuis wrote were intercepted by our agents. They revealed the single-minded fidelity with which he served the Princess Dowager; they revealed too his hatred of the Queen, whom he pursued with venomous enmity. He reported every titbit of scandal that he could collect about her, distorting her words to show her in the most unfavourable light, attributing to her none but the basest motives. The least offensive of the terms in which he referred to her was "the Concubine." In his eyes she was evil incarnate, the sorceress blighting the scene with her spells. It seemed to me reading his calumnies that he himself was ensorcelled.

I was less distressed by his prejudice when it was directed against Cromwell and myself, whom next to the Queen he regarded as his bitterest enemies. It was interesting to read his version of our crimes, to contrast it with the unvarying courtesy of his bearing in our company. I did not hold his inconsistency against him, I was grateful to him for it, for the excellence of his manners which spared us both embarrassment. He kept public business and social intercourse in separate compartments of his mind, so that he could spend an evening with me happily at Lambeth playing chess, returning home to write to the Emperor denouncing me as King Henry's evil genius, and advising him to demand as a condition of reconciliation that I be handed over as a scapegoat.

Much more important was the information which we found in his letters revealing who were the men of standing in the country with whom he was in treasonable correspondence. A name recurring frequently among them was that of John Fisher, the prelate renowned for his orthodoxy into whose see Margaret and I stole as castaways on our voyage to Sandwich. He was a man well past his prime, twenty years older than myself, who in the course of his long career enjoyed the confidence both of the King and of his father, and played a distinguished part in public life. Everyone respected him for his piety and learning, his self-denial and intrepid courage.

I try not to judge him harshly, knowing how bravely he met his end, but there is clear evidence that prejudice grew on him till it poisoned his moral standards. False values perverted him till he, a priest of Jesus Christ, could invite the King's enemies to invade his own country, to kill, to bereave, to destroy. Chapuis wrote to the Emperor that "in the opinion of that holy man, the Bishop of Rochester," he would please God better by attacking England than the Turks.

Credit is due to the King for the forbearance shown so long to the man who defied him. Fisher was left undisturbed, except for a period of two months at the time of Queen Anne's coronation, when tension was too dangerous to allow him freedom to aggravate it. He was held in comfortable confinement in Gardiner's house at Southwark, released afterwards and sent back to Rochester. When the conspiracy surrounding the Holy Maid came to light he fell under deep suspicion as he was known to be a fervent believer in her supernatural power. Even so he was charged only with misprision of treason, with concealing but not with taking part in the plot.

Sir Thomas More, living in retirement in his house at Chelsea since ceasing to be chancellor, was included on less adequate grounds in the indictment. Cromwell sent a message to both on the King's instructions, assuring them that if they asked for forgiveness they would receive it, and More took him at his word. He wrote a personal letter to the King explaining frankly, gracefully and respectfully the extent to which he was to blame and expressing his regret.

If Fisher too had approached the King directly he would, I am sure, have received the same clemency. He preferred however to put in a formal defence to the charge, declaring that he had nothing with which to reproach himself. He denied that he had ever been privy to treason (Cromwell, knowing what Chapuis had told the Emperor, raised his eyebrows when he read this) and persisted in expressing veneration for the nun, heedless of her own confession and of the events that led to her exposure. There was nothing for it but to put him on trial with her other accomplices, against whom proceedings were being taken by bill of attainder; but he was excused on grounds of health from appearing before Parliament in person. When sentence was passed he escaped the punishment of the chief offenders. He was condemned to imprisonment and forfeiture of his goods; soon afterwards he was allowed to compound both for a fine.

He was set free, but his freedom was of short duration. One cannot fail to be sorry for him, even sorrier for More, his companion in misfortune, when a succession of events entrapped them over which they had no control.

The first blow was the enactment of a statute declaring the validity of the King's marriage to Queen Anne, vesting the succession to the Crown in her issue, and appointing a commission to take an oath from all the leading subjects of the realm swearing obedience to the decision. It was a very necessary measure to ensure unity at home at a time when dangers accumulated against us abroad. I was myself a member of the commission, and as anxious as any to obtain conclusive results; but I shrank from putting the oath to More and Fisher, foreseeing too clearly their answer. It was impossible however to leave them out. They were both men of great reputation, notoriously unsympathetic to the policy which the Act was framed to promote. If we had failed to summon them the concession would have been attributed to weakness, and the example would have had a deplorable effect in the country.

Few duties more distasteful have been laid on me than that interview when More was summoned to Lambeth to take the oath. He treated us with great courtesy, seeming to feel for us as much in our reluctance as we did for him in his danger. Any ground that his conscience left free he conceded readily, accepting the King's absolute authority in secular matters. He would pledge his loyalty to the Queen, support the right of any child of hers to succeed to the Crown; but he refused to accept the annulment of the King's first marriage, insisting that power lay with the Pope alone and that my judgment at Dunstable was invalid. The effect was that he accorded the title of Queen while he denied that of lawful wife, and would swear allegiance to an heir whom he pronounced illegitimate. It was a distinction worthy of the subtlety of his intellect, and he himself was satisfied with its logical consistency; but among the bulk of the nation unskilled in the law and perplexed enough already by the course of events, it was likely to provoke such confusion that the whole foundation of public confidence would collapse.

No argument however could move him. At my request he withdrew from the room while we considered what to do. The discussion that followed was inconclusive. We were unhappy and uncertain, anxious to escape from the quandary, all except Hugh Latimer, Bishop of Worcester, who exulted loudly in More's downfall, claiming that it was retribution for the suffering inflicted on Frith and other Protestant martyrs.

The morning was warm for April, and as the dinner hour approached we moved out into the garden. Latimer still laughed and chattered exuberantly. He had a habit of grasping a man's shoulders, almost embracing him as he talked. His demonstrative gestures and ringing tones made him conspicuous. Even from a distance I could hear every word that he said. It occurred to me that More himself might be here out of doors, and I feared what he would think of this. I glanced round the garden anxiously, but at first I failed to observe him.

Then my attention fell on an old summerhouse that had been damaged by fire and never repaired. More was sitting just inside on the windowsill out of the glare of the sun. Our eyes met, and there was an expression in his so ironical and yet so merry that it was as if an inhabitant of another world, one of the ancient gods perhaps of Olympus, looked down in detached amusement on the follies of mankind. I was bitterly ashamed, felt defiled by Latimer's clowning. If it was necessary to the safety of the realm that More should be condemned, it was nonetheless an occasion for the gravest regret, a tragedy demanding the sacrifice of one of the wisest and best of Englishmen.

This incident made me more anxious than ever to save him from himself. I wrote to Cromwell suggesting that he should be allowed to take the oath in a limited form, to swear to the succession but not to the preamble of the Act, in which the validity of the King's marriage is defined. It would be made publicly known that he had sworn, but the exact words of his oath need not be divulged, and no one would have reason to suppose that they differed from the ordinary. I pointed out what a salutary effect it would have on everyone, including the Princess Dowager and the Emperor himself, when the news spread that even More submitted to the King's will.

Cromwell, who shared my respect for More and enjoyed his friendship, favoured the plan; but when he put it to the King he was unable to persuade him. The King's view was that too much hung on the issue to risk any relaxation of pressure, and that in any case he could not offer concessions to More without including Fisher, who would be sure to boast of his triumph. I was doubtful indeed myself whether More's own conscience would allow him to be silent, when he found that the extent of his submission was misunderstood.

Fisher was the next to be called for interrogation, and as the proceedings dragged on for more than a week he was placed in my custody at Lambeth, treated as a guest but held in reality as a prisoner. His presence was a strain on both of us. Even in so large a house it was difficult to escape from him. When I came into a room wanting to be alone he always seemed to be there waiting for me, to preach me a sermon without any of More's subtlety and wit on a theme disagreeable to my principles. It was more than patience could bear when I had to listen to the same sermon again as I sat on the tribunal. At last I cut the argument short, handed him a copy of the oath and told him with some asperity that he must either swear it or take the consequences. He refused, and both he and More were committed to the Tower.

Every possible consideration was shown them there, comfortable accommodation, permission to receive and often even to visit their friends. The general opinion was that after a suitable lapse of time, when the succession was firmly established, both would be released. The King was fond of More and spoke of him with regret, and Fisher was so old and frail already that with every passing year he became less dangerous an enemy.

I fully believe that no great harm would have come to them if fortune had not chosen the moment to deal a fatal blow. Pope Clement VII was dead, and Cardinal Farnese who succeeded him as Paul III had been among King Henry's supporters in the Court of Rota, and was anxious now to effect reconciliation with England. As soon as he was elected Pope he announced his intention to call a general council of the Church, at which all the problems distracting Christendom could be reviewed, and so that England might be represented with suitable dignity he looked for a sufficiently eminent Englishman on whom to bestow a Cardinal's hat. By cruel mockery of fate his choice fell on Fisher.

I have heard it said that his motives were genuinely conciliatory, that he was unaware of the disgrace in which Fisher lay or underrated its importance, and that he expected King Henry to be flattered by the promotion of an English prelate to the Sacred College. If so, his advisers were guilty of a monstrous blunder, unless they misinformed him deliberately to stir up trouble. The effect in England was what anyone should have foreseen. King Henry regarded the appointment as a studied insult and was beside himself with anger. It only exacerbated his feelings when, as a further gesture of goodwill, the Pope made a Cardinal also of our old friend du Bellay, Bishop of Paris. In King Henry's mood of brooding suspicion this was proof that du Bellay had been bribed to desert him.

I was present when the Pope's emissary, arriving with the red hat, sought permission to present it to Fisher in the Tower. The man fled when the King shouted:

"Take it back to Rome and tell the Pope that the head will follow."

Fisher's head was not sent to Rome, it was impaled above London Bridge and later thrown in the river. A felon's death rewarded a life of uncommon holiness and virtue. My distress was still greater when More suffered the same fate shortly afterwards. The event did more harm to the King's cause in Europe than anything that had happened since the dispute with Rome arose. More enjoyed international esteem. Learning, humanity, religion itself suffered irreparable loss from his death, and England was condemned as a haunt of murderous barbarians.

13

Chapuis spread the story that the Queen was responsible for
More's execution. Like most of his calumnies it was swallowed
with avidity by her enemies, but no one believed it who was in
touch with events. She had no great quarrel with More, who
went as far as his conscience allowed to acknowledge and assure
her rights. There were many whose death she had better reason
to contrive, if that had been her way of behaviour. Sustained
rancour however was not in her nature. She was very capable of
storming at More to his face, quite incapable of venting spite
behind his back.

Even if she had, the King would not have listened. He discouraged his wife from interference in public affairs, having had
to put up with too much in the past from the Princess Dowager.
He bears the blame for More's death alone. It was his habit to
brood over troubles, magnifying them into an obsession, till motives were seen distorted, the most monstrous fantasies became
credible and affection was poisoned. In this mood he was as
dangerous as a wounded beast. It is proof of his greatness that
my devotion and admiration persisted in spite of his faults.

The origin of the stories against the Queen was probably her
friendship with Latimer. Many assumed that because he rejoiced
over More's downfall he was not content till he pursued him to
his death. It is an injustice to Latimer to suppose so.

However, his growing influence on the Queen produced an
estrangement between us of which I am ashamed. I was too
accustomed to regard myself alone as her spiritual adviser, and he
was not wrong when he suspected me of jealousy. It took me
time to understand that in his honesty and earnest benevolence
she found the comfort that she needed, that he was better fitted
than I to guide her in religion. In my company she was a child
of the new learning, ready to talk with animation of the classical

past, of the rebirth of mind and art which fascinated her generation; but when I turned the conversation to theology she quickly lost interest. It was easy to know when she was bored, she became flippant.

Latimer was no more interested than she in doctrinal argument. His religion was practical, it carried her into a world hitherto unknown of people living on the verge of destitution, and he had difficulty at first in restraining her from immediate largesse, too indiscriminate to be of lasting benefit. He succeeded in diverting her to more fruitful projects, the endowment of a fund for the education of young men of promise from humble homes, and the provision of tools to enable the unemployed to support themselves by handicraft.

These activities were not only of use to the poor, they were also a healthy distraction taking her mind off the anxieties and vexations which beset her. Conflict was inevitable from the outset in her relations with her stepdaughter, Princess Mary, a stubborn girl of eighteen who could never forgive her for taking her mother's place. It is odd to reflect that that girl is now Queen of England. I still think of her as she was when I first saw her, a pale, dejected wraith, dark and fragile-looking, hovering in the background at Greenwich when her sister was born. She glowered at the festive visitors to the palace; but none received more baleful glances than I did, I who presided over the court annulling her mother's marriage. She would not have believed me if I had told her how sorry I felt for her.

Yet the chance came soon afterwards to put my compassion into effect. Some indiscreet words of hers were overheard and carried by talebearers to Queen Anne. I do not know how much the offending phrases were distorted, but the report reached her that Princess Mary cast doubts on the baby's paternity. As was to be expected, it provoked a hurricane. The King was informed, and between the two of them the storm rose to such a pitch that nothing, it seemed, could save Princess Mary from arrest.

I was leaving the palace when I got the news, and I turned back at once, praying but scarcely daring to hope that I should be able to restore peace. I knew that to argue with either in such circumstances was to add fuel to the conflagration. The only chance was to turn their anger by making them laugh.

Luck favoured me. Inveighing against Princess Mary, the King denounced her as an unnatural daughter, and I reminded him that she would be Prince Arthur's daughter, not his, if his first marriage had been upheld:

"Your late brother," I added, "makes a habit of posthumous daughters."

The remark was not very witty, but the erudite flavour appealed to him. He was proud of the argument, already regarded it indeed as his own, which deprived the first marriage of the support claimed for it in the passage of Deuteronomy. At the memory of his triumph he laughed, the tension was broken, and he turned to the Queen, who lay in bed still weak from the pain of child-bearing:

"Arthur can have Mary if he likes, sweetheart, but we'll keep Bess."

The Queen laughed too, and I detected a note of relief. The aspersion cast on her child frightened as well as insulted her. I left them making arrangements for the christening on the following day, at which I stood godfather.

No more notice was taken of Princess Mary's offence, but I cannot believe that she remained ignorant of the danger which she escaped. I wonder if she remembers it today, when she is Queen and I am her prisoner.

Poor girl, she had little else in those years to remember with gratitude. The King would not allow her to live with her mother, fearing that, if she did so, she would learn to view events in so prejudiced a light that she would become lastingly estranged from him. His fear was well-grounded, but the remedy chosen produced the same result and cost her great unhappiness. She was made to share a household with her half-sister under the care of Lady Shelton, the Queen's aunt. Yet it was a sensible arrangement in many respects, particularly as her health was far from strong. Lady Shelton was kind to her and looked after her with diligence when she was ill. There was the further advantage of course that she was guarded from the intrigues in which the disaffected wished to involve her.

The King's purpose was not to humiliate her. Nevertheless the contrast was galling when she saw the honour paid to the child who took her place. She deserves high praise for the sweetness with which she behaved to her little sister, playing with her devotedly, refusing to vent her embitterment on an innocent victim.

There was no such gentleness in her behaviour to her stepmother. The strain which circumstances put on them was enough to prevent understanding, and it was reinforced by incompatibility of temperament. The Queen was warm in all her impulses, quick to offer affection, quick to take anger. She made conciliatory gestures inspired by sincere compassion and was exasperated when they were rebuffed. Quarrels followed in which she lost her temper, and the harsh words that she used remained unforgotten and unforgiven, however she herself might wish them unspoken and try to make amends. Her stepdaughter was too conscious of her wrongs, too proud to relent.

The arrangements by which the King's two daughters shared a single household had the disadvantage for the Queen that her pleasure in visiting her own was marred by the other's sullen hostility. It was a relief when, as often happened, Princess Mary refused to greet her, retiring to her room on a sudden plea of ill-health; but it was also, as the Queen was well aware, a deliberate slight, putting her to shame before the servants. Lady Shelton much distressed was helpless on these occasions, lacking the strength of will or the means to compel obedience.

An incident attracted disagreeable publicity when Lady Shelton took her charges to Richmond, and as the distance from Hampton Court is not great the Queen planned to ride over and spend the day with them. She set out attended by a large party of courtiers including the Dukes of Norfolk and Suffolk. Perhaps she hoped that the presence of so distinguished a company would persuade Princess Mary to mind her manners.

I had the story from Lady Shelton herself. She was very loyal to the Queen, but gentle and rather ineffective, harassed by the responsibility of her task. When the party arrived she received them alone, stammering uncomfortably over the familiar message that Princess Mary had a headache and asked to be excused from paying her respects. As soon as she could she led the Queen to the nursery to see the little Princess Elizabeth.

They walked along the passage, leaving the others to follow. The door of the nursery was open, and as the Queen looked in the child toddled towards her clutching the ledge of the skirting-board for a few steps before sprawling again on all-fours. The Queen was delighted; it was the first time that she had seen her stand upright, and she put out her arms and waited for the child to approach. Then as progress was slow she stooped to pick her up, laughed and glanced over her shoulder to speak to her companions.

She broke off abruptly, and her face flushed scarlet. Except for Lady Shelton there was no one in the passage behind her. All had slipped off, and she guessed whom they went to see.

She controlled her feelings in the presence of the nurses, who withdrew deferentially to the far end of the room. For an hour or so she stayed there, playing with the child, talking to Lady Shelton, discussing warmer clothes for the coming winter. No word that she said betrayed surprise that she was deserted, but I needed no description to imagine the danger-signal gleaming in her eyes. When at last she left she carried the child in her arms.

The passage led into the hall at the foot of the stairs. By unlucky chance she reached it just as the rest of the party led by the Duke of Norfolk came down from the visit which they had been paying to Princess Mary. They drew back awkwardly, and the baby as if responding to a warning of danger broke into a terrified wail. The Queen handed her to Lady Shelton, but the wails persisted. The procession of courtiers waited uncertain, bunched on the stairs.

Then the Queen's eyes met the duke's, and her temper flared: "Run away, Uncle, for God's sake to Rome or hell or where you like. Your face may cure Mary's headache, but it makes Bess sick."

She brushed past him roughly and strode across the hall. No one dared to follow.

Although they had plotted to humiliate her they were abashed by the storm which they provoked. None of them, least of all her uncle, had the courage to stand up to her. They waited meekly till she sent word that they were going home at once. As soon as she mounted she urged her horse to a gallop. Few kept pace with her over the ten miles to Hampton Court.

She had little reason to feel affection for her uncle, the Duke of Norfolk. Her mother's early death and her father's second marriage, of which the Howards did not approve, cut her off from that side of the family, and the rift was widened when the old duke died, the victor of Flodden, her father's friend and benefactor. The present duke was a lesser man in every respect, as puny in mind as in stature. He was a useful servant however to the King, too ambitious to jeopardise his career by rash disloyalty. The Howards were not of the old aristocracy, but they had growing influence especially in the eastern counties, and their support was needed to ensure a balance of forces in England favourable to the Crown.

By temperament the duke feared and disliked change, and he hated the ministers, both Wolsey and Cromwell, who helped to carry out the King's policy in Church and state. He regretted the quarrel with Rome, but became more reconciled when the result was to make him uncle to the Queen of England. He began to take interest in his niece for the first time, and as long as her position remained secure he made much of the kinship between them, deferring to her advice in the affairs of the family, even in the choice of a wife for young Lord Surrey, his eldest son. His submission to her judgment pleased her, she enjoyed planning other people's lives, and with her usual impetuosity she tried to arrange a marriage for Surrey with Princess Mary. The King, as might have been foreseen, refused his consent, and she turned her attention to Lord Oxford's daughters to choose a bride among them for her cousin. Surrey, a high-spirited, overbearing young man, much admired already as a poet, was mated to Lady Frances de Vere, known unkindly at court as the "white hen." The Queen's efforts seldom enjoyed success in proportion to her confidence.

In return for his deference the duke expected favours from his niece, and she was too good-natured, too easygoing to refuse them. She even agreed at his request to offer a place among her maids-of-honour to his paramour, Elizabeth Holland. His quarrel with his duchess was of long standing, pursued on both sides with implacable violence. She accused him of putting the servants on to tie her up and imprison her; he retorted that she was off her head, a furious maniac. Whether the fault lay with his cruelty or her tantrums, I do not know; but he banished her from Kenninghall, his seat in Norfolk, installing this woman Holland there instead, who was formerly employed as the children's nursemaid to wash clothes and scrub floors.

It was a squalid story, and the appearance of the new maid-of-honour when I saw her at court did nothing to allay my distaste. Her pale blue eyes had a hard glint, her features too sharp an expression. I should have preferred a simple country girl reeking of scrubbing brush and slop pail to the pretentious airs with which she aped courtly manners, tried to disguise her origin. The Queen incurred much blame for so unsuitable an appointment. She did not like the woman, but was anxious to please her uncle.

Her reward was that his allegiance failed when it no longer suited his advantage. He began to make overtures to her enemies, to treat her with the insolence which I have described on the expedition to Richmond.

For a long time I refused to believe the rumours that grew about an estrangement between her and the King. There was such warmth in the relation between them when they were happy together, they both had such enjoyment of life, shared so many tastes and interests, that no danger, it seemed, could arise to the marriage, no true ground ever be given her for jealousy. He always liked to be surrounded by pretty faces, but he was rare among kings in the high standard of behaviour that he set himself. In the long years of his marriage to the Princess Dowager only a single occasion of infidelity was known, and that was during his absence on campaign in France. The fruit was the boy who became the Duke of Richmond.

When the rival was pointed out to me, reputed to be the Queen's supplanter, I was still unalarmed, so unlikely I thought her to steal the King's affection. She was a woman of some thirty or so years, Lady Jane Seymour, who had recently come to court from Wiltshire, where her family had property. Her chief advantage was a fine complexion, rather too pale but of impeccable texture, and the regularity of her features, marred only by a protuberance at the end of her nose, which shone like a knob unless it was carefully powdered. What spoilt her however was her mouth, small, pinched and thin-lipped, with the upper lip excessively long. It had an air of tight prudence, almost of parsimony, that accorded with the sourness lurking in her blue eyes.

There could be few greater contrasts than that between Lady Jane and the Queen, the former dependent on elegance, the reinforcement of art, the latter whose beauty like a wildflower's glowed most richly in informality, wind-blown with hair dishevelled.

It was unbelievable that the King could really be attracted by the newcomer, but his behaviour in her company soon left no room for doubt. If further evidence were needed it was available from the Queen herself, not only from her low spirits, her strained expression, but also explicitly in indiscreet outbursts of indignation with which she relieved her feelings, often in the most ill-chosen company. Her most dangerous confidante was her sister-in-law, Lady Rochford, who, always eager to dabble in intrigue, made scatterbrained plans to help her which aggravated the harm. The silliest was an attempt to discredit Lady Jane by spreading scandal about her, representing her as a woman of loose morals. The stories were flagrantly untrue, lacked even plausible evidence, and Lady Jane whose virtue was known to be beyond reproach ignored them contemptuously. The outcome was to put the scandalmaker herself to shame; she became a laughingstock.

The King did not laugh however; he was very angry and banished Lady Rochford from court. He revenged himself on the Queen by paying more marked attention than ever to her rival, who went about demurely triumphant like a sleek white rat gnawing her way to power. She began to profess friendship for Princess Mary, visited her frequently. They had a subject of mutual interest in their common hatred of the Queen.

At last she felt so sure of her influence that she ventured to come into the Queen's presence wearing, in a conspicuous position, a locket holding the King's portrait which he had given her. The Queen was enraged, snatched it from her neck and ran to him with it to reproach him. If the report which spread afterwards is correct, his reply was to order her curtly to give it back:

"Stop whining at treatment that was good enough for the daughter of the King of Spain."

The words are cruel and unjust. It is an explanation, but no excuse, that when he yielded to passion he scarcely knew what he said. What disturbed me most was the reference to the Princess Dowager, recalling the obsession that preyed on him. He parted from her to assure the succession, to escape the curse which lay in his imagination on her womb. Was the birth of a daughter to the Queen not enough to allay his fear, to satisfy him that the curse was expiated? The effect which such doubt could have on him filled me with forebodings: they would have been agonising if I had known all that was at stake.

An event occurred now to which the Queen attached great hopes, and in her readiness to believe in the benevolence of fortune she recovered much of her bloom and gaiety. The King proposed that the little Princess Elizabeth should be betrothed to the Duke of Angoulême, the youngest son of the King of France, and the plan was received with sufficient favour for emissaries to be sent from France to discuss it. The Queen went out of her way to be gracious to them, entertained them as often as she could, held long consultations with them in her room. It seems that she also wrote in secret to the Queen of Navarre, the friend of her childhood, sister to King Francis.

Gontier, the secretary to the mission, handed her the reply at a ball, and many observed her agitation as she took and read it. Her voice rose incautiously, and her words were overheard when she told him that she was in great trouble, that King Francis alone could save her, and begged him on his return to impress the urgency of her need on his master. Then she looked round, saw that she was watched, that her behaviour attracted curiosity, and she left him abruptly and hurried on to join the King.

No one ever knew what message her letter or its answer contained; but the purpose which she had in mind can be guessed from the subsequent course of negotiations for the betrothal. A condition which the English pressed was that the young prince should be sent to England to live at court till his bride was old enough to be married. It is easy to see how well this suited the Queen. She was sure that if the boy spent much time here as one of the family the King would grow fond of him, that the future son-in-law would come to be regarded as a son. There would be no need of Lady Jane to carry on the dynasty. King Henry would have his male heir to succeed him, and Queen Anne's daughter would be the mother of the next.

It was a dream that lay within the bounds of possibility, and if the plan after all were unnecessary, if she herself bore a son, no harm would be done, Princess Elizabeth would still be Duchess of Angoulême, in close line of succession to the French throne.

Her brother Rochford went to France to take charge of negotiations. His determination and vigour cannot be doubted, but his task was harder than his sister led him to expect. King Francis objected that, if his son had to live in England, he would become a hostage liable to reprisal whenever French and English policy diverged. It may be that, to achieve the alliance, King Henry would have waived the condition, attaching less importance to it than the Queen did; but he was seriously disturbed when the French, for their own part, demanded to be released from the substantial pension paid for the last ten years to the English Crown in reward for services after the battle of Pavia. In that defeat, one of the greatest disasters in French history, the flower of the French army was destroyed, King Francis himself taken prisoner. English support alone enabled France to recover, hindered the Emperor from extending his victory.

King Henry regarded the pension as well earned, and he needed the money now more than ever to strengthen the coastal defences against the Emperor's threat of invasion. He refused to expunge the debt.

When Rochford returned from France he had to break the news to his sister that his mission was a failure, no terms for the betrothal could be agreed. Her disappointment was pitiable to watch, expressed with none of her accustomed violence but in silence and helpless dejection. It was as though a vital spring had been cut off in her soul, leaving her too hurt to protest. The happiness of her girlhood in Paris, the affection shown her by the Queen of Navarre, her own attachment to that remarkable woman—all this held radiance in her memory, was a refuge into which her imagination could escape. It survived even the rebuff when the Queen of Navarre refused to meet her at Boulogne; but on the present occasion much more was at stake than dignity; her marriage, her whole life was in danger. In desperate need she appealed to France for help, and the friendship on which she counted betrayed her, the dream was illusion.

There was small chance, if she had known, that King Francis would listen to her entreaty. Her name was too closely linked with the cause of reform, her friendship with Latimer attracted too much attention. She was an embarrassment to him when he sought alliance with England against the Emperor, but without being drawn into King Henry's quarrel with the Pope. On the very day that he received her letter he was riding in procession in Paris, herding a gang of French Protestants to torture and the stake.

Relief came to her from an unexpected quarter. For several days Lady Jane was not seen at court, and the rumour spread and was confirmed that she was back at home in Wiltshire. Her disappearance occurred so soon after the arrival at court of Lady Shelton's daughter, Madge, that at first it was thought that the King had exchanged one favourite for another. He liked Madge Shelton and made no secret of it. She was very young, not yet eighteen, retaining much of the freshness of childhood, unable in spite of her shyness to disguise the exhilaration inspired by her first experience of the court. Her simplicity charmed and amused him, but there was no sign of any serious infatuation. When he fell in love it was nearly always with a woman of mature age. An exception, as I shall describe later, is the second Queen Catherine; but although she was not much older than Madge she was more experienced, knew how to catch a man's eye and lead him on.

Good evidence that Madge was no rival is the affection that persisted between her and the Queen. They were cousins, but the difference in age was such that the Queen treated her almost as a daughter.

There could be no doubt that Lady Jane's departure greatly improved relations between the King and Queen. He became his old self again when he was with her, genial and affectionate. The consideration with which he treated her, the care which he took to save her exertion, indicated a possible explanation of events, and in a short time it was no longer conjecture, but common knowledge. She was pregnant.

It was as if a cloud were lifted from the court. There were smiles for her everywhere, and the courtiers who had shunned, even insulted her while she was in disfavour made haste to return to their allegiance, eager to ingratiate themselves with the mother of the future heir to the throne. Her uncle, the Duke of Norfolk, outdid them all in obsequiousness. Chapuis alone remained glum, unable to feign pleasure in her triumph; but he had other grounds as well for his despondency, and they were of a sort that deserved sympathy. He had received a message from Kimbolton Castle, where the Princess Dowager was living in Huntingdonshire, to let him know that she was gravely ill. For the past year she had been suffering at intervals from a digestive disorder, retching and vomiting; but the attacks were now increasing in violence, and fear was felt for her life.

The King was annoyed that the news reached the Emperor's ambassador before he was informed himself; but one cannot blame the dying woman for turning in her pain and weakness to the one friend on whose devotion she could rely. Others might deplore her death as a setback to political schemes, Chapuis in tears would mourn a personal loss.

He asked for permission to go to Kimbolton to visit her. The King was reluctant, well aware of the many plots in which Chapuis was involved, and suspecting that he would make use of the visit to promote them. He agreed at last on condition that Stephen Vaughan went too, the same emissary whom Cromwell sent to escort me on my way back with Margaret through France. Vaughan spoke fluent Spanish and had orders to keep his eyes and ears open when Chapuis and the Princess Dowager met.

From what he told us on his return, it seems that the precaution was unnecessary. The Princess Dowager was a little better when they arrived, but still very weak, and their first interview lasted no more than a quarter of an hour. Later after resting she saw Chapuis in private, and he was with her again for an hour or two on each of the four days that he stayed there. Although Vaughan was seldom present while they talked he was experienced in gathering information, and he expressed the firm conviction that she was in no condition, and Chapuis himself in no mood, to discuss politics. They met as old and dear friends; it was indeed touching, he said, to watch them together, and she seemed to recover strength and cheerfulness from company so congenial. He described his last glimpse of her when they left. She came out into the courtyard to see them off, leaning heavily on the arm of her attendant, but laughing as merrily as if she were a girl again in her father's palace at Granada when the Spanish clown whom they brought to amuse her gave a parting display of his antics.

Chapuis was much reassured, believing that she would soon be restored to health. His last words to her were a promise to see the King about having her moved to a more convenient house.

He rode back to London by easy stages, leaving on the Wednesday morning and arriving on the Saturday night. Early the next day he sent a servant to Cromwell to seek an audience for him with the King, so that he might thank him for the visit to Kimbolton and give an account of the Princess Dowager's health. The servant brought back word that she was dead. She died on Friday January 7th at two o'clock in the afternoon.

As often happens when anyone of importance dies suddenly, a story spread that she was poisoned, and Chapuis was among those who believed it. There is so little ground for the calumny that it scarcely needs refutation. Her digestive trouble was of long standing, and her doctor was a Spaniard whose loyalty to her has never been doubted. In fact, as is clear from a surgical examination carried out after her death, the weakness that killed her was a disease of the heart, which had a black incrustation over the surface and within the chambers.

The King's behaviour after her death provoked unfavourable

comment. Even the most frivolous were shocked when he appeared at a ball at court dressed in the brightest yellow, danced with exuberant hilarity and sent for little Princess Elizabeth whom he carried round in his arms, showing her off proudly to each of the courtiers in turn. His outburst was an offence to good taste; but its source was a sudden and uncontrollable impulse of relief from nervous strain, rather than heartless disrespect for the woman who lived with him for twenty years as his wife. She died while he was in the glow of reconciliation with the Queen, expecting her to bear him the son for whom he longed. Accustomed as he was to attribute all his fortunes good or ill to divine guidance, he was filled with devout gratitude for an event which, as if to herald the child's birth, removed the last obstacle to an undisputed succession. When he dandled the little princess she was the symbol of her unborn brother.

A few days later he had a fall from his horse, and although he suffered nothing worse than bruises the shock seemed to sober him. He spoke tenderly of the Princess Dowager, recalling happy memories of the past, and he gave orders for the body to be embalmed and suitable arrangements to be made for a funeral worthy to do honour to his brother's wife, the former Princess of Wales. A date at the end of the month was appointed for the ceremony, to be held in the abbey church at Peterborough where he prepared her tomb. In years to come, when the abbey itself was dissolved, he insisted that the church should be retained for public worship. Few kings' daughters have a statelier monument.

I am afraid that the Queen's behaviour was no more decorous than his own when the news arrived from Kimbolton. This was the sort of occasion too likely to show her at her worst. All the scruples which she used to express to me about the Princess Dowager, all the compassion which, intermittently but none the less sincerely, she felt for Princess Mary, all restraints even of polite convention were forgotten. The messenger came to her when she was washing her hands in a silver basin, a work of great beauty and value, designed for the King by Cellini himself. On hearing what he had to say she tossed out the water and gave him the basin to keep, a reward more than adequate if he had saved her life. Many over-heard her cry of triumph:

"Now at last I'm really Queen."

Her brother Rochford did not share her jubilation. When he dined with me at Lambeth he had a worried frown. He saw as I did that the Princess Dowager's death could be a source of danger, that if the Queen's child were another girl, and the King looked again for someone else to give him a male heir, he would have less difficulty than before in carrying out his intention. In the eyes of the Pope he was a widower free to marry whom he chose. I prayed fervently that this time the Queen would bear a son.

She herself was convinced that it was a boy whom she carried in her womb. Her confidence inspired happiness, and when she was happy she was good-natured, anxious for others also to have reason to rejoice. Now that she had time for reflection she was ashamed of the lack of feeling with which she greeted the news of the Princess Dowager's death. She sent Princess Mary a message through Lady Shelton inviting her to court and promising to be a second mother to her, assuring her that if she obeyed the King as supreme head of the Church her former rank and privileges would be restored. Princess Mary however rejected the overture with scorn. She cherished stubbornly as a legacy from her mother the duty of obedience to the Pope, and she was in no mood in any case to forgive her stepmother for the past. The effort was more perhaps than could justly be expected from a girl in her position and of her temperament; but the Queen could not be brought to understand this, she was bitterly mortified by the rebuff, inacces-sible to reasoning, inconsolable in her tears.

The offer was made of course with the King's consent. He him-self was eager for reconciliation with his daughter now that the chief cause of dispute was removed by her mother's death. Her unresponsive attitude did not deter him; he even went in person to talk to her, and further visits followed of whose outcome noth-ing was divulged. The few companions who shared his confidence allowed no hint to escape of another motive prompting his journeys. Everyone supposed that Lady Jane Seymour was still in Wiltshire, no one suspected that he met her in Princess Mary's room.

I myself was fully occupied at the time with preparations for the Princess Dowager's funeral. It would have been unsuitable in the circumstances for me to officiate; but the burden of arrangements fell on me, to ensure that nothing occurred to provoke embarrassment or controversy. I went down to Peterborough for a final conference with the Abbot, then came home to Lambeth. At the hour appointed for the service I sat alone in my room, trying to make peace in my mind with the dead woman.

At the same hour, as I heard later, the King and Queen were at Greenwich. They sat together at first, then he rose and excused himself, saying that he was going to the chapel to be alone to pray. He was away a long time, and when nearly two hours were gone she grew anxious, fearing some mishap to him. At last she went to look for him herself. The chapel was empty, almost dark in the winter afternoon; but a light shone in the vestry, and she peeped in. She found him there sitting in a chair, with Jane Seymour on his knees.

The shock was the greater because she had no warning that her rival was back. Her pangs came on prematurely, and she was barely able to walk back into the palace. By the time that a doctor reached her it was too late to prevent a miscarriage. As she lay in pain she was told that the child born dead was a boy.

14

Three months remained before the storm broke, months of gloom and foreboding. It was not in the Queen's nature to show meekness under provocation. Even while she lay on her sickbed she reproached the King bitterly for his infidelity, blamed him for the loss of his son and heir. There were witnesses of the quarrel, and his retort was repeated, gaining relish as it passed from mouth to mouth among her enemies:

"I'll have no more boys from you, my girl."

Not even the harshness of the words so appalled me as the fanatical obsession underlying them. He regarded the miscarriage as proof that the curse persisted, that he was not yet purged from the defilement of incest incurred by union with his brother's wife. No matter whether he loved Queen Anne—and it was clear in spite of all that he said and did that he still hankered after her in his heart—superstition, a mistaken sense of duty convinced him that a further sacrifice was needed, that no heir would succeed him unless he fathered a son on Lady Jane. The conflict within him exasperated his temper, goaded him to violence.

My distress put a barrier between me and Cromwell, the only interruption that I can recall of our friendship. Although his own life was free from amorous intrigue he was indulgent in his judgment of others, and he took the Queen's unhappiness less to heart than I did. His son was married to Lady Jane's younger sister, and the connection carried more weight with him than he cared to admit. At the King's request he gave up the rooms kept for him at Greenwich Palace, and they were offered to her brother, Sir Edward Seymour, and his wife, who moved in at once. The King was able to entertain his favourite there without scandal.

Catarrh, a succession of heavy colds, kept me much at home for the rest of the winter. In ordinary circumstances it would have been tiresome, but now I was grateful for an excuse that spared me from attendance at court. The King always nervous of infection wanted no one around him who came coughing and blowing his nose. I spent the time chiefly at Knole, where Margaret put up with my sniffling without complaint. It was a great luxury that I had no need there to guard my words, that I could talk to her of events, tell her what I thought of them, reveal my inmost hopes and fears, knowing that my confidence was safe with her, that her advice would be sensible and to the point. In the past year or so she had grown into a woman, able to accept responsibility, understanding the ways of the world better but no more afraid of exploring them than was the nymph on the island in the Pegnitz, or the page who accompanied me across France and around the sights of London. I am filled with gratitude whenever I think of her courage in marrying me, of the cheerfulness with which she bore the consequences, so hard for anyone of her gay and open nature, the daily weariness of concealment and subterfuge, the lack of freedom.

For hours, even days on end at Knole I could put off the outer world entirely, cease to be Archbishop of Canterbury, slip back into the life which my father led unremarked at Aslockton. When my cold allowed I rode out to shoot in the woods, in bad weather I had my books to amuse me in the library. At dinner Margaret and I sat alone together, and afterwards the nurse brought our little daughter not yet three years old down to play. Our pleasure in the house was unmarred by foreknowledge, we never thought that in little more than a year we should have to give it up to the King.

Among the few visitors whom we entertained there, in whose discretion I had sufficient trust, was my friend Alexander Aless, a Scottish divine living in exile. He was the first of many eminent foreigners who took refuge in England, looking to King Henry for protection from Papist bigotry. I relied greatly on Aless' advice during these months in the work on which I myself was engaged, the preparation of formularies of faith to guide the Church in the first stages of its independence from the see of Rome.

As work proceeded questions arose on which it was necessary to consult the King. Choosing a mild day towards the end of March, when I was clear of my cold, I rode over to Greenwich to discuss them with him. I arrived in the early afternoon, hoping to catch him as he finished dinner; but at the palace I was told that he was out hunting, and Lady Jane Seymour with him. I asked for the Queen, and they said that she was at home and would see me. As I followed the servant who led me into her presence, tears filled my eyes. I recalled my first glimpse of her when she rode at the King's side, radiant and lovely, in the hunting party at Waltham. It wrung my heart that now she was left behind here to brood, while another woman usurped her place.

I found her sitting out of doors in the sheltered quadrangle, listening to a melody played to her on a little spinet by Mark Smeaton, a musician who had recently been appointed a groom of the chamber. The details of the scene remained clearly in my memory when later events gave them a terrible importance, and I can swear that she was paying no attention to the man, barely conscious even of his presence except that his music soothed her. He broke off as I came out of the house, and Amanda who was with her, nosing in a drain, barked vociferously, then recognised me, ran to meet me and jumped up in greeting.

I knelt to the Queen, and she told the servant to bring me a chair and set it beside her. She seemed pleased to see me, asked kindly after my health; but I felt that her mind was elsewhere, that she barely attended to my answer. There was a pause, and when she spoke again her question startled me, it was so abrupt:

"Does God really demand sacrifice to atone for sin?"

I knew that she was thinking of the King's obsession, of his fear of a curse that denied him an heir, and I assured her in words as plain as I used to him that the very idea is incompatible with divine love, a monstrous error. She nodded as if she agreed with what I said, but her frown persisted:

"If God casts no curse, who does? Is it a power greater than his own?"

I was in a dilemma in which I often found myself with the King. If I expressed disbelief in the curse I forfeited her confidence in my judgment; if I accepted the premise I had no answer to her question. While I hesitated she added still more disconcertingly:

"You can call the power evil, but it must be appeased."

I do not know what I should have said in reply; Amanda deprived me of the opportunity. A succession of piercing barks cut off all conversation, and as I looked round at the steps leading down from the house I understood the reason. The servant had left the door ajar, and Lady Jane's little dog came through, a sour-tempered white poodle, much given to snapping and snarling, but bewildered at the moment as he sought in vain for his mistress.

Amanda's din swelled to frenzy. Like most spaniels she was a great coward; but at a safe distance, on her own ground and in familiar company she could afford to bluff. The poodle was taken aback and hesitated, then his tail dropped between his legs and he slunk away. As soon as she was sure that he was in flight Amanda pursued, taking care to pause for a vociferous challenge whenever she was in danger of catching up.

The Queen's eyes brightened as she watched, and she added her own voice gaily to encourage the chase. It comforted me to see the quick change in her mood, and I rose to take my leave, unwilling to resume discussion of a problem in which I could help so little. As I left the quadrangle her laughter still rang in my ears, echoed by the dancing tinkle of a tune that Smeaton struck up on the spinet.

The closing notes of that interview haunted me when I recalled them. She laughed too recklessly, wildly, as if the dog-fight were no more than the chance occasion, a secret knowledge the true source of her mirth. My uneasiness was increased by stories reaching me of her behaviour at court, of extravagant gaiety, even coquetry, lighthearted but incautious familiarity with her friends among the courtiers, especially Wyatt and Norris. She· was by nature too free in her manners, incapable of prudence, too vain of her beauty to resent or repel admiration; but no circumstances could be more inappropriate than the present to indulgence. I had the impression that a perverse spirit drove her, an exhilaration born of defiance, that she deliberately showed herself at her worst.

All business was suspended in Holy Week, and I went down to spend it with Margaret at Knole. My secretary, Ralph Morice, came too. He was more a friend than a servant, my constant companion since I became Archbishop and an indefatigable transcriber of my letters and other documents. I had no secrets from him and never regretted my trust. It was always a pleasure to Margaret when he accompanied me; she liked him and could talk to him without restraint.

We were sitting at dinner on the day following my arrival, all laughing over Amanda's pursuit of the Seymour poodle, when we were interrupted by a hubbub of voices and clatter of feet in the passage. The quarters which I occupied were at the back of the house, to be out of sight of the curious, but this had the consequent drawback that we ourselves had no warning from the windows of a visitor's approach. We sprang up in alarm; Ralph hurried to the door to see what was happening, and Margaret made ready to dart away into hiding. She was not given the time. The door opened, a man brushed past Ralph and strode in. I was about to protest angrily when I saw that it was Rochford.

His eyes met Margaret's as she stood facing him, blushing and frowning, unable to escape. He stared at her, then suddenly with a broad grin and without waiting for an introduction he bowed: "Haven't we met before?" he asked. "Or was it your German brother?"

His memory for faces was inconveniently tenacious. It was a long time since I had introduced him to a young landgrave at Hampton Court.

I was appalled by the misadventure. I knew him well and was fond of him; he was accustomed at Lambeth to break in on me without ceremony, but here it was different, and I blamed the servants bitterly in my heart for letting him in. He was not a man to whom it came easily to hold his tongue. Luckily for us he was too full of the news that he brought, too eager to share his jubilation, to allow even so fruitful a source of gossip to divert him. He turned from Margaret to me, seemed to forget her at once as he began to talk, and she slipped out unobtrusively behind him. I do not know what impression he retained of her, what suspicion she aroused. In less than a month his mouth was shut forever.

He was in high spirits however on that afternoon at Knole, believing that the new wind of diplomacy blowing from the continent would sweep away all the clouds that threatened his sister. His news both astonished and delighted me. The Emperor sent orders to Chapuis to seek an audience with the King, to propose a treaty of reconciliation and alliance. The terms remained secret till the King received them; but Rochford, who had his own sources of information, was able to give me a very accurate forecast. In return for English help against the Turks, and in any measures necessary to repel the French in Flanders and Italy, the Emperor would use his influence with the Pope to obtain full absolution for King Henry, recognition of his marriage to the Queen and of the legitimacy of Princess Elizabeth. This was a remarkable change in the Emperor's policy, but it was in plain accordance with his political interest. Since his aunt's death he had little reason to pursue a quarrel which damaged the prosperity of his Flemish trade, least of all when exaggerated reports reaching him of the wealth accruing from the dissolution of the monasteries raised hopes of a useful loan from King Henry to replenish his own habitually empty treasury.

Rochford was overjoyed, cock-a-hoop, already predicting eclipse for Lady Jane Seymour. When he left I escorted him out of the house, and he walked with me laughing and joking, making fun especially of poor Chapuis given so uncongenial a task. But as he mounted his horse his tone became grave:

"Don't be afraid that the Queen will betray her religion."

Then he waved his hat to me cheerfully and rode away. That image of him lingered in my memory.

The King put off the audience till the Tuesday after Easter, pleading the religious festival as excuse, desiring time no doubt to think the matter over. When the day came I was at Greenwich myself to see Chapuis perform his errand. He arrived in good time and stood talking to the Boleyns, father and son, while he waited. His affability deserved respect in view of the blow that his master had dealt him, upsetting all his careful plots, making him play a leading part in restoring the Queen whom he hated. It must have been peculiarly galling to him that the order came at a time when he himself was reporting her imminent downfall. The story indeed may be true that the Emperor left his ambassador's despatches unread.

Cromwell came late. I saw him exchange glances with Rochford as he hurried to join the group where Chapuis was standing. Then the bell rang for mass, and we all moved off towards the chapel, Cromwell and Rochford flanking Chapuis on either side. There was a larger attendance than usual that day at court. Even if few were aware of the Emperor's proposals it was known, and sufficiently rare by now to arouse curiosity, that the King and Queen would attend mass together, and that afterwards he would dine with her in her room.

We waited in the antechapel for the King to take his place. He seemed to be in excellent humour, pausing to greet Chapuis cordially as he passed. Rochford and his father had contrived it that Chapuis stood facing the door, catching the eye of everyone entering. The next to enter would be the Queen, whose approach was already announced. I watched in some amusement to see what he would do when she came. It was his habit at court to avoid her, to retreat out of her way rather than pay his respects. We all knew in what terms he spoke of her behind her back.

He himself perceived the danger of his position. He edged away surreptitiously to one side, till he was in the corner between the door and the wall. The door opened inwards and, as he clearly intended, would screen him when it was pushed. There was a dry humour in his smile as he glanced at Rochford, an air of caustic triumph.

The door behaved just as he wished. He was completely hidden as the Queen came in. The crowd in the antechapel parted to make way for her, expecting her to walk straight on into the chapel to join the King. No one could have foreseen what she did. She stopped, looked deliberately over her shoulder. Some familiar imp of mischief seemed to prompt her, to warn her who was there. Her eyes sought and found Chapuis, and he could not ignore her without flagrant discourtesy, especially inopportune in view of the Emperor's instructions. He pulled himself together, stepped forward and greeted her with a courtly bow. She responded with malicious punctilio.

This seemingly unimportant incident provoked interested comment. Many observing the reconciliation between the King and Queen, and suspecting that something was in the air without knowing what, believed that Chapuis was at last persuaded of the uselessness of resistance, that he saluted the Queen in token of submission. Princess Mary and her adherents were indignant with him for paying homage to the "Concubine," and it was long before they allowed him to forget his disgrace. My own feeling was mainly of relief that the Queen had so far recovered her spirits as to resume her habit of impish mockery.

After mass we followed the King and Queen to her room for dinner. The party included most of the leading courtiers and foreign ambassadors; but Chapuis remained behind and dined elsewhere. I overheard the Queen ask why he did not join them, and the King soothed her, declaring that it was not out of any disrespect. This was true, as it seems; for, however glad Chapuis may have been of the excuse, he had reason of state for his absence, being detained in earnest conversation with Rochford.

During the meal the Queen's vivacity betrayed the elation which she was unable to restrain, and as always in such circumstances her discretion suffered. She expressed sympathy for the Emperor in his continual wars with the French, shocked many present by the indelicacy of the taunt which she aimed at King Francis:

"Why can't the French King put an end to his squalid troubles without upsetting everyone else?"

All knew, including the French ambassador, that she spoke of the venereal disease of which King Francis was a victim. It was heartbreaking to listen while she exposed herself to the disapproval even of her friends.

When dinner was over we all retired, leaving the King and Queen alone. Rochford passed us on the stairs, going up as we came down, and I wondered if his errand were connected with his conversation with Chapuis; but when he rejoined us later downstairs he stood aloof, unusually reticent, refusing to be drawn when anyone tried to get him to talk. For several hours we waited there, uneasily expectant. The knowledge seemed to gather without words that great issues were being decided overhead.

When at last the King came down the Queen was not with him. He beckoned to Chapuis, grasped him by the arm and drew him aside into the recess of a window. Many inquisitive glances were cast at them as they conferred there in secret. In a few minutes he called to Cromwell and Sir Thomas Audley, the chancellor, and they made haste to join him. There was an ominous note in his voice of impatience, vexation.

The talk was resumed, and a great hush fell on the rest of us as we watched the little group by the window. Although their voices were lowered it was clear from their gestures and expression that the discussion was not going smoothly. Suddenly Chapuis spread his hands as if to disclaim responsibility, then he withdrew across the room, choosing whether by chance or design a place next to Sir Edward Seymour, brother to the Queen's rival.

Without him the debate seemed to grow still more acrimonious. One of the casements of the window was open, and a fresh breeze ruffled the curtains so that they swayed across the recess obscuring my view from time to time of the three who argued there. The King's back was turned, but Cromwell faced me, and with every glimpse that I caught of him his temper seemed to be mounting. He was one of the few who dared to bandy high words with the King, and as each inflamed the other the King's voice rose, provoked to fury:

"Her blood be on her own head."

I saw Audley frown as if in warning that the exclamation could be overheard, and the argument was resumed in a lower tone. It seemed to advance no more smoothly. Cromwell's face became purple, and at last with an abrupt gesture he turned away, snorting and growling to himself. He spoke loudly, addressing the company at large rather than the King:

"I'm dying of thirst, I must have a drink."

He crossed the room to a chest by the door, where he sat alone. A servant brought him a glass of wine.

The King paid no attention to him, but went on talking to Audley till Chapuis approached with a quizzical smile to take his leave. They parted with formal expressions of politeness, the King's as chilly as an insult.

For several days afterwards Cromwell was ill in bed. His furious argument with the King brought back a weakness afflicting his lungs, and he was barely able to sit his horse as he rode home to London. Chapuis who accompanied him had an anxious journey, less concerned to promote the Emperor's policy than to prevent King Henry's chief minister from falling on his head in the road.

When Cromwell was well enough to see me I visited him in Throgmorton Street. The events still rankled so bitterly in his mind that it was hard to get him to speak of them with coherence; but at last I pieced the story together, as much of it as he was willing to divulge. He was delighted, he told me, when Chapuis brought him the Emperor's proposals. This was the opportunity which he sought to establish King Henry as arbiter of Europe, holding the balance between Empire, Papacy and France. Chapuis assured him that the independence of the Church in England would be maintained, that the Pope would be content with the restoration of a nominal suzerainty, leaving the King in control of the revenues. Cromwell was very willing to give Queen Anne his allegiance again on such terms.

He informed the King, who was no less favourably impressed, particularly by the security afforded to the succession by Papal recognition of the legitimacy of his issue. The Queen too was exultant, as was to be expected, and her father and brother shared her jubilation. This was the state of affairs when Rochford visited me at Knole, glowing with hope and confident in the success of the negotiations.

In the days which followed till Chapuis had his formal audience with the King he had further meetings to discuss the terms with Cromwell. Difficulty arose from the Emperor's insistence on English support against the German Protestants, with whom he was once more in conflict. Cromwell strove to whittle the condition down, to concede no more than an assurance of sympathy for the Emperor's cause; but Chapuis demanded a binding commitment, reinforced by suppression of Protestant teaching in

England. He argued that if the Pope was to accept King Henry's authority in the Church no occasion must be given to find fault with its doctrine, to doubt its orthodoxy.

Disagreement persisted on this question even till the Tuesday, and Rochford was deputed to carry on the argument, to obtain the best terms from Chapuis that he could. They were still arguing when we went up to dinner without them in the Queen's room, and it is clear that Rochford was on his way to report the outcome when I passed him later on the stairs. Not even Cromwell knew what took place between the King and Queen while they were alone; but remembering the extravagance of her behaviour at dinner I am sure that already she foresaw and was steeling herself for a terrible decision.

When the King came down and led Chapuis off into the window he was in the grip of violent emotion. Cromwell told me that as soon as he joined them he knew that the battle was lost. The King's mood, so genial before, so ready to encourage the negotiations, had changed in a few hours to an unreasoning obstinacy. He rejected every overture with scorn, spoke as if it were a condescension to treat with the Emperor at all, till at last, as we witnessed, Chapuis withdrew in protest. The only result of the further conclave was that Cromwell himself lost his temper.

I never learnt how far Rochford succeeded in mitigating the Emperor's terms. When I asked Cromwell he grunted:

"It would have cooked Latimer's goose."

The words fed my suspicion that the Queen played a decisive part in the proceedings, and this was confirmed by some incautious remarks from Lady Shelton, in whose company the Queen spoke freely. I knew that she would consent to no compromise that endangered her friends. If she shamed the King by her loyalty, stung him with her burning reproach, it is easy to understand his ill-humour, his unaccommodating attitude when he talked to Chapuis. He would not wish to admit that he allowed his wife to thwart him.

Cromwell very evidently blamed her for the disappointment, and he did not forgive her. Thenceforward he worked hand in glove with the Seymours for her undoing. The King resumed his coldness towards her, avoided her society, and she sank into listlessness and depression. Lady Jane was restored to favour.

On May 2nd I was at Knole when I received an urgent message from Cromwell asking me to return to Lambeth at once. Appalling news awaited me there. The Queen was in the Tower under arrest charged with adultery. What I heard of the events preceding the disaster did nothing to lessen my bewilderment. She was with the King at the May Day tournament at Greenwich, looking, people said, unusually happy, so seldom was she invited now to accompany him to an entertainment. Norris was among the competitors, and it happened that as he rode towards her she dropped her handkerchief. He leapt from his horse and picked it up with a flourish, but instead of wearing it as a favour he used it to wipe his brow, then gave it back to her on the point of his lance. Gossip made much of this incident in view of what happened. In my own opinion it was no more than lighthearted burlesque, a private joke between them.

A few minutes later the King rose suddenly without explanation, called Norris to his side, and they returned together to Westminster. The Queen was left to watch the rest of the performance alone.

She spent the night at Greenwich, and on the following day at dinner—a nightmare meal where she sat surrounded by frightened faces and vainly awaiting a comforting message from the King—as the cloth was removed for dessert her uncle, the Duke of Norfolk, and other lords of the council entered, announcing that they came to examine her on grave charges which had been laid against her. Her uncle who presided at the examination made up for his past subservience by the coarseness of his insults.

The examiners committed her to the Tower. There was a painful delay while they waited for the tide, then she was put on a barge and taken up the river. It was the same journey that she made less than three years before in such splendour to attend her coronation. The constable of the Tower, Sir William Kingston, received her when she disembarked. He was no friend of hers, a partisan rather of the group of nobles with whom Chapuis conspired; but he seems to have treated her with as much humanity as his grim duty allowed, and there is no reason to disbelieve his account of her behaviour. When she asked if she would be put in a dungeon he told her that he had the King's orders to give her the same lodging that she occupied before she was crowned. On hearing this she burst into tears, and he quoted her words: "It's too good for me. Jesus, have mercy on me." Then she sank on her knees in prayer on the stone floor.

It puzzled me to hear of her self-abasement if she was innocent of the crimes of which she was accused. Later I understood better, when I knew more of the motives underlying these events.

Not even this bare outline of the facts was known to me on my first arrival at Lambeth. My belief was that the whole trouble arose from some terrible misunderstanding, which would yield when the truth was revealed. In this conviction I sat down to write to the King to express my sympathy. Much as I should have liked to write to the Queen also, I could not without his permission as she was his prisoner.

My letter needed careful composition if it was not to do more harm than good. It would be presumptuous to insist on the Queen's innocence when I knew nothing of the evidence; but I hoped that he would be impressed by the tribute which I could honestly pay to her character, when I assured him that I never had better opinion of a woman than I had of her, and that next to himself I was more bound to her than to any creature living. I was obliged to add, as of course was only right, that if adultery were proved against her it deserved to be punished; but there was no doubt in my mind that proof was inconceivable.

I had barely finished writing when a messenger came summoning me to an inquiry at Westminster, and I left the letter lying on my desk and made haste to cross the river to the Star Chamber, where the chancellor and other lords of the council awaited me. They treated me with courtesy, but it was plain from the questions that they put that they were trying to elicit information damaging to the Queen. In answer I could only declare what I had said already in my letter to the King, that she enjoyed my unqualified love and respect.

When they saw that I had nothing to reveal they told me more of the charges on which she was arrested. These included not only adultery with Norris and the musician Smeaton, but also conspiracy against the King's life and incest with her brother Rochford. Each item was more incredible than the last. Was it likely that a woman living as she did under the constant scrutiny of the court, vulnerable to every breath of gossip, would be able to commit repeated acts of adultery without arousing suspicion long before this? What had she to gain from the King's death, which would deprive her of her standing in the kingdom and leave her at the mercy of her enemies? The most preposterous charge of all was that of incest with her brother. It is appalling if a man cannot love his sister without incurring calumny which defiles and poisons the natural ties of blood.

I left Westminster confused and distraught, unable to believe either that the charges were true or that the King would accuse the Queen without adequate evidence. Back in my study at Lambeth I picked up my letter and added a postscript, telling him of the interview in the Star Chamber of which he would receive a report. My intention was also to comment on the information given me, but try as I would I could not think what to say. I could only express my sympathy and regret.

For the next week or so I watched the course of events with the helplessness of nightmare. Norris and Smeaton were under arrest as her accomplices, Rochford too, and they were soon joined in prison by Sir Francis Weston in consequence of a rash remark which she made to her attendants. These women had orders to repeat whatever she said, and as one of them was Lady Boleyn, her aunt by marriage, from whom she had long been estranged, her words were unlikely to lack embellishment. It would have made all the difference to her comfort if, instead of this gorgon, she could have had her real aunt, Lady Shelton, her father's sister, to look after her.

There was nothing against any of the prisoners beyond tittle-tattle, reports of idle words, frivolous behaviour. Much of it was probably true. The Queen was by nature much too free in her speech and manners, too heedless of her own dignity and of that of others. Her faults were not hidden, strict decorum was offended

by them ever since she came to court. They afforded no more
ground now than in the past to convict her of moral turpitude,
of an infidelity wholly at variance with her character.

The charges were no less hard to believe of the men themselves.
Norris was the King's trusted friend and companion, proud to
enjoy the Royal favour and anxious to retain it. Weston I did
not know well, but I doubt whether she did either. She became
involved with him only because he made eyes at her cousin Madge,
whom she intended for Norris. As for Smeaton, she was on
familiar terms with him as with all her servants; but she had
not the art to disguise her feelings, to show as little interest as
she did in his presence, if he had been her lover. It is true that,
unlike the others who affirmed their innocence and hers to the
end, Smeaton broke down and signed a confession; but being
of humble birth he suffered cruel treatment in prison. There are
few men who cannot be made to plead guilty under torture.

She was more distressed for the sake of her friends than for
herself, she wrote to the King to plead on their behalf; yet she
was so little able to restrain her careless tongue that her chance
words reported and distorted helped to aggravate their danger.
Even Wyatt fell under suspicion from this source. She told Lady
Kingston, her gaoler's wife, that ballads would be written about
her in time to come, and that no one could do it as well as
he. At once he too was arrested. In prison he was not content
to deny his own guilt, he defied her accusers by insisting that
she herself was innocent on every count. In a sonnet written
shortly afterwards he laughs off the storm which he provoked:

> Sephame said true that my nativity
> Mischanced was with the ruler of the May.

There would have been nothing laughable in the fulfilment
of the astrologer's forecast if the King's affection for him had
not prevailed. He was released and sent to Allington Castle, his
father's house on the Medway, to live there for a time under
supervision. He even managed to get his sister Mary added to
the Queen's attendants in the Tower. She loved the Queen, and

her presence would be a great comfort, mitigating the hostility of the rest.

Wyatt's courage and loyalty put me to shame as I waited helplessly at Lambeth, a passive spectator of events. Yet there was nothing more that could be done since my letter to the King remained unanswered. From what I heard he was at Westminster distracting himself with feverish gaiety, entertaining Lady Jane at York Place, Wolsey's old home now converted into a Royal palace. His behaviour was that of a man nagged by conscience and doing his best not to listen.

The whole course of events defied understanding. Even if he despaired of male issue from the Queen, wished to put Lady Jane in her place, there was no need to trump up false charges bringing disgrace both on her reputation and on his own justice. The Roman court would be ready enough, if he sought it, to pronounce the annulment of a marriage never recognised by the Pope, and he himself, left a widower by the Princess Dowager's death, would be free to marry again. A wrong would be done, but less atrocious in its consequences than his present course of action.

I had an uneasy feeling as I worried over the mystery that the same superstition that inspired his fears for the succession directed his choice of measures to exorcise them. There was a disturbing flavour of it in a complaint which he made to one of his friends, snapped up eagerly by the gossip of the court, that when he married the Queen she ensorcelled him. She herself seemed to be infected with similar delusions if her words to Kingston were correctly reported, that there would be no rain till she left the Tower, a threat that aroused alarm as prolonged drought already retarded the crops. I myself was more alarmed by the credulity with which stories like this were received. There was enough darkness in the case without adding that of witchcraft.

The commoners were put on trial first. The indictment against them brought a surprise; a statement was submitted affirming that Lady Wingfield, a former attendant on the Queen, had been a witness of acts of adultery. It was the strongest evidence yet offered by the Crown, relating to deeds, not to words only. Lady

Wingfield however was unable to swear to it in person, having died in the meantime. The deposition read in court was the work of a woman who attended her in her last illness and professed to be repeating what she told her.

The story left room for many questions. Did the woman remember what she heard and repeat it accurately? Was she ever in Lady Wingfield's confidence to the extent that she claimed? There could be no answer, Lady Wingfield was beyond reach of the court's inquiries. The woman concerned was pointed out to me in the street, and I thought that she had a rapacious expression, would not easily resist a bribe; but it is unjust to condemn a person on the face alone, and I know nothing against her. The court accepted her evidence, and all the prisoners were condemned to death.

The trial of the Queen and her brother followed after the weekend. Twenty-six peers were summoned for the hearing under the presidency of her uncle, the Duke of Norfolk, who expressed no reluctance. Her father was not among them, he implored to be relieved of the duty and was excused. Less fortunate was her old suitor, Henry Percy, now Earl of Northumberland. He was forced to sit among her judges; but in the middle of the proceedings he was taken ill and allowed to leave. He was never of strong constitution, and the shock of this ordeal was too much for him. He died a few months later, the last of his line.

I could not have borne to be present myself, yet I longed to be informed of the Queen's demeanour, to have clear knowledge to resolve my doubts, to shape my own judgment. So I sent my secretary, Ralph Morice, to stand among the spectators, and he brought me back a full account of the trial. He told me that, as always when the need was great enough, the Queen rose to the demands of the occasion, her dignity recalled that of her coronation as she curtseyed to the peers assembled to judge her and sat down to await their questions. She answered them with the firm intelligence of which she was capable when she set levity aside. Few around Ralph in the crowd failed to respond to her wit and charm, and he thought that she made a favourable impression on her judges also, that many were convinced by her defence. If so, they were not enough to save her. Her uncle treated her with hostility from start to finish, and it was he who pronounced sentence of death, either at the stake or on the block as the King directed.

Her brother's trial followed. It is not true, as has been asserted, that his wife gave evidence against him. However unsuited they may have been to each other, however shallow her principles, there was no malice in her nature. The only ground that I can find for the calumny is that she did in fact write to the King; but far from incriminating her husband it was to sue in vain for his pardon and release. The rest was added by her enemies when she herself fell into trouble a few years later, and stories were eagerly sought to blacken her character.

Rochford defended himself ably. His demeanour made such an impression on those present that at the end of the first day's hearing odds were laid of ten to one on his acquittal. Although I scarcely dared cherish hope I could not help being encouraged by the report. The disappointment was all the harder to bear the next day when he was condemned and sentenced like the others. He himself probably destroyed any chance of acquittal when he was handed a note bearing what purported to be a remark made to him by the Queen and overheard. He was told to confirm that the words were hers but on no account to divulge them. He retorted at once by reading them aloud. They referred to the King and were indelicate as well as defamatory.

Both the Queen and her brother were to die. It seemed that nothing remained but their execution. I was too stunned by the event to think clearly yet, to appreciate the causes and consequences. I should have liked to visit the Queen in the Tower to offer her what comfort I could; but I was uncertain whether the King would grant leave, whether she herself might not resent it as an intrusion. She had her own chaplain with her, a priest called Devett, who was active in the performance of his duties, keeping the sacrament for her in a recess at the back of her room, accessible to her prayers. Might she not prefer to rely on him rather than me for spiritual strength? He came to her free from painful association with the past, reassured her as I could not by his confident faith in the efficacy of material symbols.

The King himself resolved my doubts. He sent me orders to go to the Tower to hear her confession, adding that I was to take care to report anything whose effect annulled her marriage. This warning surprised and offended me. How could I reveal what she said without violating the secret of the confessional? How in any case, even if she were guilty, was the validity of her marriage impaired? It was one thing to pass judgment on his first marriage in strict accordance with the law, quite another to annul the second whose legality I myself confirmed.

Nonetheless, if she wished to confess to me, I could not refuse her. I set out at once for the Tower. At that time it was unfamiliar ground to me. King Henry seldom used it as a residence, preferring the greater comfort of Greenwich or Hampton Court, or even his new palace at Westminster, the former York Place. As I disembarked at the stairs and crossed the drawbridge to enter the ancient stronghold its grim associations chilled me, recalling not only the turbulence of the past but also the prisoners more recently immured here, a list that included More and Fisher and ended with the Queen of England.

There was nothing resembling a prison in the room in which I found her, the presence chamber itself with its canopied chair of state, where she sat as if enthroned. As I came in she rose to greet me, and I knelt and kissed her hand. I expected her to lead me at once to the chapel, but instead she sat down again and invited me to do the same. While I waited for her to speak I watched her covertly. Sunlight poured in through the window, revealing the gloss of her dark hair which hung loose over her shoulders and the inwoven pattern of the damask in her plainly cut black silk dress. It shone on her face also, but the lines traced there by anxiety, the disfiguring pallor of the last few months had vanished. Her appearance recalled the first occasion that I saw her, on her hunting expedition with the King at Waltham. The same excitement flushed her, the same secret awareness lit her eyes.

She told me that what she had to say was better revealed here than in the confessional, and that I was free to act on the information as I thought fit. I was relieved to hear it, but her next words struck me like a blow:

"When I married the King I swore to him that either I bore him a son or my blood washed away the curse that denied him an heir."

Then she asked me if I knew what she meant by the old religion. It is a phrase that has come into use recently of the doctrines taught by the Pope; but at the time of which I write, at so early a stage of the breach with Rome, I could give it no meaning. She smiled at my ignorance and explained that she spoke of a creed that was old when Christianity came here, and which survived in remote places in spite of the efforts of the Church to suppress it. She told me that in the country round Blickling Hall in Norfolk where she was born nearly everyone high and low belonged to a coven, the name given to the conventicles of thirteen in which the cult was organised. The servants who had charge of her on her mother's death were themselves believers, and in their company she attended the rites, even their great festival of Beltane celebrated on a hilltop on May Day, where a man, the king of the coven, played the part of the god, and the girls present worshipped naked.

"They meant it for the best," she explained. "It was to make the crops grow."

I listened with growing concern. Her description of the rites struck a chord in my memory, recalled stories overheard in my childhood in the smithy at Aslockton of witchcraft, devil-worship hidden in Sherwood Forest. When I grew up I learnt more of these practices, knew that they were condemned as mortal sin in the Bible and by the Church; but they played as I thought so small a part in contemporary life, were so remote from my own experience that I put them out of my mind. It was all the greater shock to find a witness to the idolatry, an initiate in the Queen herself.

My dismay increased as she went on to describe the doctrine in fuller detail. Carnal licence was among the least abominable of its errors. The divine king of the coven retained his sanctity for seven years, after which he must die unless his powers were re-

newed by the sacrifice of a human victim offered as a willing substitute. Whether it were the man-god himself who suffered, or another took his place, the efficacy of the rite depended on free
will, on readiness to accept not only death but also the ceremony
of pain and humiliation preceding it. The victim was reviled,
flogged, killed, submitting to rejection on earth to be proved worthy
of the choice of heaven. Many unaccountable disappearances of
people in Norfolk could be attributed, she told me, to the Beltane
fires.

These ideas imbibed at an early age made a deep impression
on her, but they remained latent, seemingly forgotten among the
distractions and excitement of life when she left Norfolk and was
taken to Paris. Even on her return to England she was too much
occupied with events to spare a thought for them. Henry Percy
claimed all her attention, till his place was taken by the King. It
is unlikely indeed that idolatrous echoes from the past would ever
have troubled her if the King himself had not evoked them, insisting on the guilt that he incurred from intercourse with his
brother's wife and the curse that lay on the succession.

The purpose of the Beltane sacrifice is expiation, to renew the
powers of the coven and purge the guilt of the past seven years.
It was typical of her imprudence that as soon as she saw how it
applied to King Henry's own predicament she explained it to him,
telling him everything that she knew. Witchcraft—the old religion,
as she called it—is an offence condemned by the state as well as by
the Church, and it was his duty to denounce the practice and punish
the offenders.

She judged rightly for once in counting on his forbearance. The
secrets which she disclosed aroused his burning interest, he
clutched at them with all the strength of his obsession. He himself was approaching a multiple of seven in his age, the comple-
tion of his sixth term of seven years of life. I can well believe
that as he brooded he attributed the opportunity to supernatural
guidance, which offered at the crucial time the knowledge and the
means, the willing victim, to exorcise the evil besetting him. Her
own acquiescence surprises me even less, so consistent was it with
the impetuous loyalty of her character and with her sanguine con-

fidence in the benevolence of her destiny. At their secret marriage
she added a vow more secret still, undisclosed to the officiating
priest, that either she bore the King an heir or she died to enable
him to beget his line on another woman.

"I thought that when Bess was born I'd done my part," she
told me, "but it had to be a boy, and I miscarried."

She spoke without resentment. She had no pity for herself, accepting her fate with a calm conviction of its justice. There had
been moods, as I knew from Kingston, in which she shrank from
it and clung to life; but now I found only serene exhilaration, it
amazed me that anyone could look forward to death with such joy.
Her chief concern was that the rite in which she played the leading
part omitted nothing indispensable to its effectiveness. She reminded me with satisfaction that twenty-six peers came to judge
her, two covens of thirteen, the sacred number. There remained
only, to fulfil the tradition, the degradation of the victim doomed
to sacrifice.

I began to understand much hitherto inexplicable in the course
of events, the necessity for the false charges, their shameful im-
putations, even the seemingly excessive humility with which she
behaved when she entered the Tower. The purpose of her present
confession, of the King's warning, was also made clear. The victim
must be stripped of all her honours, no longer a Queen, no longer
the King's lawful wife. She herself intended me to annul the marriage.

She left me in fact no choice. The condition on which the
bond was founded must invalidate it in the eyes of the law. When
I explained this she nodded in agreement; but when I went on to
rebuke her for the sin of witchcraft, to entreat her to pray for
forgiveness, she laughed gaily declaring that far from repenting she
gloried in what she did. I have blamed myself bitterly since for my
failure to help her. I was too shocked and bewildered. Every prejudice that I cherished was outraged, my hatred of superstition, my
respect for the Crown. Instead of a friend and comforter she found
only a narrow prelate, whose charity was stifled. I refused her absolution.

Looking back after twenty years I am glad that she remained

impenitent. I see her again as she sat radiant in black under the Royal canopy, no longer Queen of England but Diana, Queen of the underworld. The faith for which she gave her life was wicked error, but the God of love whom it denied was honoured in her courage and self-sacrifice. He absolved her as I could not from the idolatry. He would not have wished to deprive her of the strength which she found there to die, would not have wished to leave her forlorn on the scaffold.

As I knelt to take leave she pulled off the ring that she wore, a slim band of gold with a single rounded emerald set in a circle of little diamonds like the head of a flower.

"Keep this," she told me. "Some day perhaps you'll think better of me."

I took it with joy as a token of her affection. It was too small to go on any finger of mine, or even of Margaret's; but when I showed it to Alice it fitted her exactly, and she wore it, sanctifying it with her love.

I saw the Queen once again before her death. She came secretly under escort to the crypt at Lambeth, her execution was deferred for the purpose for two days. A few lords of the council including Cromwell were present as witnesses; but the King's orders were to keep the proceedings as quiet as possible, and they were soon over. Without declaring my reasons I pronounced the marriage annulled.

For the rest of that day and all the next I tried vainly to distract myself with work. Nothing that I took up was able to hold my attention. Rochford was dead, beheaded while his sister suffered degradation at Lambeth, and the hours ebbed relentlessly which remained before she herself shared his fate. I could not even find comfort in praying for her, although I knelt at the altar again and again. I had yet to learn that God is not bound by outward forms. Many who deny him with their lips are nearest to him in their hearts.

My only comfort was to read the verses which she herself wrote in prison, and which Mary Wyatt copied out and sent to me:

> Oh, death, rock me asleep,
>   Bring on my quiet rest.
> Let pass my very guiltless ghost
>   Out of my careful breast.

Peace of a sort answered me as I repeated them.

There was no peace even there however when Thursday evening darkened into night, her last night on earth. I sat in my study trying to read, staring at the page with unseeing eyes, hardly knowing what book lay before me. I could not bring myself to go to bed, it was too certain that sleep would be denied. At last in the small hours I went out of the house to walk in the garden. The night was warm and the sky clear. I could see my way dimly but sufficiently as the moon had not yet set. I crossed the lawn to the river and stood there staring into the water. Its blackness had a silver sheen like the silk of the Queen's dress.

I awoke from my thoughts with a start, feeling that someone was behind me. I had heard no one approach, but footsteps were soundless on the soft turf. At this hour in the privacy of my garden I counted on being alone, and it was not without fear of the supernatural that I glanced quickly round. But the ghost was of flesh and blood, a middle-aged man, and the flowing wrap that enveloped him was merely a scholar's coarse cloak. I recognised Alexander Aless, the Scottish reformer. He was often a visitor at Lambeth; nonetheless I was surprised to meet him in the dead of night.

He seemed to hesitate as I turned, then he came quickly on again. He was clearly very distressed. His face showed pale in the moonlight, and when he spoke he was barely able to control his voice. But his first words were ordinary enough, apologising for disturbing me and explaining that he happened to catch sight of me from the bridge. I could not refrain from asking why he was not in bed, although he had as good reason in truth to ask the same of me. But he was too polite or too preoccupied to retaliate; he answered at once that he had awoken from a dream so vivid that he could not bear to lie thinking of it, and had gone walking in the road to try to get it out of his head.

I was surprised that a man like Aless should let a dream upset him, and I suppose that he read the expression in my face and was offended. His voice was strained, almost challenging, as he told me in gruesome detail how he had seen the severed head of a woman and knew who it was. Glancing round, as if even in that lonely place he might be overheard, he added in a whisper:

"It was the Queen."

If it had been anyone other than Aless I should have suspected cruel mockery inflicted from motives beyond my understanding to taunt my grief. Such behaviour however was unthinkable of the man who spoke.

"Don't you know what is to happen today?" I asked him.

He shook his head. For the past few weeks, he confessed, he had shut himself up in the house, talking to no one while he applied himself to his books. Knowing his habits, his remarkable power of concentration, I believed him; but I felt an intolerable reluctance to inform his ignorance, to tell him the truth.

The moon sank behind the trees. The unseen hemmed me in, smelling of mayblossom and water-mint, the disembodied fragrance of the summer night. It was as if another answered in my place, using my tongue as an instrument. The words have endured in my memory ever since:

"She who was Queen of England will today become a Queen in Heaven."

I could hold my tears no longer and hid my face in my hands. Aless took me gently by the arm and led me back to the house.

15

Friday the 19th May 1536 was a turning point in my life. For a time I had no will left to perform my duties. Everything that I cherished seemed to have fallen in ruin. Of those whom I loved the Queen and her brother were dead, and their father died broken-hearted shortly afterwards. I knew that the charges brought against both were false, and I had learnt from her own mouth what depths of superstition prompted them. How could I continue to serve a King guilty of such iniquity?

Yet even as I asked the question I was ashamed of my self-righteousness. Was I so free from offence myself that I could only work in the company of the immaculate? Great designs were taking shape in England in which I was called to participate, the establishment of peace and order under Royal authority, the liberation of the Church from false doctrine and foreign exaction. The result would be much better of course if those who achieved it were themselves without sin; but in human affairs no achievement at all is possible unless one bears with imperfection.

My respect for the King could never be the same again, but the feeling into which it changed was the more lasting because it was founded on experience. Hitherto I had tended to belittle his faults, dazzled by the greatness of his position. I was in no danger of doing so now, having seen what victims they claimed. Yet it was possible to draw a distinction between his motives and the actions which they inspired, to respect the former even while I abhorred many of the latter.

Not even the horror of the past weeks shook my belief in the aims which we pursued under his leadership, and to whose success his exalted rank and the force of his character were indispensable. I knew how much weight his personality carried from the impression which it made on me myself. Nothing that he did, however outrageous, could alienate my affection for him. For the next ten years he and I worked closely together. He was often unreasonable and wrong-headed, his rage could bring death; but he had a geniality that warmed our association, so that I enjoyed and looked forward to his company and relied with unfailing confidence on his strength.

Nevertheless it was a severe strain on my resolution that on the very day of the Queen's death I had to issue a dispensation removing a bar of consanguinity, more fancied than real, to enable him to marry Lady Jane Seymour. Greatly to my relief I was not asked to officiate at the wedding, which was celebrated quietly at Wolf Hall, her home in Wiltshire. Many commented on the indecent haste with which the ceremony was pressed on, so that the meats served to the guests were baked while Queen Anne was beheaded in the Tower. The official reason given for the urgency was that, unless the marriage took place at once, it would have to wait till Rogationtide and Whitsun were over. Even so it would have meant no great delay.

My own opinion is that the King yielded to his bride's insistence. Beneath her meek and staid demeanour she had a fund of sullen obstinacy, and she was not so sure of her fascination that she could afford to give him time to change his mind. She did not like it when he told her, in the interval between the trial and the execution, that he meant to write a tragedy about the Queen, and even if the impulse passed without effect there were other signs of irresolution to shake her equanimity. The contradictions which racked him were shown by the very care that he took over preparations for the Queen's death, allotting her the rooms of state in the Tower for a prison and sending for an expert swordsman from France to ensure that the stroke would be swift, her agony not prolonged by a clumsy headsman. I was told that even this Frenchman inured to scenes of the sort was dazzled by the brightness of her eyes, and a scarf was brought to blindfold her to enable him to carry out his duties.

There was however another motive which may have contributed to the King's haste to celebrate his remarriage. The Queen herself told me that her blood was intended as a sacrifice to fructify the woman whom he married next. It is, I believe, a tenet of this gruesome creed that the magic is most potent when consummation follows immediately. If that was the idea in the minds of the newly wedded couple it received a semblance of confirmation from events, when Queen Jane conceived and bore a son. I rejoiced with the King in the fulfilment of his heart's desire, and I was honoured when he invited me to be the boy's godfather: but it horrified me to think what interpretation he put on the coincidence. I wondered if the bishops and other divines at court when the birth was announced would have cheered as enthusiastically if they had known as much as I did.

My own knowledge never marred the love and pride which I felt in my godson. I refuse to believe, it is incompatible with any true understanding of the love of God, that crime and blessing were cause and effect, nor do I believe that Queen Jane suffered divine punishment when, less than a fortnight after her delivery, she succumbed to a fever and died. Her fatal illness was the result of culpable neglect. If she had kept quiet as her physicians advised she would have recovered her strength; but instead she endured at once the strain and excitement of the baby's christening. Poor woman, she paid dearly for her ambition.

For a time I was afraid that these events would interfere with the work of ecclesiastical reform, that without Queen Anne's influence to sustain him the King would lose interest. To my relief the fear was groundless, he remained as determined as ever to resist the claims of the Pope, to assert his own authority over the Church. The task had fresh urgency for me now that I saw to what evil the abuse of religion can lead. The shock of the Queen's confession rankled in my memory. It was appalling to find that even in England the veneer of Christianity was so thin, and it seemed to me that less blame for this attached to the credulous and deluded who clung to idolatry, the "old religion" of witchcraft, than to the Christian priests responsible for their souls who failed to disseminate and explain the gospel of love.

The doctrine of the Real Presence has a terrible importance for me today when to reject it means death at the stake. Theologians want us to believe that after the prayer of consecration the "substance" of the bread and wine—the material essence binding them to experience—changes without change of appearance to that of flesh and blood. The spirit becomes matter, the symbol acquires supernatural power, and the truth to which the miracle bears witness is that of human sacrifice.

Sacrifice lies at the root of the doctrine, and my distaste for it mounted as I compared its ideas with those of the "old religion," described by the Queen. In both the blood of an innocent victim is needed to purge sin, to absolve the sinner from the forfeit incurred. In the heathen ceremony murder is committed, while the Christian sacrament enacts the rite in symbols; but great as is the difference in practice, the principle remains the same of an angry deity appeased by unmerited suffering.

There is nothing in the gospels to support such a view of the Incarnation. God took on human flesh and lived as a man among men to reveal his true nature to us, and he suffered the inevitable fate of perfect goodness in a fallen world, he was rejected and crucified. The stress is laid on the example of the life rather than on the necessity of the death. It is right of course to speak of self-sacrifice when we describe the great act of divine love; but the word is used in the transferred sense of pure renunciation, it has lost its original association with the priest's knife and the altar.

As these thoughts took shape in my mind I longed to discuss them with my friends, but I had to be careful in whom to confide for fear of exposing myself to charges of heresy. There were many even in the reforming party who would have been offended by my speculations if they had known of them, few to whom I could talk as freely as I did to Cromwell. He indeed, vicegerent for the King as supreme head of the Church, listened to me always with good-humoured, if at times cynical tolerance. It was easier perhaps for him as a layman to examine issues of this sort without prejudice. In any case he was fond of argument, accustomed readily to consider both sides of every question. The keenness of his comments even where we disagreed helped greatly to clarify my opinions.

He and I were at once in our respect for the divine gift of reason, our abhorrence of superstitious credulity. I never discussed the Queen's confession with him. I do not even know how far he was aware of the circumstances that prompted her death, although he played a leading part in the tragedy. After her death he never mentioned her name to me, nor I to him. Each knew what the other thought, and that our friendship could only continue on a foundation of silence. He did not ask for my approval, and he would not have had it; but I loved and respected him for what he was, in spite of much that he did.

Wyatt also whose devotion to the Queen was beyond doubt remained his friend, and I was thankful not to have to choose between them, when death had already deprived me of so many whose company I cherished. It helped to reconcile me even to those most active in support of the Seymours that events soon arose which threatened us with a common danger, obliterating differences and tightening the bond between us. The rebellion so long plotted by Chapuis broke out in the north, starting in Lincolnshire and spreading across the Humber into Yorkshire, gaining strength with the capture of York and the surrender through Lord Darcy's treachery of Pontefract Castle. The rebels described their uprising as the Pilgrimage of Grace, a crusade against heresy and schism; but although there may have been a few genuine enthusiasts the bulk of their support arose from causes far removed from religion.

A number of recent incidents aroused indignation in the counties affected: Cromwell's stern action for instance in summoning the grand jury of Yorkshire before the Star Chamber to explain the acquittal of a notorious murderer, and his suppression among the clothiers of the West Riding of lucrative fraud. Behind these lay deeper and more widespread causes of unrest. The north felt that it was the victim of unjust discrimination, proving by corrupt administration, neglected trade the truth of the proverb, "Out of sight, out of mind." There was reason in the complaint, as Cromwell himself recognised later when he reorganised the King's council in the north to remove abuses. The pity is that before the grievance was allayed the sufferers were led astray by troublemakers, incited to sedition and bloodshed.

As news arrived of the successes won by the rebels great alarm was felt in London. The King had no established force of his own for use in emergency. He had to rely on the loyalty of the nobles who mustered their retainers. His first intention as the men as-

sembled was to lead them north in person, but he was persuaded
to give up the command to the Duke of Norfolk, from whose estates most of the army was drawn. He himself remained in the
capital to quell any disaffection that arose there, and commissioners
were appointed in the neighbouring counties for a similar purpose.
In Kent the task fell on me.

Knole was no longer mine. Margaret and I were living at my
house at Ford on the road from Canterbury to Reculver, which
she preferred to any other that I could offer. She loved the view
from the rising ground beyond the garden, which looked out across
the coastal plain to the estuary already widening into ocean, a sheet
of water seemingly illimitable except in the clearest weather when
the distant shore of Essex could be dimly traced. She used to sit
there for hours, often taking our baby daughter—little Meg she
had become—to show her the sea. When I laughed at her, protesting that the child was too young to understand, she shook her
head gravely:

"I want her to get used to it. She may have to."

To my sorrow I knew that she was right.

Neither of us had the chance to make expeditions up the hill
while the rebellion lasted. I myself was too busy, she too fearful
of hostile eyes prying where they could for information to use
against me. Whatever the true causes of the outbreak, those who
fomented it were careful to avail themselves of the screen of religion, complaining of the breach with Rome and the dissolution of
the monasteries, and as Cromwell and I were closely associated
with these policies we became the chief target of invective, denounced as the King's evil counsellors responsible for every misfortune recalled or invented. Ribald ballads deriding "Crim and
Cram" circulated through the country, and Cromwell himself sent
me a copy which amused him. His worst crime, to judge from
the verses, was to be born a brewer's son, an unforgivable offence
in the eyes of those whose lustre lay only in their quarterings.

My own past was busily combed for similar shortcomings. Walking out early one morning I found that someone had fastened a
truss of hay over the front door, a facetious allusion to the story
that I worked as an ostler at the Dolphin in Cambridge. I ordered

a servant to remove it before Margaret came down. She would be alarmed to know that an enemy could approach so near, even climb the porch at night to leave us a token of his wit.

It amazes me that, among all this malice and calumny, no one so much as hinted that I was married. I was utterly at the mercy of my servants, any of them by speaking could have ruined me, but all kept my secret faithfully. Margaret herself behaved as if she had the gift of invisibility, as if she had been out gathering fernseed on St. John's Eve. She did everything that she was told, except when I implored her to seek safety in Germany. She replied stubbornly that it would be time enough if the rebels won.

There was little danger in fact of a rebel victory in Kent. Although I fussed over my duties, making a show of vigilance, my office of commissioner was something of a sinecure. The only trouble that I had was with my old adversaries, the monks of Christ Church at Canterbury, who, counting on impunity while my attention was occupied elsewhere, were breaking the law to carry on a lucrative trade in relics. Meanwhile the fate of the kingdom hung on the issue of events in the north. The Duke of Norfolk preferring negotiation to battle invited the rebel leaders to meet him at Doncaster, and terms were agreed which he referred to the King. The most important was a promise to hold a Parliament at York at which northern grievances would be redressed. When Cromwell heard the news he was very angry, pointing out that this was disorder which Chapuis had been plotting for years, that it had offshoots ramifying through society, and unless it was stamped out vigorously it would recur still more dangerously later. The King however approved of the duke's conciliatory policy; he sent for the leader of the rebels, a lawyer from Richmond called Aske, who came to London under safe-conduct. They seem to have reached understanding on many of the issues in dispute. Aske returned satisfied to Yorkshire.

We barely had time to breathe a sigh of relief. Within a week or two the work was undone, Cromwell shown to be right. The revolt was too ill-organised, disrupted by conflicting ambitions, to submit to leadership. Aske's followers defied, disowned him, took up arms again. While they threatened to seize Hull and Beverley the Duke of Norfolk gathered his forces, and this time his orders were to suppress mercilessly till the insurrection was crushed. It was an easy task. The rebels had no concerted plan, and he was able to intercept their marauding bands and eliminate each in turn. All the leaders were captured and brought to trial. A stern example was necessary to avert further danger to the realm; but I was sorry for Aske, who was sentenced to death like the rest.

The defeat of the Pilgrimage of Grace was less a victory for reformed religion than for the group of nobles led by the Duke of Norfolk. The King learnt how heavily he depended on them for support. The lesson was reinforced a few months later when the Pope, in alliance with the Emperor and the King of France, published the bull of deposition which his predecessor, Clement VII, threatened but always deferred. Reginald Pole, the King's cousin —who flits on the edge of my story, stirring up trouble for us in exile till his recall by our present Queen to supersede me as Archbishop of Canterbury—was sent from Rome to establish contact with the disaffected in England. Although he ventured no nearer than Flanders he succeeded with help from Chapuis in hatching a plot in which many of his family were implicated, his two brothers and his cousin, Lord Exeter, the "White Rose," who as grandson of King Edward IV was next in succession to the Crown if King Henry died without an heir. Our agents, including friends of mine among the German Protestants, informed us of his doings just in time to save the country from civil war.

Threatened from abroad by a concert of European powers, with a bull of deposition fostering subversion at home, the King and his ministers were in no mood for leniency. All those inculpated were sent to the scaffold except Sir Geoffrey Pole, the younger brother, who saved his life by betraying his kin. Reginald alone suffered no harm, out of reach and out of danger, rewarded by the Pope with the rank of Cardinal.

The execution of these sentences depleted the older families, especially those descended from the Plantagenet kings, and comparative newcomers like the Howards, of whom the Duke of Norfolk was the head, were left predominant. The effect was to remove any likelihood of a violent upheaval, any attempt to unseat the dynasty and replace it with another branch of the Royal line. The duke was a timid man, who kept his ambition in check till it could be indulged in safety. He aimed no higher at present than to be the first of the King's servants, and much as he disliked the policy of reform in Church and state he was careful to confine himself to means within the law to bring pressure on the King and discredit Cromwell, his principal rival.

For a few years longer Cromwell's influence prevailed. I received whole-hearted support from him in my efforts to clean the Augean stables of the monks of Canterbury. The exploitation of miracles imputed to relics is among the most degrading trades which superstition fosters. The pious are swindled as no miracle of course takes place, and the love of God is outraged by the pretence that he can and will set aside the laws of nature for payment of money.

Since the exposure of the claims of the Holy Maid, and the disgrace which followed, the monks preferred to collect this revenue from more orthodox sources, in particular from the shrine of Thomas Becket behind the high altar in the cathedral. This Becket, who was Archbishop of Canterbury between three and four hundred years ago in the reign of King Henry II, was murdered in the northwest transept of the cathedral by four knights claiming to act on the King's orders. He was in fact during his tenure of office a stubborn opponent of the King's policy, conspiring with the Pope and other foreign powers. After his death his own offences were forgotten, and his bones encased in an iron chest were enshrined in a magnificent tomb glittering with gold and jewels, which acquired prodigious sanctity when he was canonised as St. Thomas of Canterbury, saint and martyr. Pilgrims came from far and wide over the years to worship there, and for a suitable fee the monks would open the lid to show his skull cloven by the murderer's blow. Monastic greed throve on the offerings.

Among the chief wonders with which the credulous were enticed was a red stain on the floor reputed to consist of Becket's blood, miraculously preserved at the spot where he was killed. It was a source of perpetual offence to me, sure as I was that it sprang from shameful deception; but no matter what I suspected it remained there plainly visible, unchanged according to tradition for centuries, honoured devoutly as a pool of the saint's lifeblood. One morning I was alone in the transept with my brother Edmund, my archdeacon, whose feelings towards the miracle were the same as my own. As we came to the railings guarding the sacred spot we paused as often before and stared at it in impatient resentment.

"The pity is," I muttered, "we've no proof."

He said nothing, frowned as if lost in thought; then suddenly he left me, hurried across to the sacristy and returned with a small knife and a sheet of foolscap. As he stooped under the railings and knelt on the ground I began to understand his purpose. I glanced round warily. No one was in sight, the cathedral was empty.

We carried out our experiment without interruption. The stuff came off easily, breaking into powdery flakes, but I watched with impatience while he worked. There would have been grave scandal in Canterbury if anyone had seen the Archbishop and his brother on hands and knees in the transept of the cathedral, scraping up the blood of St. Thomas and tipping it into a scrap of paper.

I had a friend interested in natural science, and I showed him my specimen without disclosing its origin. He declared that it was a kind of red ochre imported from Sienna, and his opinion was confirmed by the master of a workshop dealing in paint. With this evidence in my hands I felt that I could take action. I referred the whole matter to Cromwell, who informed the King, and permission was given me to dismantle the shrine, to extirpate the abuse for good.

An absurd story has been told that we arraigned Thomas Becket at a posthumous trial, and perpetrated other indignities on him of the sort that our enemies practise on the corpses of those who defy them. Neither the King nor Cromwell, nor indeed I myself, would have lent ourselves to such mockery. The bones received decent burial in consecrated ground, but the place was kept secret so that superstition could not follow them. The title of St. Thomas of Canterbury was abolished by Royal proclamation, the man Becket stripped of supernatural attributes.

As the donors of the treasure were dead or unknown the ownership lapsed to the Crown, and I made haste to deliver it before the monks could claim their pickings. We filled two enormous chests with precious metals and jewellery. They were so heavy that it took eight of our strongest men to carry them out of the church.

My success at Canterbury encouraged me to promote with Cromwell's active support a measure especially dear to my heart, the publication of an English translation of the Bible. I believed that only good could come of enabling people to test at the source the claims of the Christian hierarchy, to read for themselves what the Son of God said and how he and his disciples lived. My first idea was to divide the New Testament among chosen bishops, each of whom would translate a gospel or epistle, so that the work would bear the stamp of authority. Cromwell scoffed at this plan, asking what sort of help I expected from men like Gardiner and Stokesley who disapproved of an English version on principle. I should have wasted less time if I had listened to him. Few whom I approached were anxious to cooperate, and even when I persuaded them they made little progress.

In the end I had to fall back on the book already available, known as Matthew's Bible. Matthew was a pseudonym adopted by John Rogers, chaplain to the English House at Antwerp. His name carried less weight than the bishops but his output was more reliable, even if it leant heavily on the earlier work of Tindale which bore the stigma of heresy. Cromwell persuaded the King to license the publication in England, and the clergy were ordered to provide a copy in every church for the use of the public. My own share in the achievement was chiefly to write the preface.

Even when I wrote it I had a premonition of danger which marred my satisfaction. I quoted at length the warning given by two learned fathers of the Church, St. John Chrysostom and St. Gregory Nazianzen, who taught that there is a right and a wrong way to read the Bible, that the only true purpose is to learn how to lead a better life. Whatever fails to help can be neglected without loss, or if the cause lies in lack of understanding the advice should be sought of a teacher qualified to explain. The ignorant are guilty of great harm who thrust an interpretation on an obscure passage, defending it fiercely for no reason except that it is their own, using the words of the Prince of Peace to provoke strife and hatred, so that, as St. Gregory complains, "all our holiness consists in talking."

My presentiment was borne out by events. My preface went unread or unheeded. The English Bible was no sooner placed in the churches than the self-opinionated began to quarrel over it. They became intoxicated with their own pretention to learning, hurled texts at each other even in the ale houses, and the resulting disputes led to blows. Priests complained of troublemakers in the congregation who interrupted the sermon, often the liturgy itself, leaving their places and striding across to the desk where the Bible was kept, to read a passage aloud from it in a voice that drowned the priest's own, usually from a chapter of disasters in the Book of Revelation.

The scandal arising from such incidents did grave harm to the cause of the reform. The King's answer was to forbid anyone without authorisation from the clergy to read the Bible aloud or expound its contents. Those in the King's council who feared reform of any sort took the opportunity to demand severer repression. Among these were the nobles led by the Duke of Norfolk.

The first warning of the storm was the appointment of a committee of bishops, over which Cromwell presided, to advise the King how best to promote unity of faith. We were still sitting when the Duke of Norfolk announced in the House of Lords that our deliberations were fruitless, and that the King wished the House itself to give an opinion on six articles, which he recommended as essential to true religion.

When I saw the list I was appalled. It seemed that every tenet of orthodoxy received support, regardless of the abuse that it engendered. The most unpalatable item from my own point of view was that which reaffirmed the condemnation of a married priesthood. For three days the proposals were debated. I took part myself to plead as vigorously as I could for their rejection, feeling in their intolerance, their refusal to compromise a spirit repugnant to my fundamental convictions. The King was present on the first day and the last, so that I was able to address my arguments to him in person. His face could be very impassive if he wished, but he was seldom able when he was annoyed to disguise his anger. I was certain on this occasion that he listened to me with patient attention, if not with sympathy.

My opposition was without success. The House approved of the articles by a large majority, and arrangements went forward to draw them up into a bill for parliamentary enactment. I was myself on the committee that shaped the clauses dealing with enforcement; but my influence carried no weight there, the penalty appointed for almost every offence was death, and if a priest married he was not only liable himself to be hanged, his wife was also.

My heart sank when the completed bill was shown me, and a cowardly temptation urged me to resign my office and escape abroad. I was ashamed of the impulse when I considered the effect, the deadly blow to the King's authority if his enemies could taunt him with the flight of his Archbishop.

Shortly before the bill came up for its first reading he himself sent me a message, that I had his permission to remain absent from the debate if I wished. I was grateful for his kindness, his intention to save me unnecessary distress, but I did not take advantage of it. I felt that on so grave a matter I must follow my decision consistently through to the end. The bill was deplorable, unsound in doctrine and savagely vindictive in its penal clauses; but for reasons which I could guess, and on which the safety of the realm depended, the King supported its promoters. Even so I could not have brought myself to vote in favour if I had not believed that his ultimate purpose was to allay religious strife, and that he would find means of disappointing those who already exulted in the triumph of bigotry.

Although I did not speak in the debate my presence was taken by the other reforming bishops to denote approval, so that even Latimer and Shaxton who stayed away at first came in before the third reading to occupy their places and record their assent when the bill became law. They were made soon afterwards to resign their sees, Latimer that of Worcester, Shaxton of Salisbury, they were both too single-minded to hold office with any comfort while the Act was in force.

I am afraid that I was not thinking of their troubles, or even of those of the nation, as the result of the vote was announced and the bill was taken away for the King's signature. The words of the clause tolled in my mind which condemned a priest's wife to the gallows. Heedless of ceremony I hurried out of the House of Lords, urged the boatman to row me as fast as possible across to Lambeth. Arriving I rushed to my room to change my clothes, ordered the best horse in my stables to be saddled, then with a single groom I set off at a gallop for Kent.

The distance to Ford is over sixty miles. We covered most of it during the hours of darkness of the short June night. There were few people on the road, and I do not suppose that any knew who I was. My old riding cloak bespattered with mud, my lack of any suitable retinue were disguise enough. Those whom we passed probably took me for a courier bound with despatches for the ports.

Margaret was at breakfast and came running out into the passage when she heard my voice. Her eyes met mine in silent question, and tears filled them when I nodded. She knew what the threat meant of the six articles as I wrote to warn her during the drafting of the bill, telling her what we must do if the measure became law. She did not try to protest or argue now. The danger was urgent, and she acted with sense and speed. A box small enough to be carried on horseback was packed ready, filled with a few clothes and other personal belongings for herself and Meg. I could not bear to watch her as she completed her preparations. Her movements were brisk, her face, her every gesture so disconsolate, forlorn.

The nearest port was Sandwich. Although the silt that obstructs navigation already deprived it of much of its foreign trade the harbour was still accessible to ships of light draught, and I relied with confidence on finding a captain there willing to oblige me. Within an hour or so we took the road, with a single servant added from Ford to carry the box strapped to his crupper. I was anxious to keep the party as small as possible so as not to attract attention. Margaret rode her own horse, and Meg already four years old sat on a pillion on mine behind me, clinging tightly to my waist.

At Sandwich my friends received me with the sympathy that I expected, and with little delay they found me a ship bound for Rotterdam. As the very existence of my wife and child was unknown I had no fear for them in the Emperor's dominions, and the captain promised to put them on a boat trading up the Rhine to Mainz, where Osiander could call for them. It was a cloudless morning as we rode to the quay, and Meg chattered gaily, delighted by her first view of a seaport, the ships entering and leaving, the bright colours of paint and sails gleaming in the sunshine. Margaret and I kept silence. I understood the effort that she was making, her fear that if she spoke her voice would break in tears.

We dismounted, the groom led the horses away, and for a few moments we were alone. As we stood there the emotion which she struggled to control overcame her, suddenly she yielded. She flung her arms round my neck, clung to me sobbing:

"Come with us, Tom," she begged. "Come away too. We can all live so happily together in Germany."

I knew that I must refuse, but I had not the heart to utter the words, to explain once more the reasons why I must stay in England. My own tears flowed freely as I kissed her. Meg who was watching us set up a loud wail of alarm. The sound recalled Margaret from her grief, she let go of me, stooped, picked Meg up and soothed her.

She did not speak again till we came to the ship. At the gangplank she turned and kissed me lightly on the forehead, held Meg towards me so that she could do the same.

"*Auf wiedersehen,*" she whispered.

The ship was ready to depart. The crew cast off the mooring ropes, hoisted sail. Margaret and Meg stood hand in hand in the stern waving their handkerchiefs. I watched as they glided out into the river, passed out of sight round the bend of the shore, and the last glimpse of sail was lost in the haze out to sea. I remembered the desolation of our parting at Regensburg, but this time I wondered if we should ever meet again.

16

Ford was haunted by too many ghosts of happiness, and I returned at once to Lambeth. When I attended court I found everyone talking of the new Act of Parliament, "the whip with six strings," and from the glances that I intercepted I was aware that all expected my imminent downfall. My hurried departure from the House of Lords after the debate had been observed, and it even became known that I travelled down into Kent. The conclusion drawn was that I was trying to escape abroad. No one guessed my true purpose.

My spirits were at the lowest ebb. Both my private and my public life seemed to be ending in disaster, and it increased my uneasiness to receive a message announcing that several lords of the council including the Dukes of Norfolk and Suffolk were coming to Lambeth to pay me a visit of state. The Duke of Norfolk was the leading advocate of the six articles, and I knew that he would rejoice in my undoing.

The other duke was less to be feared, but no more likely to offer me support, although there were few at court who enjoyed closer friendship with the King.

When the day came I waited in trepidation for my distinguished guests. My only comfort was to learn that Cromwell would accompany them. I knew how strenuously he opposed the six articles. His present mission was evidence that although his advice was rejected he retained his place as the King's minister, it was also an assurance to me of at least one friendly face to relieve my discomfiture if the purpose of the deputation was reprimand.

I was not kept long in suspense. As soon as the polite greetings were over the Duke of Norfolk made himself spokesman for the rest and addressed me with gracious civility. He told me that they were sent by the King for no other purpose than to assure me of his continued confidence and regard. I could not help admiring the suavity with which he delivered a speech so uncongenial to him. He excelled, if in nothing else, in polished manners.

My chief feeling however was unbounded gratitude to the King, who, knowing my distress and anxiety, took so prompt an opportunity to reassure me, chose the most public means possible to re-establish me in the eyes of his council. My gloom lifted, the visit dreaded in anticipation began even to promise enjoyment. I saw that Cromwell shared my cheerfulness, that he seemed to be un-discouraged by the recent events in Parliament. The only flaw in my contentment was the ill-concealed hostility with which he was treated by one or two of the lords present. The behaviour of the Duke of Norfolk was especially embarrassing. When we sat down to dinner he ignored Cromwell completely, turning his back on him to lavish excessive affability on myself. Cromwell betrayed no resentment; he ate in silence, watching them all with a sardonic smile.

As the meal proceeded my discomfort increased under the flow of the duke's compliments, which were patronising where they were not insincere. He praised my respectful demeanour towards noblemen of rank, contrasted it with Wolsey's presumption and impertinence. Having started on Wolsey he pursued the theme with exasperating insistence, rejected every effort that I made to deflect him. Cromwell came into the King's service from Wolsey's, and I knew that he retained a loyal affection for his old master.

The duke's voice mounted deliberately as he vented his rancour:

"The King's treasury would be fuller today if he'd got rid of that scoundrel sooner."

Cromwell could endure no more. He leant forward and spoke quietly and drily:

"The only money misspent to my knowledge while I served him was that paid to the Duke of Norfolk to grovel to the Pope."

I do not know to what incident in Wolsey's policy he referred, but it was a damaging accusation now when the Pope was the King's declared enemy. Both dukes sprang to their feet, shouting in fury. For a moment I feared that they would draw their swords, but Cromwell remained seated, coldly indifferent. I made haste as we had finished dinner to rise and say grace.

Afterwards, to forestall any resumption of the quarrel, I asked them if they would care to see the portrait recently made of me by the German painter, Hans Holbein. It hung in the gallery, and as I waited at the foot of the stairs for them to go on up ahead I saw that Cromwell lingered at my side, and for a few minutes we were alone. He winked at me, grinning derisively at the backs of the dukes and their fellowers as they mounted; then in a hurried whisper he told me that, although the six articles had become law, there was great hope that they would not be rigorously applied, and that the King was anxious that I should put my reasoned objections in writing for his consideration. He added with his twisted smile:

"You were born in a lucky hour. Say or do what you will, the King always takes it well from you."

They were words that I have never forgotten, so great was my satisfaction; but I suffered a pang of remorse when he sighed and muttered:

"I wish that where I'm concerned he were as unwilling to fall out."

There were indeed many stories of conflict between them, they were both of too forceful a nature. Nevertheless it was clear that once again his influence was restored, and that his enemies, bitterly as they resented it, dared not attack him openly.

I obeyed the King's command with alacrity, taking pains to assemble my arguments against the "whip with six strings." My habit in work of this sort was to dictate my ideas to Ralph Morice; then I revised his notes, and he made out a fair copy. I little guessed to what trouble, even danger the procedure would lead on this occasion.

Ralph was still working on his copy when urgent business summoned me to Croydon. So I left him at Lambeth to finish the task, telling him to follow me when it was ready, so that I could look it through. He did as I said, I gave the work my final approval, then sent him back with it to Lambeth for safekeeping till I could deliver it to the King. I impressed on him the need to guard it with the greatest care. My attack on the articles was outspoken, and if enemies in the council got hold of it I was likely to be indicted on a capital charge, from which the King himself could not save me without violating the Act of Parliament. Ralph knew this, and I was sure that I could rely on his discretion.

On his return home however he was unable to enter his room. My almoner, expecting him to stay longer at Croydon, had locked up and gone out with the key in his pocket. Ralph himself was in a hurry as his father was in London and wanted to see him. Unable to put the treatise safely away in his desk, and afraid to leave it anywhere else, he tucked it under his belt to carry on his person while he went on his errand. It was a decision for which I cannot blame him. He could not foresee the succession of misadventures awaiting him. I give the story as I heard it from his own mouth.

He crossed the Thames and boarded a wherry to travel to St. Paul's steps. His fellow passengers were some soldiers of the King's guard absent from duty without leave and hoping to slip back unobserved. They were dismayed as they reached Southwark to find a concourse of boats against the shore, clustered round a raft where dogs were baiting a bear. The warden and troupe belonged to the household of little Princess Elizabeth (employed much against the wishes which I expressed as her godfather), and the King himself was there to watch.

The soldiers begged Ralph to let the wherry turn in among the sightseers, so that they would be lost in the throng. Reluctantly he agreed to the delay, and they poled the boat vigorously towards the raft, ramming and jostling others who obstructed their passage. He began to suspect that they were less concerned to escape notice than to enjoy a close view of the show.

Just as they approached the raft the bear, maddened by its tormentors, leapt into the water to escape them, splashing and clawing at the surrounding boats which were jammed together too close to move. Some fended it off with oars, but Ralph's companions were less successful; the wherry lurched as it clutched the gunwale, and in the confusion it clambered on board with the dogs in pursuit. There was frantic panic; the soldiers jumped across into another boat, and some of them fell in the water. Ralph shrank back into the stern, while the wherry rocking uncontrollably filled and sank. In the shallows by the shore on an ebbing tide it did not have far to sink. It settled in the mud, and he was left sitting up to his waist in water.

The dogs and the bear continued their battle in the water-logged hulk, and the bear getting the worst of it kept backing towards Ralph, till its hinder quarters pressed against his knees. In his terror he kicked, and it turned on him; but the dogs distracted its attention again, and he was able to crawl out wet to the skin from beneath. By this time rescuers were coming to drive the beast off, but as he stood up a fresh consternation overwhelmed him. The precious document, tugged loose in the struggle from his belt, was floating away on the tide.

He pointed to it and shouted to the bear warden, who grabbed a pole and fished it out; but instead of passing it back to Ralph he examined it suspiciously. He was a surly man who liked to give trouble, and although the writing can have meant little to him he handed it, while Ralph watched anxiously, to a priest standing on the bank. After a brief glance the priest threw up his hands in horror, exclaiming that it was rank heresy and ought to be reported to the King's council for the writer to be hanged.

Ralph announced in a voice as peremptory as he could make it that he was secretary to the Archbishop of Canterbury, and demanded back his master's property. But his words did more harm than good. To those like this priest who detested the new ideas in religion my name smacked of hellfire, and resentment glowed the more fiercely since my speech in the House of Lords opposing the six articles when they were introduced. The bear warden in addition had a personal grudge. He knew that I disapproved of his sport, that I tried to dissuade those in charge of the young princess from engaging him.

The King had already gone, disgusted by the general disorder, waiting only to see that all in the water were safe. There was no one to whom Ralph could appeal. He tried to bribe the warden, but the man rejected the coin and turned away with muttered threats, clutching the document tightly while he collected his dogs and bear to take them home. Ralph's appointment with his father was forgotten. He hurried instead to Cheapside where he knew a grocer called Blage, between whom and the warden there was close acquaintance, if not friendship.

Blage, anxious to oblige a customer, agreed to act as intermediary, and a plan was concerted between them. He would invite his friend to supper for which Ralph would pay, and under the mellowing influence of good food and wine combined with a bribe three times as large as that previously offered he would coax the treatise back. The plan was carried out, the supper served and eaten; but when Blage began to speak of the missing document, revealing how much Ralph would pay, the warden leapt to his feet in a rage and strode to the door without a word of thanks even for the meal. His own bear might have had better manners.

When Ralph received Blage's report of this he was in despair, and as he ought indeed to have done at first, he went to Throgmorton Street to see Cromwell. He found him setting out for Hampton Court and told him the whole story. Cromwell listened in silence, then called to one of his servants to dismount and give his horse to Ralph. He knew that the King and his council were at Hampton Court and guessed rightly that it would be the warden's destination. They rode at a good pace and soon caught up with the man travelling on foot. He was stepping out grimly, too bent on his purpose to look at them, barely even yielding room for them to pass as they trotted by. They reached the palace long before him, and when he arrived they were waiting in the hall and heard him inform the guard that he had an important communication for the Bishop of Winchester.

I can imagine the man's dismay when instead of Stephen Gardiner he met Cromwell, who snatched the papers out of his hand, demanding fiercely to know where he got them. Ralph testified that the handwriting was his own and the document my property. Then putting on his most intimidating manner Cromwell lashed the man with his tongue, threatening him with mutilation and the gallows for meddling with a privy councillor's affairs. It was too easy a victory perhaps, with Cromwell's high position and influence pitted against a wretched bear warden; but Ralph's description of the man checked any impulse in me to pity him. Like most bullies he was a coward, and when he was persuaded that he had more reason to fear punishment than to expect reward he slunk sullenly away.

As it happened I myself was at Hampton Court, having ridden on from Croydon. Seeing Ralph and Cromwell in the hall I joined them, and was much surprised when the latter handed me a wad of stained and sodden paper. He grinned at Ralph as he remarked:

"Here's tinder that might have lit both of you at the stake, if the Bishop of Winchester had dried it."

Then Ralph made full confession of the accidents to which my treatise had been exposed. I could not help laughing at his account of the bear sitting on his lap, and I laughed even more heartily in my relief at the warden's discomfiture.

"Your sentence for the offence," I told him, "is in two parts. The first is a ducking in the Thames, which has already been inflicted; the second is to take this filthy mess and write out a fair copy."

As Cromwell and I walked on towards the presence chamber I thanked him profusely for his help, without which I should indeed have been in great danger. He barely listened to me, he was still chuckling to himself over the incident. I think what amused him most was the warden's blunder in rejecting the bribe offered him, getting nothing out of his mischiefmaking except a supper with the grocer Blage.

Ralph copied out the treatise again as I directed, and when it was ready he gave it to Cromwell, who himself delivered it to the King. I do not know what influence my arguments had on the King's mind. The fact is however that while the Act remained in force little vigour was shown in putting it into effect, and few suffered the harsh penalties which it imposed. The King seemed to be content with a gesture to conciliate the Duke of Norfolk and his party, unwilling to allow them to translate their threats into deeds.

Those who regarded the Act as a prelude to Cromwell's downfall were disappointed. He had suffered no more than a temporary setback, was securely established again in power, enjoying the King's favour. His influence could be detected in the prosecution of a number of preachers who assumed licence to revive interest in miracle-mongering shrines.

It was in foreign policy however that Cromwell had what seemed to be his greatest success. King Henry had been a widower for two years, and his ministers anxious to find a wife for him in Europe with powerful connections helpful to English interests, urged that his choice should fall on a French princess. Cromwell was resolutely opposed to such a match. He saw nothing to be gained from a close alliance with France. He had his own plans ready worked out for the King's marriage, believing that he had found a bride exactly suited to the need of the times in Lady Anne, sister of the Duke of Cleves. The ducal family adhered to the Catholic tradition, but Lady Anne's sister was married to the Elector of Saxony (son of my old acquaintance at Nuremberg), an active leader of the Protestants. The King's fear of doctrinal vagary would be allayed by the news that the bride offered him was a Catholic, and the Emperor would be more easily reconciled to her. At the same time it would give satisfaction to the German Protestants that the sister-in-law of the Elector of Saxony was to become Queen of England.

The Duke of Cleves was flattered by the honour proposed for his family, and he made haste to annul the arrangements already made to betroth his sister to a son of the Duke of Lorraine. Meanwhile Cromwell was doing everything possible to persuade King Henry, relying not only on political argument, but also on a portrait painted by Holbein, who visited Cleves for the purpose at his special request. I have seen the portrait and recognise the likeness, as in all Holbein's work; but the expression and pose are not what I associate with Lady Anne of Cleves.

King Henry was charmed by it. The Duke of Cleves was asked to send his sister to England for celebration of the wedding.

My own introduction to the new Queen was in unpropitious circumstances. She arrived in the middle of winter, and the weather was appalling. At Calais she was kept waiting a fortnight while a gale blew out of the northwest, and although when at last the wind changed they made a quick crossing, embarking at noon and reaching Deal in the twilight, there was still a heavy swell very distressing to anyone like herself who had never been to sea before. She was so exhausted when she landed that she had to spend the week-end at Dover Castle.

Word was sent me that she would come on to Canterbury on the Monday, and I rode out with a number of other bishops and dignitaries of the county to meet her on Barham downs. It was a bitterly cold afternoon with driving rain, and as she was muffled in voluminous wraps I had little chance to form an opinion of her face and figure. My impression was of someone tall and slim.

This was confirmed when I visited her later at St. Augustine's Abbey, a Benedictine house where I lodged and entertained her in Canterbury. I must admit that on entering the room I glanced at her with curiosity, and I hope that I did not betray the shock that I received. I saw a young woman looking rather more than her twenty-four years, with angular features, a sallow complexion and high forehead framed in tight bosses of black hair. There was nothing displeasing in the face; on the contrary it was strong and sensible, and an amiable placidity shone in the fine dark eyes. Yet my heart sank as I looked at her, knowing how much depended on the impression which she made on the King. She had none of the lively charm of her namesake, the first Queen Anne, nothing either of the elegance of Lady Jane Seymour. I could not even attribute her shortcomings to the fatigue of the journey. She seemed to be completely recovered, and when she found that I understood her German, in spite of some difficulty with the dialect, she was soon chattering away happily.

Every word that she uttered added to my dismay. I felt sure that I should like and respect her, equally sure that the King would find her company tedious.

He himself was so impatient to see her that on New Year's Day he rode out secretly with a few companions disguised in grey coats to meet her on her way at Rochester. The result of the meeting was just as I feared. He was cruelly disappointed, so much taken aback that he forgot even to give her the New Year's present which he had brought, a muff and tippet of sable. Nevertheless in spite of his agitation he stayed to supper, holding himself in check and treating her with civility. He relieved his feelings later on his return to Greenwich, where Cromwell had to bear the brunt of his rage.

I am sorry for Cromwell but even sorrier for Lady Anne of Cleves. It is true that as she knew no English, and the King's manners in her presence were faultless, she may have been unaware of the extent of the disaster; but no woman is so insensitive as to be wholly mistaken about the emotion which she arouses in a man, no self-delusion could persuade her that the King had fallen in love. She had further reason for anxiety when she received orders to wait at Dartford, while the ambassadors who accompanied her were summoned to Greenwich to attend a meeting of the council. An impassioned argument was going on there, and searching questions were put to them about her proposed betrothal to the son of the Duke of Lorraine. The King hoped to find legal grounds in it to disclaim his own offer of marriage. He was in a desperate state of mind, appalled at the thought of marrying a woman for whom he had conceived such distaste.

A hard choice lay before Cromwell. He knew that if he argued with the King, and convinced him against his will, the price would be a lasting grudge. On the other hand, if he yielded, the great plan for a Protestant alliance would be wrecked. It was proof of his courage that he chose the first course, proof too of the force of his reasoning that his arguments prevailed. The King was made to see, however reluctantly, that by renouncing the marriage at this stage he would estrange both the Duke of Cleves and his brother-in-law the Elector of Saxony, and that the result could only be to comfort the Emperor and the King of France and leave England stripped of allies to face a hostile coalition alone. So the bridal party at Dartford was given permission to continue its journey to London, and the wedding was celebrated with fitting magnificence on the feast of the Epiphany.

For four months from January to May the King and his new Queen lived together as man and wife. It is hateful to pry into the secrets of their intimate life, but the interest which these provoked was inevitable in view of the importance to the nation of a fruitful issue, of the birth of a second son to the King to reinforce the dynasty. He himself was to blame if rumours spread to whet prurient curiosity; many of the remarks which he made to his friends, and which at once were repeated, were as indiscreet as they were coarse. The only excuse that can be offered is that he was living under great strain, and indeed I had never before seen him so listless and depressed.

His lack of reticence appalled, yet the very savagery of its expression directed me to a possible explanation. I remembered the scabrous secret which Rochford divulged at his trial, asserting that it had been confided to him by his sister when they were discussing the King. It is no disproof that soon afterwards the King begot a son on his marriage to Lady Jane Seymour. Impotence is gradual, irregular in its onset. The danger was even more to be feared now when he was four years older, weakened by pain from a gangrenous sore in his leg. There is no shortcoming more embarrassing to a man's vanity, and King Henry would not be the first of his sex to cover his mortification by imputing inadequacy to the woman, disparaging her physical charm.

Perhaps the marriage could have been saved if there had been intellectual companionship to fill the place of desire. She was not stupid and soon picked up a broken English, but as I feared when I met her they had few interests in common. She read no books, except to spell out a textbook on needlework; she played no instrument and had no ear for music. I remembered what Margaret told me about the noble families of Germany, that they denied education on principle to their daughters, condemning literary and musical taste in a woman as a sign of lightness of morals. Margaret added that she herself had a thoroughly disreputable upbringing, taught at an early age both to read and to play the lute.

If the former Duke and Duchess of Cleves had been equally unconventional their daughter might have had more success with the King of England. As it was, his heart ached for the company of his first Queen Anne.

The blame lay of course on Cromwell, and I watched with admiration the spirit with which he bore it. His enemies led by Gardiner and the Duke of Norfolk thirsted for his blood, and the failure of his policy supplied them with insidious weapons. Yet he betrayed no uneasiness, he gave the impression indeed that his position was impregnable, and the success of his bold tactics seemed to be confirmed when the King made him Earl of Essex and Grand Chamberlain of England.

I wrote to congratulate him on the honour, and he sent a short letter of thanks; but I saw little of him in those days, his time was too fully occupied with cares of state. All through the month of May he retained the King's confidence.

When I attended the House of Lords on the 10th of June I had no suspicion of what was in store. Cromwell was in his accustomed place, and the morning's business was unremarkable. After dinner there was a meeting of the council, and it did not even occur to me that the council chamber was unusually full. My thoughts indeed had begun to stray, turning over and fitting together phrases for a cherished project of my own, the composition of a litany in English to be chanted in processions in place of repetitious invocations of saints, meaningless to those who know no Latin. I was aroused by a clatter at the door. An officer of the Royal guard from the Tower strode in, marched up to Cromwell and bowed:

"My Lord of Essex," he announced, "I arrest you for treason."

A shocking scene followed. Cromwell tried in vain to speak, to defend himself before his fellow councillors; there were too many who interrupted, shouting abuse. He shouted back, lost his temper, clutched his cap and flung it to the ground but the words which the gesture enforced were lost in the din. The Duke of Norfolk himself tore the George star from his neck, another stripped off the Garter. Pushed and dragged, he was taken to the gate which leads to the river, where a barge was waiting to carry him to the Tower.

Again and again I have reproached myself for sitting still, doing nothing to help my friend while he suffered indignity. Yet what use was it to join in the scuffle, to pit myself against such numbers? No one could save him but the King, by whose orders he was arrested. I hurried home as soon as I could and wrote to the King, striving not to give up hope but oppressed by foreboding as I recalled my similar effort four years before on behalf of Queen Anne. The first part of the letter was the easiest to write, in which I spoke of the great services which Cromwell rendered, "he that was such a servant in my judgement, in wisdom, diligence, faithfulness and experience, as no prince in this realm ever had."

Every word of the tribute was true, but I was at a loss how to go on. It was the same difficulty that perplexed me before. How could I declare charges to be false of which I had no sufficient information?

When at last I resumed my letter I wrote that, "if he be a traitor, I am sorry that ever I loved and trusted him," and I expressed sympathy for the King in his disillusionment. If, as my conscience still urges, I was disloyal to my friend in admitting the possibility of his guilt, I knew that my only chance of helping him would be destroyed by a blunter approach. I hoped that the context made clear how incredible the postulate of treachery seemed to me, and that the King thought well enough of my judgment to reconsider the evidence.

The letter remained unanswered, and my confidence ebbed. I heard that I myself was expected shortly to join Cromwell in the Tower. Everywhere at court I had to listen to his former cronies denouncing him, those who cringed before him for favours only a few days before. I stayed away as much as possible and shut myself up at home alone in my room.

I was recalled to my duties by the King, who ordered me to convoke the clergy to give an opinion on the validity of his marriage. Without Cromwell to restrain him he was determined to get rid of the Queen. The proceedings that followed reminded me uncomfortably of the two earlier occasions of a similar sort, and I feared the taunts to be expected from our enemies in Europe. Much to my relief, I was not left to be sole judge; the whole convocation pronounced on the issue, and the answer given was unanimous that the marriage was void. No fault can be found with the decision, even if the arguments were flimsy which relied on the abortive betrothal to the scion of Lorraine. There was ground enough for annulment in the evidence that after four months of cohabitation the Queen remained a virgin.

When I informed her of the verdict she distressed me by collapsing in tears; but it soon became clear that the impulse inspiring them was terror, that she expected to be condemned like her namesake to death on the scaffold. When I reassured her she recovered her equanimity, agreed readily to submit to the Act of Parliament by which our findings were given effect. Some have blamed her for the complaisance with which she consented, without even a protest to save her dignity. It is true that she was not a thin-skinned woman, but when all the circumstances of the estrangement are considered she emerges less humiliated than the King.

He himself, having obtained his freedom, behaved to her with generosity, endowing her with an ample income and estates at Richmond and Bletchingley. The only condition imposed was that she must reside on them, not return to Cleves. As long as she was in England her brother dared not endanger her safety by taking action to avenge her wrongs. She lived there in comfort and honour, no unwilling prisoner, never seeming to regret in exile the dull obscurity of her brother's court.

At the time of the annulment however I had little room for her in my thoughts. I was too much concerned with the events which were dragging Cromwell to his death. A bill of attainder was introduced in Parliament. No evidence worthy of the name was offered to convict him of treason, but he was too vulnerable to escape unscathed when the expenses of the treasury were investigated. Another scarcely less dangerous line of attack was to accuse him of heresy, for although he had no taste for theological speculation his hatred of clerical pretention was often expressed with indiscreet violence. Many of the stories rang true about his intervening to save heretics from punishment.

The bill was carried by acclamation in a House dominated by the Duke of Norfolk and his faction. I myself with others of his friends left before the question was put to the vote.

I still waited with dwindling hope for an answer to my letter from the King. I do not know what arguments were used to poison his mind, but I doubt whether he was convinced in his heart of the prisoner's guilt. Twice he sent emissaries to the Tower to put further questions, and I was told that there were tears in his eyes when he read a message which they brought back to him, a very moving letter indeed in which Cromwell thanked him for all his kindness in the past, for treating him "more like a dear father than a master." Much later he complained to me of the pressure which the peers were able to exert, having taught him during the northern rebellion how vitally the Crown depended on their support.

The arrangements for Cromwell's execution were kept as secret as possible for fear of a popular demonstration in his favour. His openhandedness, his genial accessibility to suppliants seeking redress of wrongs made him greatly beloved in London, and when the news of his death became known the humbler quarters of the city were heavy with sorrow. So too was I at Lambeth, deprived by the headman's axe of a leader whose wisdom I trusted, a friend whom I had grown to love. I recognised my feelings in the sonnet in which Wyatt described his own:

> The pillar perished is whereto I leant,
> The strongest stay of my unquiet mind;
> The like of it no man again can find,
> From east to west still seeking though he went.

With Cromwell dead it was indeed as if a pillar had fallen on which the kingdom rested.

17

Nobody was appointed to fill Cromwell's place as vicegerent. For the rest of his life King Henry bore responsibility alone both in ecclesiastical and in secular affairs. His ministers advised, he allowed none again to control him. The effect was to bring me into closer contact with him in the administration of the Church. Cromwell no longer stood between us, an intermediary able and accustomed to give orders on his own authority.

If anyone had predicted such an outcome I should have been utterly incredulous in the first weeks after Cromwell's execution. The general opinion was that I was destined to share his fate. Many even of my supporters blamed me for remaining in office and I myself longed to resign, to retire into peace and academic seclusion at Cambridge. It was an enticing prospect, but I felt that it would be an act of cowardice, even of disloyalty to the King to abandon him to evil counsellors.

For the time being my enemies were triumphant, reaping the fruit of plans carefully laid. I do not know whether it was by design or accident that Lady Catherine Howard, a niece of the Duke of Norfolk, was chosen to be among the maids-of-honour allotted to the Princess of Cleves on her arrival in England; but there can be no doubt of the eagerness shown by the duke and his party when the King picked her out for attention, or of the deliberate skill with which they fostered the attachment. I blame Gardiner especially who offered his house at Southwark, the official residence of the see of Winchester, for clandestine meetings. As soon as the contract with his German wife was annulled the King married her maid-of-honour.

The new Queen was only eighteen, first cousin of the Boleyns but a great deal younger. However sternly one deplored the political intrigue of which she was the instrument, it was impossible to bear her any personal ill-will. She was so artless and good-humoured, a merry scatter-brained child, like a plump kitten with her light-brown hair and tanned complexion, and her shortness of stature that made her look even younger than she was. She had no real claim to beauty; her fascination lay in the bloom of youth, in an unsophisticated simplicity which I took for frankness till I caught the sly expression lurking in her large blue eyes.

On her mother's death her father, left with a family of young children, sent her off to his own stepmother, the old Dowager Duchess of Norfolk, who brought her up with little care, letting her run wild with servants of untrustworthy character. Among the results of this neglect was an utter lack of dignity; she was incapable, never learnt the art of behaving as a Queen. It used to be said of her cousin Queen Anne that in rags she looked most a goddess. Dressed up in the stateliest robes poor Queen Catherine remained a slut.

The King however was blind to any shortcomings. In his eyes she was adorable, he called her his "rose without a thorn." He had fallen passionately in love and believed that his passion was returned. It was reassuring to his self-esteem that at the age of forty-nine he was able to win the heart of so young a girl. He underestimated the extent to which she was dazzled by the Crown.

In the light of subsequent events I am filled with pity for the new Queen. Among all the pleasures and honours of her high estate she was haunted by the memory of escapades whose exposure could ruin her. It is clear that the secret began to pester her almost as soon as she was married, that associates privy to her misbehaviour in her grandmother's house mustered quickly to seize the opportunity offered them, to demand favours in a tone verging on blackmail. That she was frightened into yielding, tried to buy them off was foolish but understandable. Her irresponsibility was more evident when she even encouraged them to resume relations on the old terms.

Nothing of this was known to me or anyone else at court at the time. The King and Queen lived quietly, with less pageantry than usual, partly because money was lacking in the treasury, but also, and even more compellingly, because he desired to enjoy his happiness in undisturbed privacy. He gave orders that petitions commonly submitted to him in person should be directed instead in writing to the council, so as not to trouble him with public business. A Queen of whom he was so fond was in a position to exert effective influence; but she took no interest in politics, and those who built their hopes on her were disappointed. Her uncle chided her for this, and she answered him back tartly and they quarrelled. She was becoming imperious, no longer the submissive niece, and seems to have had as little taste for his lectures as her cousin.

In the spring of the following year there was an abortive insurrection in Yorkshire fomented as usual from abroad by Cardinal Pole. Order was quickly restored, but the King was advised that his presence would make a useful impression, and he set off with the Queen on a progress of state to cover Yorkshire and Lincolnshire, the principle seats of unrest. He took a large company of peers with him, leaving Lord Hertford, Audley and myself in charge of the government in his absence. Hertford, formerly Sir Edward Seymour, was Queen Jane's brother ennobled after her wedding. In spite of my prejudice against the Seymours I respected his character, and already our acquaintance was warming into a friendship destined to grow in strength in later years.

In any case I was pleased to be chosen for the triumvirate. The choice refuted the stories current about my impending disgrace, and I remarked with satisfaction that most of my leading opponents were kept by the King close at his side under his watchful eye.

My pleasure was short-lived. While the King was in the north a man called Lassels came to see me, and the news that he brought made me wish that anyone rather than I held responsibility. He told me that his sister Mary used to work for the Dowager Duchess of Norfolk, and that while she was in attendance on Lady Catherine Howard she acted as go-between for her with at least two lovers. He added that his sister kept silence to avoid scandal, but that when Lady Catherine was married to the King the facts preyed on her conscience, and on his advice she sent him to lay them before the council.

This was the first known to me of any slur on the Queen's character, and my impulse was to dismiss it as calumny. Yet strictly as I examined John Lassels I could find nothing that threw doubt on his good faith. He was an earnest young man, straightforward, of rigid scruples, who spoke with an air of genuine concern. I arranged for him to bring his sister to give me the story from her own mouth.

When she came I was less favourably impressed than with her brother. It was clear that she had neglected her duty, conniving at, even encouraging misconduct in a young girl who at the time when this began was barely thirteen, and I suspected that malice was the motive prompting her present confession, as the Queen refused her employment in the Royal household. Nevertheless she gave her evidence with such assurance, was so precise in the details, that I felt bound to refer the matter to my colleagues, Hertford and Audley. Their opinion was that on the King's return he must be informed, and the disagreeable task was laid on me of informing him.

When I visited him at Hampton Court I found him in jubilant spirits, delighted both with his entertainment and with his companion on the journey, more in love with her than ever. My heart ached as I thought of the blow that I had to inflict. For three days I waited to break the news, making various excuses to myself to leave him longer in ignorance. Then on the Sunday I could bear the deception no longer, and I sat down to write a report of what I had learnt from John and Mary Lassels, choosing my words as carefully as I could to spare the King's feelings, but suppressing nothing of relevance. The next morning, All Souls' Day, as he was coming out from a mass for the dead I slipped the paper into his hand. He took it with a puzzled frown, but perceiving my agitation he folded it in silence and put it away in his pouch.

Several hours passed before he sent for me. He was making a great effort to control himself, and his manner was quiet and composed as he pointed to my report:

"There's no word of truth in this," he told me. "Of that I'm certain. But for my own peace of mind and the Queen's sake the lie must be sifted to the dregs."

Then he gave me my orders. I was to go back to Lambeth at once and summon and examine the men named as the Queen's lovers; but the proceedings must be strictly in secret, no breath of scandal allowed to attach to her. He would consider what to do when he heard the result of my examination.

The first of those accused by Mary Lassels was a musician called Manox. Any hope to which I clung of establishing the Queen's innocence was scattered when he came before me. He broke down at once under my questions and confessed his guilt, seeking only to mitigate it by insisting on the still more shameful behaviour of the other man, Francis Derham, who was his rival and successor.

Derham was of rather higher rank, a distant kinsman and retainer of the Duke of Norfolk. It would not have been easy to get hold of him without attracting attention, if it had not been for the lucky chance that he was suspected of an act of piracy committed in Ireland, and we were able to arrest him on that charge. Like Manox he admitted to amorous relations with Lady Catherine Howard, but he put forward an unexpected defence. He claimed that they pledged troth to each other, and as the betrothal had been consummated she was his wife. I summoned and interrogated a number of women employed by the Dowager Duchess at the relevant dates. They drew a horrifying picture of the conditions prevailing in the household, of the failure of the old duchess to protect young girls little more than children placed in her charge; but on the point at issue they supported Derham, they had heard him address Lady Catherine as his wife, seen him share his money with her, and she herself had said nothing in protest. I kept all the witnesses in custody to make sure that they would not chatter in the town, while I returned with a heavy heart to Hampton Court to present their evidence to the King.

He received me in private when I arrived, and although I had prepared a written report he was so impatient to know its effect that much against my will I had to tell him in hastily chosen words. For a moment or two he sat silent while I waited for an outburst of rage, then suddenly he rose to his feet, turned away from me and hid his face in his hands. To my embarrassment and distress he was sobbing, helpless in tears.

A meeting of the council was convened at Hampton Court soon

afterwards, and he took the unusual step of attending it in person. He had recovered his composure, and his voice was stern as he announced that grave news relating to the Queen had come to him, and that he desired the council's advice. He added that for the present nothing was to be divulged and forbade even a minute to be taken of the proceedings. Then he read aloud my report of the original charges and of the examination of the witnesses. While he spoke I watched the faces around me. Most of them wore an expression of shocked surprise; but I seemed to detect uneasiness in one or two, especially Gardiner and the Duke of Norfolk, and I wondered whether they were altogether ignorant of the Queen's past. They were the first to express condolence when he finished.

As he could not bear to meet the Queen again it was decided that he should leave by river that very afternoon to stay at Oatlands Park, his palace at Walton. Meanwhile a deputation was appointed including myself to inform the Queen that she was accused of premarital incontinence and perjury, of going through a form of marriage with the King when her troth was plighted to another. It was the first of a series of confrontations, each more painful than the last. She was too much taken aback to say much on this occasion, except to protest her innocence. I had the impression however that the shock was not so much of a strange and monstrous accusation as of a blow long feared, suddenly inflicted. As soon as we had given our message we took our leave, and most of the council went on to join the King. I stayed behind at Hampton Court to await instructions.

The Queen was confined to her rooms, and rumours quickly spread of the frantic state to which she was reduced, of fits so violent that her reason was in danger. When this was reported to the King at Oatlands he sent me orders to seek audience with her, to explain the enormity of her offence and the appalling penalties to which she was liable, but to end by assuring her that he would show mercy and spare her life. I made haste to do as I was told, but when I came into her presence she was in such terror that my heart shrank from harsh rebuke. At the first word that I uttered she sank to her knees moaning and weeping, working herself up into a frenzy till my voice was lost in her screams. When at last her agitation died down and I was able to make myself heard I disobeyed my instructions, and speaking as gently as I could I gave her the news at once that the King had intended me to reserve to the end, to follow his reprimand:

"Don't be afraid," I implored her. "The King will be merciful."

She grew calmer then, and although she continued to weep they were tears no longer of fear but of gratitude. I took the opportunity to try to get her to admit her guilt, to express contrition. Above all it was necessary that she should acknowledge her betrothal to Derham and its consummation, so that I could annul the King's marriage and set him free. At the first approach to the subject however any trace of composure gave way, and another storm of agitation threatened. It seemed that I could do nothing with her for the time being, and I left.

In the evening I visited her again. She was still barely in control of herself; but I was able at last to check her outbursts with soothing words and even to lead the conversation in the desired direction. By degrees I brought her into a quieter state of mind, till she was ready to concede that Derham had been her lover. For her own sake I persisted, arguing that he was also her husband; but she denied it obstinately. She saw only that if she were his wife she ceased to be Queen; she could not or would not understand how much her safety depended on the legal impediment. At last however I believed that I had enough evidence to prove it in spite of her, and I went back to my room to compose my report to the King. It was discouraging to learn the next morning that, in conversation with her attendants after my departure, she withdrew the greater part of what she told me and insisted that Derham ravished her against her will.

Sir John Dudley carried my letter to Oatlands, a man destined later to play an important part in my life but at that time little known to me. He was courteous, obliging, reliable, and I was glad to have a colleague so sagacious to advise me and share my burden. Before he set out he and I discussed the matter fully, so that when he saw the King he was able to comment on my report and explain my grounds for thinking that marriage with Derham could be established. To his surprise, and my own when he informed me, he received orders that all mention of the earlier betrothal was to be suppressed. The rest of the story however would now be made public, and I was told to prepare the Queen to leave Hampton Court and travel to Syon House at Isleworth, a former convent of Brigittine nuns recently dissolved, where she would be kept prisoner. All her maids-of-honour except four were to be discharged.

The reason for the decision soon became known. Wider inquiries had revealed that the Queen's association with Manox and Derham did not end when she married the King. Manox found employment among her musicians, and on her journey in the north, while she and the King were staying at Pontefract Castle, she met Derham and had the incredible folly to admit him into her household as a gentleman-in-waiting and her private secretary. He returned to London before her, so that no suspicion of this reached me when I arrested and examined him in her absence. It may be that he used blackmail to obtain his position; it is also true that a secretary who shared her secret was almost indispensable to answer many of the letters which she received. The effect of the new evidence was nevertheless disturbing.

Worse still, another actor was added to play a part in the tragedy. Derham, pressed to explain his relations with the Queen, diverted the attack by attributing similar guilt to her cousin, Thomas Culpepper, a man of unsavoury reputation convicted not long before of a peculiarly brutal rape, for which he escaped punishment only because he was a kinsman of the Duke of Norfolk, more closely related than Derham and of better standing. Derham swore that on the Queen's journey in the north she had a secret assignment with Culpepper at Lincoln, and several of her women bore witness in corroboration that for two nights running she did not return to her room till after two o'clock in the morning.

I was less inclined to doubt the story when I heard that Lady Rochford had been arrested, accused of acting as go-between to enable the guilty couple to meet. She retained employment at court even after her husband's execution, and the new Queen treated her with favour because of the ties of kinship. At the time of the visit to Lincoln she was in charge of the Queen's household, and I was sure from what I knew of her character that Culpepper's plans could rely on her for active encouragement.

The King was stunned with horror. It was bad enough to learn that the Queen came to him already soiled when he married her; he had now to accept the fact that, while they were living together, while he lavished affection on her and she professed to return it, she was deceiving him, carrying on intrigue with former lovers. He was no longer interested in proving that one of them was her lawful husband. The effect would only be to save the man from punishment. It would also of course mitigate her own offence, and I saw to my regret and foreboding that his heart had hardened against her, and that no argument in her favour would be allowed to prevail. The mercy which I promised in his name was offered to a woman guilty of concealing her past, of nothing worse than perjury; it would not be extended to an adulteress.

At an assembly held in the Star Chamber, to which as many peers, magistrates and other dignitaries of the realm as was possible were invited, a public statement was read on the King's behalf announcing the Queen's disgrace and the circumstances which provoked it. The foreign ambassadors were present, Chapuis among them. He had been away for more than a year on business and had just returned. As I looked in his direction his eyes caught mine, there was a sardonic gleam in them. I knew that he was thinking of the first Queen Catherine, challenging me to deny that all this trouble falling on the King was the fruit of my annulment of her marriage.

The compilation of evidence dragged on for months, the more painful as I myself was chosen to play the chief part in the investigations. The King was unwilling to entrust them to anyone connected with the Howards; on the other hand he shrank from exposing the wretched girl to the venom of political enemies, and he paid me the compliment of believing that I should treat her with impartiality and consideration. I had many interminable interviews with her at Syon House, and both Derham and Culpepper were brought to Lambeth for me to examine them. Each denied carnal knowledge of the Queen since her marrige, each asserted it of the other. She herself weakened their credit when, in her eagerness to divert herself of blame, she insisted that they both forced her, quoting incidents not only from the old days in her grandmother's house but also recently at Pontefract and Lincoln. When she saw her mistake she tried to take back what she said, and I am doubtful how much weight it deserved to carry. She was more composed than in the first days at Hampton Court, and the bouts of frenzy which dismayed me there were not renewed; but her balance of mind remained shaken by her experiences, and she spoke at random to serve whatever seemed to be her interest, regardless of the truth.

My orders were to do nothing to extract evidence of her betrothal to Derham, and my conscience smote me, knowing that she could have relied on it for defence; but she refused to admit it in any case, clung to her rank. She showed more courage than her accomplice Lady Rochford, her elder by many years, whose nerves gave way under the strain, and who lost her reason entirely, fell victim to frenzied delusions. The King's doctors laboured to restore her sanity so that she would be fit to plead to the charge of treason.

The first to be put on trial were Derham and Culpepper, and both were found guilty and condemned to death. There was evidence enough to support the verdict, but Derham's guilt seems the lesser as he could justly argue that in law the Queen was his wife. Nevertheless he was made to suffer the full torment of *peine forte et dure* at the gallows, while Culpepper died quickly by the stroke of the axe. The Duke of Norfolk was able again to exert influence on his behalf.

The Queen was indicted by bill of attainder, and Lady Rochford's name was added when the doctors declared that she was clear enough in her mind to understand what was done. Before the debate in Parliament I saw the Queen for the last time, visiting her with other lords of the council to hear her confession. It was a painful occasion, and her words were drowned in her tears.

The Duke of Suffolk told the House of Lords that she confessed to her crimes in full. The bill was carried, and she and Lady Rochford were removed to the Tower.

Two days afterwards the sentence was given effect, both prisoners were beheaded. It seems that the doctors were right about Lady Rochford, that she had indeed recovered her self-control. Eyewitnesses report that she behaved with composure on the scaffold, died with pious submission.

The question has occurred to me at times whether this death was prompted by the same motive as Queen Anne's, whether Queen Catherine too was a sacrifice to restore the King's failing powers. She declared that she was not with child, and everything known confirms that she spoke the truth. I am unable however to believe that King Henry was twice guilty of the unholy rite, if only because she was by character incapable of filling the part.

18

Much alarm was felt after Queen Catherine's execution by those who helped to promote the marriage. They knew what pain the King was made to suffer, and they feared that he would exact heavy retribution. In the event they were reassured. The only members of her family whom he punished were the few who had guilty knowledge of her doings. The Duke of Norfolk wrote an abject letter dissociating himself from his niece—from both his nieces, he added as a precaution, remembering Queen Anne—and he retained his position and influence.

An uneasy partnership persisted between him and the King. Although strong government was already beginning to bear fruit, earning favour for the Royal authority among those engaged in manufacture and trade, the heritage of the civil war was too recent, and dynasty not yet firmly enough established for the Crown to rest secure. The resources and armed retainers of loyal nobles were still needed in an emergency. Their support was indispensable to the King, and they demanded a price for it. Already it had cost him the fall of Cromwell.

By now the pieces were rearranged on the European chessboard. The Emperor stood allied with the Protestant princes of Germany, at war with France, and when he made overtures of friendship to England they were accepted. War with France as usual brought war with Scotland, a danger the more pressing as we had no moat of sea to guard that frontier. For thirty years we had enjoyed freedom from anxiety there, ever since the great victory won at Flodden when the Scottish army was destroyed and King James IV himself killed, leaving a son only a year old to succeed him; but now King James V was grown up, married to a French wife, estranged from his uncle King Henry by religious conflict. Scotland became a sanctuary for English malcontents who professed allegiance to the Pope.

Tempers were on edge on both sides of the frontier, and the Scots may be right that we were the first to cross it. King James at once raised an army and marched south into Cumberland, where on marshy ground by the Solway an English force caught him up. The result was a defeat for him almost as crushing as that at Flodden. He was unlike his father only in escaping with his life.

He had not long to live. His health was never robust, and the misfortune broke his heart. At the time of the defeat he was without an heir, but his Queen was about to bear a child. He waited anxiously for news at his palace of Falkland, and a messenger was sent there to tell him that she was delivered of a daughter. Within a week he was dead.

For the second time in a generation Scotland was condemned to the weakness of a long regency. The sovereign was the baby girl, Mary, a week old.

These events provoked great jubilation in England, and thanksgiving was celebrated in all the churches. I went down to Canterbury to attend the service and preach the sermon in the cathedral. Friends warned me while I was there that trouble was brewing, that I had enemies working secretly to destroy me; but I refused to listen, derided the stories as idle gossip of the cloisters. I was elated by the victory in Scotland, by the King's alliance with the Protestant leaders in Germany. My mind was full of dreams of reform, of enlightenment shining from the Church in England to irradiate all Christendom. There was nothing in the business, I told myself, beyond the usual squabbling of the prebendaries.

I must go back three years to explain who these prebendaries were. When the larger houses of religion shared the fate of the smaller houses Christ Church priory at Canterbury was dissolved, and the King demanded that peculiar care be taken in the redistribution of its revenues, that an example be set that would do credit to his policy. Many of the purposes to which the money was devoted were indeed admirable, especially the endowment of lectures in divinity and the humane arts and sciences, to be attended by scholars from Oxford and Cambridge, and the foundation of a grammar school for sixty children. I tried to eliminate an unnecessary provision from the plan, whereby twelve prebendaries were paid to live in comfort with nothing to do except make mischief in the cathedral chapter.

My arguments did not prevail, and the prebendaries were appointed. Worst of all, they were recruited mainly from the leaders of the dissolved priory. When seven places were filled with monks I wrote in despair to friends at Cambridge to ask them to recommend candidates from the university for the few left. Among the names sent me was that of Nicholas Ridley, and I remembered our meeting in his uncle's room at Queens'. I picked him out at once for an appointment and have never ceased to be grateful for my good fortune. He could not of course leaven the lump, but in all the troubles that followed I knew that I could count on one unswerving friend.

An issue on which I had my way was over the choice of six salaried preachers attached to the foundation. I convinced the King that opposing views should be equally represented; but I repented of my experiment when I saw the bickering that resulted, and I had to intervene to restore discipline. It was unfortunate for my reputation for impartiality that the first to be punished was Serles, the most violently opposed of all the preachers to reform. He used language so extravagant in a sermon advocating the worship of images that I could not ignore it without neglecting my duty. He appealed from me to the King's council. The council sent him back, instructing me to impose a term of imprisonment. I obeyed, but made the term as short as possible, a few months. Nevertheless he accused me of prejudice, bore a grievance that rankled.

This was the background to the warning which I received when I visited Canterbury after the victory won against the Scots. I knew that the prebendaries grumbled, reviled me in my absence; but I did not believe that there was anything more to be feared from them now than in the past. Even Nicholas had no details precise enough to convince me of a plot.

Such troubles were far from my mind as I walked on a still evening in April in my garden at Lambeth, enjoying the last glow of the sunset on the river. When I heard music, I saw that it came from a barge moving upstream, flying the Royal standard. I made haste to mount on to the bridge to salute the King as he passed.

To my surprise the rowers drew in towards the shore. The music stopped, and the King himself came out of the cabin, beckoned me to the landing stage. When I was within earshot he invited me on board. Thinking that he had a party with him for his entertainment, and not wishing to intrude, I suggested that I should bring out my own barge and follow; but he would take no refusal, insisted on my joining him, and as the gangway was lowered I obeyed.

I was wrong in thinking that he had a party of friends. It seemed that the cruise was for his own pleasure alone. The cabin was empty when we entered, and he turned to me with a genial smile:

"Ah, my chaplain, I've news for you. I know now who is the greatest heretic in Kent."

At the same time he drew out a sheaf of papers from his sleeve.

The friendliness of his tone was so much at variance with the sense of his words that I was more bewildered than alarmed, although I felt sure that the description was applied to myself. While I hesitated what to say he thrust the papers into my hand, bidding me read them. They were depositions attested by the majority of prebendaries at Canterbury and some local justices, reporting a long list of incidents which reflected discredit on the orthodoxy and even the honesty of my diocesan administration. The source of the information was mainly hearsay, gossip passed from mouth to mouth, and I noticed that the most assiduous collector was Serles who had seemingly devoted himself to the task ever since his release from prison.

The chief targets of complaint were my subordinates, especially my commissary, Christopher Nevinson, who had married my niece; but the attack was aimed at me as much as at him when it spread the cruel calumny that his wife's mother, my sister Emmet, was guilty of bigamy. The fact is that her first husband deserted her many years before. I do not know the exact circumstances; but he was a miller, and one day he walked out of the mill without a word and never came back. The only occasion on which I met him was at my mother's funeral, and I had no chance to form an opinion of him; but my other sisters told me how shamefully he neglected her, drinking more than was good for him and spending his money on women of light conduct. Then he vanished altogether, and she came to me in despair to ask my advice. I took the responsibility of telling her that she had the right to presume him dead, and when she explained that a neighbour, Henry Bingham, wanted her to be his wife I gave the union my blessing, and they were married. I liked Henry and respected him, as did the whole family.

Nothing in the depositions distressed me as much as this slander directed at Emmet. A great deal that was said about me myself was so ridiculous indeed that if I had not been in the King's presence I should have laughed aloud, especially at the story that I preached a sermon booted and spurred in the cathedral, disparaging the sacrament of the altar. The only germ of truth that I could recall was an occasion when I was about to go out riding, waiting on the steps for my horse to be brought round, and Serles came up and engaged me in an argument about the Real Presence. The man's untimely verbosity annoyed me, and in the heat of the moment I probably answered with imprudence.

When I had finished reading I handed the documents back to the King. Knowing their contents I was all the more puzzled by his demeanour, which had none of the sternness, even fierceness to be expected. I told him that I should welcome a thorough investigation, and he laughed:

"Yes indeed, and I've already chosen the judge. The investigation will be in the hands of my Lord of Canterbury."

This took me aback. While it afforded gratifying evidence of his goodwill it put me in an invidious position, judge in my own cause. I pointed out how difficult it would be for me to avoid the appearance of bias; but he replied that he trusted me to tell him the truth, brusquely dismissed my objections and ordered me to appoint a commission to serve under me in Kent. I had no choice but to obey, and I did so the more readily as the charges to be investigated contained nothing in which I was conscious of offence. There was not even a hint of my marriage, and I marvelled again at the discretion shown by all in my confidence. The nearest that my accusers came to the secret was the story, quite true in itself, that I received monthly letters from Germany, addressed to the Fleur de Lys tavern in Canterbury. They were wrong however when they attributed these to a treasonable conspiracy carried on with the German Lutherans to subvert the King's policy in England. The letters were from Margaret, who wrote every month without fail to give me news of herself and little Meg.

I was congratulating myself on my escape when, as if the King read my thoughts, he glanced at me with a quizzical glint in his eye:

"Perhaps you'd rather tell me here in private why the Act of Six Articles is without force in your bedroom."

My astonishment was so great that my face, I am sure, blushed scarlet, the very image of guilt unmasked. He laughed heartily at my discomfiture, then added that he knew of my marriage from the outset, that Vaughan guessed and that Cromwell's spies confirmed the fact. He kept it to himself, he said, waiting till he made up his mind about me, even then he was unwilling to reassure me, for fear that I should relax my precautions and arouse suspicion among opponents in the council. His voice became stern as he insisted that the Act of Six Articles was necessary to satisfy public opinion and could not be revoked.

Then his geniality returned. He told me that the lack of frankness between us irked him, and he was anxious to clear it up. I had his permission to recall Margaret to England, but she must live unacknowledged and secluded as heretofore. The difference would be that in future we knew that he shared our secret.

Hearing this I was so overcome with joy and gratitude that I could not restrain my tears as I knelt to thank him.

Looking back at my interview on the Royal barge I have often wondered how much the leniency of the King's attitude reflected the influence of the widowed Lady Latimer, formerly Lady Catherine Parr, who was about to become his wife. When I got to know her better I learnt to respect her as much for the sweetness and gentleness of her disposition as for her wit and intelligence. I could well believe that she pleaded on my behalf. She was an accomplished woman, a friend of scholars, giving ready support to any movement that fostered enlightenment. During her husband's lifetime however she kept these interests to herself, knowing that they would arouse his disapproval. He indeed clung so fondly to old traditions that when it first became known that the King would marry his widow there was loud rejoicing among the opponents of reform. Even Gardiner expressed satisfaction, little guessing how soon he would change his tune.

There was similar expectation when I arrived at Canterbury. I heard from Nicholas that the other prebendaries were boasting that Lady Latimer would persuade the King to dismiss me and put Gardiner in my place. He knew nothing as yet of their plot, of the information laid against me, but when I told him he agreed that it afforded an explanation of their confidence. He was delighted by my account of the favourable reception given me by the King, and laughed heartily when I complained of my embarrassment, my reluctance to preside over the investigation.

"I'd rather have your discomfort than theirs," he exclaimed.

I cannot deny that there was comedy in the scene when I broke the news to them, the dismay that lengthened on their faces, their clumsy efforts to wheedle and fawn. All the same I felt that it would be invidious to sit in judgment in person. I delegated the task to my chancellor, Richard Cox.

Leaving him in charge of the proceedings I returned to Lambeth. If my mood was exultant it quickly received a salutary shock. A day or two passed, then one evening when I had gone early to bed a servant woke me to say that a messenger from the King was waiting. I dressed, hurried downstairs, and found Sir Anthony Denny, one of the most trusted officers of the Royal household. He told me that he had orders to summon me on urgent business. Much puzzled and disturbed I went out with him. His boatman was at the steps, and we crossed at once to Westminster, to the new palace.

Denny led me to the gallery where he left me, and when I entered the King was alone. I knelt in homage and he signed to me to rise, then for some time he sat silent, frowning as if uncertain how to begin. His appearance shocked me, so striking was the change from the genial exuberance of his manner on the barge. The light from the chandelier above his head twinkled on his jewelled doublet, enhancing his excessive corpulence, reflecting an unhealthy pallor on his face. Although he was two years younger than myself

I felt with a pang of anxiety that I was looking at an old and sick man. When at last he spoke his voice was tired and strained.

He told me that there was grave uneasiness in the council over the information laid by the prebendaries of Canterbury, that many of the lords denounced me as a heretic and complained that if I conducted the inquiry no one would dare to speak the truth. These, I reminded him, were the very objections which I put to him myself, and he nodded irritably, muttering that he was no more convinced by them now than then. Nevertheless my enemies were pressing to have me committed to the Tower, and he had yielded to the extent of authorising them to arrest and examine me. His purpose, he explained, in summoning me at so unusual an hour of the night was to warn me that the plan would be carried out early the next morning.

His words took me so much by surprise that I had nothing at first to say except to thank him for his consideration. Then as I reflected how little ground these lords had for their complaint, how innocent I was of any intention harmful to religion or the peace of the realm, my courage returned. I was able to declare in all sincerity that I had no fear of the outcome, knowing that he would insist on a fair trial.

When he heard this he laughed bitterly:

"Lord God," he exclaimed. "Can anyone be so simple? Don't you see that once they've got you in prison they can find three or four rascals anywhere to swear what they like without fear of contradiction?"

The rebuke abashed me. I listened attentively while he directed me how to behave, bidding me demand that my accusers be produced so that I might answer them face to face:

"And if they refuse, as I think they will," he concluded, "show them this."

He pulled a heavy signet ring from his finger and handed it to me. It was the token that he used to withdraw a case from the council for his personal jurisdiction.

When I returned to Lambeth and my bed it was long before I was able to sleep. The ordeal awaiting me in the morning preyed on my mind. In addition I was worried about the King's health, failing so much faster than was apparent when I saw him on the river, and about the weakness revealed in his authority, his dependence on the support of the faction led by the Duke of Norfolk. I understood better how the balance of forces had tilted to send Cromwell to his doom.

At eight in the morning the expected messenger came from the council, and as I was waiting ready for him I set out at once for the council chamber. I was about to walk straight in as usual when a servant checked me none too courteously at the door, announcing that I must stay outside till the council had time to attend to me. The rebuff was without a shadow of right, as I was of course a councillor myself; but it would have been even more humiliating to become involved in a dispute, so I did what I was told. The lobby was full of secretaries, pages and other retainers waiting on their masters' orders, and as they all knew me as the Archbishop I was embarrassed by their inquisitive stare. Even more embarrassing was the way in which councillors, arriving late for the meeting, avoided my eye as they brushed past me to cross the threshold.

I have seldom been so glad to see anyone as I was when my own faithful secretary Ralph Morice appeared. He had come to gather news of the progress of my trial, and was amazed and horrified to learn that I was still kept waiting there for it to begin. He hurried across at once to the palace in search of any of my friends, and in a short time he returned with Sir William Butts, the King's doctor.

No one could have pleased me better. Butts was remarkable not only for his medical eminence but also for the kindness of his heart, and the King who consulted him regularly had as high an opinion of his character as of his ability. He greeted me without comment on my predicament, held me for some minutes in pleasant conversation. As he turned to go he smiled reassuringly:

"I want a few words with the King."

Soon afterwards the council sent for me and I was ushered in. It was odd to stand as a prisoner where I was accustomed to sit as a colleague; but I remembered how much ruder indignity Cromwell had to bear, and my own dwindled in comparison. The Duke of Norfolk presided. His tone was cold but civil as he informed me that complaints had been received of the heresy with which I infected the realm, and that it was his duty to commit me to the Tower to be examined. Following the King's instructions I asked him to produce the witnesses, so that I might hear what they had to say and answer them; but he shook his head, declaring that he could not allow it, they would be too frightened to speak out in my presence. As I began to protest he signed to two officers of the guard standing at the back of the room, and they strode forward to arrest me.

There was nothing for it but to show the King's ring, and I held it up.

"You leave me no choice, my Lords," I told them. "I appeal from the King's council to the King himself."

Their faces were interesting to watch. Some were indignant, aghast; but I was glad to see that many showed evident signs of relief. I had the impression that they obeyed the duke's leadership without enthusiasm, and one of them—Sir John Russell, I think—as good as told him that he was wasting their time. There was no discussion however. A strict procedure was ordained when the King intervened with this ring. The whole council rose, and we moved in a body to the palace.

We found the King seated on his throne, waiting grimly to receive us, and among the courtiers attending him I saw Butts, who caught my eye and winked. The Duke of Norfolk humbly on his knees explained the purpose of our visit. Then the King spoke, and his voice shook with anger as I have known it in his fits of rage; but although I trembled instinctively with the others I could tell that he was fully in control of himself, that in a sense he acted a part. His tone was that of pained disillusionment, indignant to learn that the councillors on whose wisdom he relied were unworthy of his trust. He accused them of abusing their authority to gratify their spite, asked what they meant by treating the Archbishop of Canterbury as a lackey, putting not only the man, but, what was worse, his office to public shame, while he waited shut out of the council chamber, a target for the whispers and sneers of a crowd of menials. As he developed the theme the faces of the offenders grew more and more anxious.

The Duke of Norfolk in fact had blundered badly, and I admired the skill with which the King took advantage of it. I do not know what plan he had in mind when he gave me the ring, but the incident in the lobby of the council chamber lightened his task. He could avoid any appearance of shielding a heretic, gave judgment instead as the guardian of dignities, both of the Crown and of the Church. All took it for granted that I was acquitted, and the duke pleaded humbly:

"We meant no harm to my Lord of Canterbury. We only wanted him in the Tower so that his glory after his trial might be the greater when he was released."

It was not a convincing explanation, but the King accepted it without remark, and I was glad to follow his example. These were men with whom I worked in almost daily contact in the business of government, and a grudge would only embarrass us all. I did not hesitate to comply when he told them to shake hands with me.

Meanwhile Cox pursued his inquiry on my behalf at Canterbury into the charges brought by the prebendaries. He made slow progress, and finally the King sent Thomas Legh, a master in chancery, to Canterbury as his commissioner. Legh was a bull of a man, tall and burly, and his methods were harsh and arbitrary, but they bore fruit. He sent armed parties to the houses of the prebendaries and their followers, searched even the clothes which they wore, the purses which they carried. Everything was examined and much of interest found, clear evidence showing how facts had been embellished, incidents inserted, to add plausibility to the case against me.

Confronted with the documents, intimidated by Legh's ferocity, the culprits made a full confession, and they were sent to prison. I had won, but when the battle was over I felt little exultation in my victory. It was a satisfaction to me as well as to them when at Christmas the King proclaimed an amnesty, and they were released.

Any grudge that I bore them was put out of my mind in any case by a throng of intervening emotions. As soon as possible after my interview on the King's barge I wrote to Margaret to give her the news and tell her to make arrangements for the journey. The difficulties however were greater than I foresaw. The renewed war between the Emperor and France provoked unsettled conditions, especially on the lower Rhine down which she must travel, and the necessary precautions brought delay which tried patience sorely for both of us.

I was glad of the distraction in July when the King's marriage to Lady Latimer was celebrated. In spite of a cold wet day, one of the worst of that inclement summer, the wedding was a gay occasion, and I enjoyed it the more because Gardiner was chosen to officiate, to enlist him as far as possible on the new Queen's side. Both the King's daughters were among the bridesmaids, and he himself seemed to put off his age and sickness and renew his youth.

There was indeed a quality in the new Queen Catherine which banished ill-humour. It was not only that she was a remarkably good-looking woman, finely proportioned, reminding me of a porcelain figure with her fair hair, regular features and hazel eyes. One had the feeling immediately in her company of great peace.

Fate seemed to decree that she should combine the duties of wife and sick-nurse. The King was her third husband. The first, Lord Brough, was over sixty years old when he married her, she herself barely fifteen. There was a similar discrepancy in age with Lord Latimer, and now at her third marriage she was likely to exchange one sickbed for another. The King's was an intermittent ailment, a form of gout. There were occasions when he seemed to be as robust as he had ever been, then the sore on his leg would break out again, with excruciating pain. It tormented him beyond endurance, maddened his temper.

News came to me at last that Margaret was at Antwerp, that a ship was already crossing to pick her up. I made haste to ride to Sandwich to meet her.

Four years had passed since she sailed away on a summer morning, and now I stood on the same quay on a November afternoon, watching the bend of the river for the first glimpse of her return.

Sails were lowered, ropes made fast to the bollards. Little Meg would be eight years old now, I wondered if she would recognise me. Then before the gangway could be put out a child leapt from the deck to the shore. I stood among a group of people, merchants and others interested in the cargo. She ran past them, barely glanced at them, ran straight to me, jumped up to throw her arms round my neck.

19

Margaret returned to live at Ford in conditions seemingly little changed. There was the same need of caution, seclusion; her existence remained a secret. It was a secret however that no longer oppressed us now that we knew that it was shared by the King. If she chafed at times under the restrictions, longed for the freedom which she found in Germany during her four years of absence, she never betrayed her feelings either by word or behaviour. Her tastes were in any case for the country rather than the town. She enjoyed riding in the fields and woods, could occupy herself happily in the house with a book or needlework. What she minded most was to be cut off from her friends; but there had always been a privileged few whom we trusted, and now the King's benevolence encouraged me to allow her to widen the circle, so that she might enjoy more varied society.

About a month after her return we were entertaining my sister Emmet and her husband, Henry Bingham, when business arose at Canterbury to which I had to attend in person, and as I should be spending a couple of nights there they asked leave to accompany me. I suggested to Margaret that she should come too, but she shook her head and laughed:

"I've lost the figure for a Polish boy. No box would hold me."

I mention this because of the stories spread later. As things turned out I can never be too thankful for her decision.

The Archbishop's palace at Canterbury was something of a labyrinth, and as Henry and Emmet were strange to it I put them in a room near mine. The library, however, was in the farther wing, and when I retired there on the second night to work, and they themselves went up to bed, the whole length of the building lay between us. I was busy and became engrossed in my book, so that at first I paid no attention when a clamour arose at this unusual hour. I was not fully aware of it indeed till a servant burst in on me to announce that the house was on fire. The passage was full of smoke, the whole place reeked of burning.

I asked the man quickly whether the Binghams had been warned, and as he was unsure I ran to the staircase. He tried to hold me back, but I tore myself from him. Neither Henry nor Emmet knew their way about the house, the multiplicity of turnings would be baffling in the smoke and darkness. There was even a danger that they had heard nothing, were still asleep.

When I reached the stairs I understood why the man wanted to restrain me. Flames crackled among the boards and banisters; one or two of the treads already caved in, revealing a glowing furnace in the well beneath. I hesitated, uncertain whether the frame would bear me if I set foot on it.

Then a figure staggered out of the room on the upper landing, and in the glare of the conflagration I saw Henry supporting Emmet in his arms. I started forward, the servant who had followed was already climbing at my side. We met Henry midway, and he thrust Emmet towards us; we clutched and tumbled with her rather than carried her to the bottom. But the stair on which Henry paused was burnt through; it yielded under his weight, and as he tried to save himself the hole widened, there was nowhere firm for him to stand. As we picked ourselves up safely on the flagstones in the hall he screamed in terror. Flames shot up round him, and he vanished into their depths.

We could do nothing to save him. The whole staircase had become a cataract of fire, and the heat was already past bearing where we stood. Emmet lay unconscious, seemingly lifeless. Between us we carried her out into the street.

A huge crowd was collected there. A conduit had been opened, and men raced to and fro with buckets whose contents they hurled in through the windows. I was grateful for their efforts, but I could see that the house was doomed. They might as well have poured water on the flames of hell. All around me I heard cries of lamentation as is common among spectators of a calamity, even those who suffer no personal loss. It seemed to me that everyone lamented except myself. I was too grieved at first by Henry's death to care for my property.

The fire had not yet reached the wing which held the library, and zealous helpers were climbing in at the window and throwing out books as fast as they could. The sight recalled me to action. I hurried over to direct them, remembering in particular a box in which I kept a collection of folio volumes of the Greek classics from the Aldine press given me by Pope Clement himself when I was in Rome. I peered into the room to see if the box could be saved.

Flames already licked the farther wall, and the tapestry was beginning to smoulder; but the box lying by the table was still unharmed. Two boys only remained there, feverishly working along the shelves and filling their arms with books. I shouted to them to leave everything else and get the box out, then to follow quickly before the ceiling fell in. They dropped what they held and ran at once to obey.

I had forgotten how heavy the box was. Neither boy was more than sixteen years old, neither very strongly built. They had a desperate struggle to move it. I watched them in anguished suspense as the fire advanced, and was just about to call to them to give up and save themselves, when by a magnificent effort they heaved their burden on to the window sill. Willing arms reached from outside to grasp it and tugged it through the smashed glass and woodwork of the casement. The boys followed head foremost. As we lifted them to the ground the whole room behind them was ablaze. No one could have stayed there and lived.

My relief was so great, I told the boys with some exaggeration that the books which they had recovered were more precious to me than any treasure in the world. This bred a legend that I had Margaret hidden in the box. She was, as I have shown, many miles away at Ford at the time.

Emmet was carried across to a neighbour's house where she recovered consciousness, and although she suffered severely from burns and shock there was no lasting injury. As soon as she was well enough to be moved I brought her to Ford, where Margaret nursed her back to health. Her body was healed, but her spirit broken. She had had to endure too many disappointments, and this last was the more cruel because she believed when she married Henry Bingham that the clouds had parted.

The palace at Canterbury has not been rebuilt, but I managed well enough without it. Later I adapted my house at Bekesbourne for official use, living there when I had business at Canterbury. The distance is only three miles, about a quarter of an hour on a good horse.

I was at Ford however in the following summer when the King passed through Kent on his way to France to take over command of his army in person. Our alliance with the Emperor, an uneasy association from the outset, was threatening to break under pressure of events, largely because of the success with which we played our part in the war. An English army besieged Boulogne, and it was clear that the French could hold out little longer; but the Emperor, far from expressing gratitude, complained of the delay, urged us to raise the siege, to join forces with him in a march on Paris. The fact was that he had no desire to see Boulogne in English hands. We were already well placed to control trade through the narrow seas, holding Dover and Calais on either shore. If we obtained yet another port there he feared for the freedom of his shipping.

To forestall any argument that might arise the King wished to be present on the spot when Boulogne fell. His health was better than it had been for months, his leg troubled him less. He insisted that he was fit to bear the strain; but he took me by surprise when he announced that he would interrupt the journey at Ford, spend the night there with his retinue. He left me little time to prepare his entertainment, to arrange for the two Margarets to be spirited away.

I was worrying over this when a further message arrived, brought by a single horseman and delivered to me in private. It was from the Queen to tell me that she would come with the King to see him off at the port, and that although she understood that my wife could not appear in public she hoped to meet her in private and make her acquaintance.

Margaret expressed dismay. She had lived so long officially invisible that she was shy of appearing even secretly in the Queen's presence. Yet I doubt whether in fact she was as unwilling as she pretended. No maturity could extinguish her curiosity, her love of new experience and adventure. She agreed that the Royal wishes must be obeyed, and her plans for flight were cancelled.

Ford is smaller than Otford or Knole; but our accommodation was not so cramped as to leave none available to which she could retire, hidden from observation yet able to receive the Queen in suitable dignity. The rooms which she chose were on the upper floor, approached by a staircase of their own, so that she could go in and out without meeting anyone. The servants employed to get them ready guessed what was in the wind, and in spite of the haste with which they had to work they took the utmost care over the arrangements. Indeed if I had not stopped them they would have carried all the best furniture upstairs, leaving me only bare walls and floor to entertain the King and his nobles.

It was lucky as things turned out that the hiding-place was so splendidly furnished. The King and Queen dined in the banqueting hall with a party of officers. As soon as we had finished the Queen made an excuse to withdraw. I knew what was her errand, and a chaplain was waiting to be her guide; but to my consternation the King rose too and accompanied her, beckoning to me to follow. I had no chance to warn Margaret how exalted a visitor to expect.

He walked slowly, enfeebled by his lameness and great bulk. When we came to the stairs I was doubtful whether he would be able to mount them; they were steep and narrow, with awkward turns not designed for ceremony. But the Queen followed close behind, supporting him when his efforts failed. I was amazed that anyone so slightly built had the strength to bear his weight. I admired even more the tact with which she kept him from knowing how much he depended on her.

He was panting as he reached the top, but jubilant, well satisfied with his achievement. When she took his arm to steady him he shook her off, then caught her hand with a gruff laugh and led her himself across the landing. One of Margaret's maids stood posted at the door, ready to show the Queen in. When she saw who else was coming she stared wide-eyed, her mouth gaped, and with a suppressed scream she darted inside to tell her mistress.

The King was not put out. He was in his most genial humour as he followed the girl into the room, and Margaret quickly collecting herself played up to him with spirit. I could see that he approved of her. He liked women who were intelligent and not afraid of him. Watching him even now in his age and infirmity, aware of the charm which he exerted, I understood how little it depended on the lustre of his position.

Margaret responded to his company as a flower to the sunshine. She was once more as I remembered her in Osiander's house at Nuremberg. My heart ached to think how nearly I had forgotten that laughing face. She blushed when he turned to me suddenly:

"Poor Cromwell could be alive today if he'd chosen me a nymph from the Pegnitz, not the muddy Rhine."

The Queen made haste to intervene. She encouraged Margaret to discuss the religious conflict in Germany, adding comments of her own which revealed the wide range of her knowledge, the fearlessness of her views. I listened at first in trepidation, this was dangerous ground in the King's presence; but he himself soon joined in, taking the theme from them and expanding it.

The freedom with which he spoke that evening was in striking contrast to the severity of the law which he enforced against heresy; but the inconsistency was more apparent than real. His mind was open to new ideas, his policy held them in check, fearing danger unless he advanced slowly.

He broke off at last and drew me aside, leaving the Queen to talk to Margaret. I was expecting something of the sort, unable to believe that the only purpose of the interview was to satisfy his curiosity about my wife. Nevertheless, looking back, I am sure that Margaret's appearance and behaviour played a part in his decision to confide in me, that he wished to see clearly into my heart before entrusting me with his son.

I do not mean to exaggerate when I use such language. Prince Edward, now seven years old, had a tutor already well qualified to look after him, my friend Sir John Cheke. It became clear however as the King spoke to me that he was thinking of a time when he would no longer be there, that although I was in fact the elder he expected me to outlive him. He reminded me that I was the boy's godfather. Then brusquely, urgently he began to talk of his hopes and fears for his son. He was anxious to ensure not only peaceful succession to the Crown but also the survival of his work to promote the strength and unity of the kingdom, and he was convinced that independence from Rome was an indispensable condition. Foreseeing that reform of the Church could and must be carried still farther in the next reign, he had been careful to choose tutors for the prince who would confirm him in fidelity to the new learning. He made me promise that after his death all my influence would be used to fulfil his intention.

It was strange to hear how freely he spoke of death, to which no one else might refer without danger of a charge of treason. He was already considering the terms of his will, and described the provisions which he was making for his son's minority. I should be myself on the council of regency and have useful support there from Hertford, whom he named with affection; but he was less certain about Gardiner, had not yet made up his mind whether to include him at all.

"I can rule him myself," he told me, "but if I put him among you when I'm gone he'll rule the roost."

He intended to leave instructions in his will to direct the order of succession if Prince Edward died without issue. In that event his elder daughter, Princess Mary, would inherit, and if her line failed the next to succeed would be Princess Elizabeth. If both his daughters died childless the Crown would devolve on the heirs of his younger sister Mary, the White Queen of France, born of her marriage to his old friend, the Duke of Suffolk.

When the King finished explaining his intentions he asked me to give him my oath to observe them faithfully, and I obeyed without hesitation. All those which affected his son's reign had my heartfelt approval. As regards the later provisions, the contingent remainders, I am afraid that I paid them little attention, unable to foresee their importance. Prince Edward was in excellent health, completely recovered from his only serious illness, a quartan ague which provoked anxiety a few years before. A long reign lay ahead of him, during which he would grow up, marry and have sons of his own, one of whom would succeed him. Nothing seemed more certain than that before he died I should be myself in my grave.

On the following morning before his departure the King summoned the lords of the council who attended him, and informed them that he had appointed the Queen to act as regent for him while he was in France, and that she would be advised by the Archbishop of Canterbury. We were a long way from the "whip with six strings."

During the next two months I travelled with her about the country, even staying as her guest at Otford which was formerly my own house.

Boulogne surrendered early in September, but before thanksgiving could be offered for the victory further despatches arrived bringing uncomfortable news. The Emperor advancing on Paris had marched into a trap, cut off from supplies and reinforcements by a strong army under the command of the Dauphin, the future King Henry II of France. His plight was so much of his own making, the strategy which landed him in it so imprudent, that many suspected that he invited the misfortune on purpose. Its effect, as his envoy announced to King Henry at Boulogne, was to leave him no choice except to seek terms from the enemy. Uncomfortable in alliance with German Protestants and English schismatics he was glad of the excuse to make peace.

We carried on the war alone. The King whose health was causing anxiety came home and the Duke of Norfolk whom he left in command of Boulogne nearly lost it at once by his negligence; but the courage of the garrison retrieved the disaster, and the town remained in our hands. The care devoted by King Henry to his navy began now to reap its reward, enabling the garrison to be supplied with food and ammunition from the ports across the Channel. It became clear to the French that nothing could dislodge us as long as we retained control of the sea, and they ceased their attacks and turned their attention to assemble as large a fleet as possible, bringing ships from as far as the Mediterranean, which they based on the new port built by King Francis at the mouth of the Seine—Franciscopolis he wanted to call it, but the grandiose name did not appeal to the local people, who still persist in speaking of it as Le Havre, "the harbour."

All through the spring and early summer England awaited invasion, and everyone from the King downwards was intent on preparations to repel it. Ships of any sort that would serve were diverted from their normal trade to reinforce the navy in the Spithead, and such was the eagerness with which the nation rallied in the face of danger that few complained of the interference with their means of livelihood.

My own diocese covered a vulnerable stretch of coast where the sea is narrowest. I obtained a number of pieces of artillery from the council, which we harnessed to horses and hauled along the cliffs, ready to greet the French when they arrived. Many of the horses came from my own stables, and I must confess that I enjoyed the days spent with them on the downs by the sea, helping to train the refractory to the unaccustomed burden. It was a pleasant change from the normal duties of an Archbishop, to urge a horse and not a man to conformity.

In July the invasion was launched, but I saw no active service. The French Admiral d'Annebault sailed straight for the Spithead, where the main English forces were assembled. His purpose was to fight a decisive battle which would destroy the naval power of England and leave the whole coast at his mercy. We awaited the outcome with apprehension. King Henry himself went to Portsmouth to review his ships.

For the next day or two I had little news in Kent of the course of the fighting, and the few reports that came through were often contradictory. Some spoke of a great battle already in progress off Portsmouth, others of a desultory skirmish in which neither side had the advantage. Finally an official despatch arrived to reassure me. The few French soldiers who landed in the Isle of Wight had been repelled by the local people, and the French fleet itself, seemingly losing heart, had raised anchor and sailed back out to sea.

The threat of invasion was not over, but it never again became dangerous. D'Annebault cruised to and fro in the Channel, maintaining the alarm. At last in the middle of August our own fleet was ready to put out in pursuit; it met and engaged with the enemy in the evening off Shoreham, till interrupted by darkness. When dawn broke the English sailors looked out at an empty sea. D'Annebault, taking advantage of a breeze that sprang up at midnight, was homeward bound for France.

His behaviour was explained by reports from our agents who watched the crews disembarking on arrival in the Seine. The men looked more like corpses than living flesh and blood. The enemy responsible for the French defeat was the plague, to which the sailors fell helpless victims, cooped up in overcrowded ships in the hottest summer in my memory.

Even if sickness did most to avert the danger, great credit accrued to the commander of the English fleet, the Lord High Admiral. This was John Dudley, whose acquaintance I made three years before at Hampton Court when he and I were left in charge there of the former Queen Catherine. He had recently inherited the title of Viscount Lisle and he plays an important part in the later pages of this story. He made a favourable impression at first sight, and the good opinion was reinforced by the modesty of his demeanour, his seemingly imperturbable suavity. It was as if his spirit had been born in velvet gloves. Few suspected, I did not myself till I knew him much better, the ruthless and insatiable ambition hidden beneath the surface.

In spite of the distinction which he enjoyed as Lord High Admiral he was still far from the summit of his career. He belonged to the group of councillors who favoured religious reform; but his influence was overshadowed in it by that of the two Seymours, uncles of Prince Edward, who were the acknowledged leaders. Hertford, the elder, was fast becoming one of the most powerful men in the kingdom, chief rival to the Duke of Norfolk, who hated him with bitter jealousy. Hertford was a very competent general, as he had shown by a successful campaign in Scotland. Norfolk with less ability suffered disgrace from his recent blunder at Boulogne.

My own early acquaintance with the Seymours was limited to a formal civility, a barely concealed hostility while their sister was usurping the place of Queen Anne; but after her death my relations improved, at any rate with Hertford. His brother Thomas was a contrast to him in most respects, sharing only a handsome appearance and military talent. It was known that he wooed the Queen while she was still Lord Latimer's widow, and that she would have become his wife if the King had not claimed her. When the King's death left her a widow again she married him.

Jealousy poisoned his relations with his brother Edward. He kept it under control for the present so that the two might present a united front against the Howards. It did not help however to commend me in his eyes that his brother and I were friends, and he did his best to avoid my company. I was surprised therefore when he drew me aside one day at Hampton Court, appalled when he went on to congratulate me on the birth of a son. His information was perfectly correct. Margaret was just delivered of a child, our son Tom.

In spite of the King's connivance my marriage was still a secret, and there was no one with whom I less wished to share it than Seymour. Uncertain how much he knew, I pretended to think that he spoke in jest. His manner became more cautious; he began to hint, wrapping his meaning in such riddles that for some time I failed to understand. Even when I caught a glimpse of the truth I felt that I must be mistaken, that a man in his position never would sink to blackmail, demanding money under threat of informing the King.

Hertford saved me from an embarrassing situation. He came up to speak to me, and his brother at once walked away in disgust. As he could do me no harm with the King I was not greatly troubled, and even when I heard that he was spreading rumours I ignored them, trusting that they would die out of their own accord. A month or so later however when we were sitting down to dinner in the hall at Lambeth I saw him to my surprise lingering at the door behind the screen, peering in at us. I sent my steward Dick Nevill to invite him in to join us.

I do not know what he expected to find if he wandered round the house; but he scowled to himself as he strode up the room at Dick's heels. When he reached my place he announced that he was sent to summon me to the King. I asked at what hour the King wished me to attend, and hearing that it was not till two o'clock I urged him to sit down with us while we finished dinner. My insistence was the more peremptory because among his stories reaching my ears was a distressing account of my parsimony, the niggardly establishment which I kept while I hoarded revenue to buy land for my wife and children. It was a calumny that wounded me to the quick, for I prided myself on the excellence of the table which I provided for the entertainment both of my guests and of my household.

We were all enjoying venison from my woods in Kent flavoured with herbs from the garden at Lambeth, and it distressed me when he was given a helping to see how inattentively he picked at it, not appreciating the good food as he should. At last his impatience got the better of him, and he rose leaving the greater part untouched on his plate and excusing himself in a manner so perfunctory as to be hardly civil. I no longer tried to detain him, and he took his leave.

A little before two I crossed to Westminster to obey the King's summons. When I was shown into his presence I found Seymour standing unhappily by the throne. The King turned to him as soon as he had acknowledged my salutation:

"Perhaps you'll tell my Lord of Canterbury now what dissatisfied you in his hospitality."

His tone was grim, and poor Seymour sank terrified to his knees, protesting that he had been misinformed and begging forgiveness for spreading so false a story. I was an embarrassed witness of his humiliation, but I understood the King's purpose when he declared:

"If you can't tell me the simple truth about a meal at Lambeth, how can you expect me to believe charges against the Archbishop's morals?"

Later I heard much that threw light on Seymour's motives. There was no personal spite in them, little as he cared whether he broke me or not. All that he wanted was money. He was a man of extravagant tastes and had overstrained his resources to gratify them. When he could extract nothing from me by threats he had the idea to reveal my guilt to the King, to provoke such a storm of anger that he could propose the confiscation of the revenues of the episcopal sees. So little was the King impressed by his mischief-making that he gave orders without my knowledge for the grant to me of lands in Yorkshire.

At this time I was much absent from town, having work that kept me in my diocese, greatly to my satisfaction. For weeks on end I could retreat to Ford, ride or walk with Margaret on the uplands overlooking the wide estuary, with no one to observe us or find fault. The task moreover which demanded this rustication was of a sort to delight me, the preparation of an English liturgy to replace the Latin in all the churches of the realm. Although circumstances prevented it from bearing fruit in King Henry's reign, it was the foundation of the book of common prayer published soon after his son came to the throne.

Secluded with my family, absorbed in my studies, I lost touch with the struggle growing between the rival factions in the council as the signs became clearer that the King's reign approached its end. No one deplored the controversy more earnestly than the King himself. I was present on Christmas Eve on one of my rare visits to Westminster when he prorogued Parliament, and many were affected to tears, as I was, as we watched his face lined with pain, his ungainly body crippled by illness, and heard him exhort us all to charity, "the special foundation of our religion."

His exhortation had little effect. Prejudice tugged against prejudice, and he could only try to preserve a balance. For the moment the advantage lay with Norfolk, Gardiner and their friends. They thwarted many reforms which I proposed for the abolition of ceremonies liable to abuse, in particular that of creeping to the Cross on Good Friday, the posture of the doomed victim approaching the idol of Moloch.

I was accustomed to attacks on myself. My alarm and anger were aroused more violently when I learnt that my opponents were even trying to entrap the Queen, whose ardent interest in the new learning they deplored. The story was much embellished by the time that it reached me; but it seems that they poisoned the King's mind against her so effectively that he signed an order for her arrest. The messenger carrying the document dropped it on the floor, where it was found by one of her women who picked it up and showed it to her. Her distress was such that she fainted away, and the King hearing that she was taken ill came solicitously to her bedside. What passed between them I do not know, except that her charm and ready wit prevailed. When the chancellor arrived with the guard to arrest her he found them strolling in the gallery, and the King's arm was round her waist.

Already the political balance was tilting in the other direction. All Gardiner's attempts to mend relations with the Imperial Court were a failure. The Emperor was in no mood for concessions to the King of England when he himself came so near attaining the crown of his ambition, the domination of Christendom. King Francis saw that while the war dragged on between France and England the Emperor was left free to do as he wished. Both sides were anxious for peace, and terms were agreed. France would make payment in compensation for the war and settlement of old debts, and King Henry in return would cede Boulogne back at the end of eight years when the money was paid. Admiral d'Annebault himself came to England to sign the treaty, and I was recalled to town to attend the reception given in his honour.

Partly because of his health, but also from deliberate policy, the King sent his son in his place to greet the French embassy. Prince Edward was nearly nine years old, tall for his age, with grey eyes and his father's red-gold hair. He had grown up strong and wiry, active both in body and in mind. His bearing indeed had a dignity beyond his years as he rode between his Uncle Hertford and me, leading the procession from Hampton Court to meet d'Annebault. As I glanced at the boy riding at my side I thought of Malory's stories of Arthur, the successor revealed by a wonderful sign when King Uther Pendragon grew old.

Admiral d'Annebault with the French nobles was waiting on the bank of the river. The prince dismounted at once, and as the grizzled Frenchman advanced and kissed his hand he replied with an affectionate kiss on both cheeks, paused as if to collect himself, then in a clear voice audible to all of us he delivered a speech of welcome in faultless Latin. Even if the phrases were the work of his tutor John Cheke, it was a feat deserving admiration in a boy not yet nine to repeat them in public without nervousness or error. D'Annebault was plainly delighted.

They mounted and rode side by side at our head as we returned to Hampton Court, where the prince still acted as host, showing the guest to his rooms.

Another incident of that visit stands out in my memory. The King, who was now so lame and infirm that he had to be carried in a chair, felt unable to bear the strain of the great banquet prepared for the entertainment of his visitors, and he invited d'Annebault to dine with him in private. I alone shared their table, and when we had finished eating he pulled himself to his feet and with one arm round d'Annebault's shoulders and the other round mine for support he paced to and fro in the room. Although the movement was painful to him it seemed to ease the flow of his thoughts, and the posture enabled him to lower his voice to ensure secrecy.

He spoke of the danger threatening both France and England from the Emperor's control of the council at Trent, which was turning the Church into an instrument of Imperial policy. He praised the care taken by King Francis to protect the Church in France from Papal encroachment, and he insisted that his own measures in England differed only in degree. Suddenly he made a remark that took my breath away, so little was I prepared for it:

"Tell my brother, the King of France, that we can set an example to edify all Christendom. Let us both abolish the mass in our dominions and replace it with a simple service of communion free from sacrificial pretence."

D'Annebault was too experienced a courtier to betray surprise. He promised civilly to inform his master of the proposal.

King Henry had never said anything before to warn me that his mind had travelled so far. My firm belief is that an undercurrent of feeling gathered force as he approached the end of his life. Although he never spoke to me of his guilty compact with Queen Anne he knew that I received her confession, shared his secret. The knowledge was a bond between us enabling me to read his thoughts when we were alone together. I was sure that he brooded over his sin with the same obsessive intensity as earlier over his marriage to his brother's wife.

If my own imagination was haunted, so too even more surely was the King's by echoes of human sacrifice in the wilds of Norfolk. They blended inextinguishably with the chant of the choir when the Christian priest stood at the altar to turn bread and wine into flesh and blood, to crucify again the innocent victim, the price of atonement. King Henry had reason to feel discomfort when he attended mass.

Few except myself knew of the message to King Francis, and no answer was received. Within a year both Kings were dead, but King Henry during the short time left him remained firm in his intention to ensure the continued progress of reform. Gardiner fell into disgrace: the immediate cause was his refusal to give up land at Southwark to the Crown. The revised terms of the King's will were made known, and the whole council swore to observe them. They carried out the plans which he confided to me at Ford. Gardiner's name was omitted from the council of regency.

The King was confirmed in the chosen direction of his policy when evidence reached him which aroused suspicion of the loyalty of the Duke of Norfolk and his eldest son, Lord Surrey. They were arrested early in December on a charge of treason and confined in the Tower. The ground of offence on which the proceedings rested was Surrey's presumption in changing the quarterings on his shield to give prominence to the Royal bearings. I know little of heraldry and can express no opinion on his claim that he was entitled to the honour by Plantagenet blood, which he inherited from his mother, the Duke of Buckingham's daughter. Even if he had the right, the question remains why he waited to assert it till his action could provoke the most challenging effect. A time when the King's health was failing offered peculiar opportunities to a noble who flaunted the Royal arms.

It was a sign of the growing strength of the dynasty, of the hold that it had earned on the allegiance of the nation, that the King was able at last to assert himself against so powerful a family, on whose favour he long depended, to whose interests he had to defer.

Surrey had the saving grace in my eyes that he wrote charming poetry. It would have been better for him indeed if, in the face that he turned to the world, there had been more of the poet and less of the heir to rank and privilege. His arrogance earned him many enemies. Little could be done in any case to save him when the full extent of the charges became known. It was bad enough that he boasted to his friends that, as soon as the King was dead, his father would seize control of the council of regency and impose his own policy on the nation. A still more heinous plan was revealed which he had concerted with Cardinal Pole in Italy, to stir up rebellion to prevent Prince Edward from succeeding and to crown Princess Mary in his place. The restoration of Papal supremacy in England would follow, and it was assumed that Princess Mary would offer Surrey her hand in marriage.

Surrey was convicted and beheaded, nor was his father allowed to escape. Proceedings were taken against him by attainder.

I was present at the debate in the House of Lords and voted in favour of the bill. It was an unpleasant task; but the King himself asked me to attend, and I had no doubt of the duke's guilt. It would have been dishonest to make an excuse to be absent in my diocese.

The King was by now very ill indeed, too weak to enjoy the few recreations left him, to be wheeled out into the garden to fish in the pond, or to play on his lute while his fool, Will Somers, sang. So that he should not be deprived entirely of the music that he loved, Somers himself had to take the lute and play to him. Listening to it he could forget his pain, cease for a time to worry over the fate of the kingdom, over the obsessive fears rearoused by the treason of the Howards.

The bill of attainder was carried in both Houses and awaited only his assent; but he was unfit to make even the short journey from his palace in Westminster, so he empowered the chancellor to affix the seal on his behalf. We were summoned to take our places for the ceremony in Parliament on Thursday, the 27th of January. Although I played my part in the proceedings I have no memory of them. I felt no pity for the man whom we condemned to the scaffold, failed even to pray for his soul. On that morning all my prayers were elsewhere. The King's mortal illness blotted out the prisoner in the Tower.

When the business of the House was over I went round to the

palace. The report was neither comforting nor alarming. The King suffered a great deal, but there was no change for the worse. I had an appointment at Croydon, and there seemed to be no reason not to keep it. So I returned to Lambeth for a hasty meal, ordered my horse and rode off into the country.

It was nearly midnight and I was in bed when the messenger came to Croydon to call me back urgently to the King's bedside; but somewhere in the recesses of my mind I was expecting the summons, I was wide awake at once and in a few minutes I was dressed. It was a bitterly cold night, freezing hard, and as I set out with the man for Westminster all my attention was needed to hold my horse up, to avoid a fall on the icy patches in the road. The moon was hidden by clouds; there was barely light to see as we galloped through sleeping villages, Streatham and Brixton, hushed except for the clatter of our hooves. I knew that there was no hope, the King was dying.

He was still alive when I reached the palace. I heard that when the seizure overcame him early in the evening the doctors hesitated to tell him what it meant; when at last they suggested that he should see a priest he refused to have anyone but me, even so he insisted on a short sleep before he sent for me. He slept for an hour or two, and when he awoke he was speechless. They feared that before I arrived it would be too late.

It was not too late, but there was no time to spare. He was conscious when I entered the room, he smiled at me; but no power of speech was left him. I held his hand and begged him to give a sign that he died trusting in the love of God. His fingers tightened on mine with a force that affirmed more surely than words. Then slowly his grip relaxed, life died from his eyes; but a great peace lit his face with its afterglow. He lay still, never moved again.

At that moment, with the last gesture of faith, he crossed the threshold, no matter whether his heart went on beating in his unconscious body for a short time longer. I left him and returned to Lambeth, knowing that there was no more that I could do. What remained of the night I spent alone in my chapel.

It was not till morning that I spared a thought for the signed order ready for the execution of the Duke of Norfolk, remembered that it became invalid on the King's death.

20

After King Henry's death I let my beard grow, as I still wear it now. Strangers who saw me assumed that I was asserting my reforming principles by following secular instead of ecclesiastical fashion. Only a few friends knew that I wore it in mourning to recall the work inspired and left unfinished by King Henry VIII.

Some may think that the work advanced more smoothly when his son succeeded him. The Church received an English liturgy and married clergy, and its chief service was transformed into an act of divine communion free from the sacrificial associations of the mass. These were achievements which I greeted with approval. If my satisfaction was incomplete it was because doubt of their permanence troubled me, the master's hand was missing.

On the Monday following his death the council of regency met to carry out the provisions of his will. We agreed that the Earl of Hertford, lawful guardian to the nine-year-old King, was the fittest among us to be preferred to rule on our behalf, and he received the title of Lord Protector carrying little short of sovereign authority. Objection was raised in later years accusing him of overriding the old King's will to further his own advancement; but I myself have never doubted that the course which we took was right. We were too large a body to govern effectively if power were shared between us, and Hertford, the young King's uncle, was better qualified than anyone for the chief place. He was with King Henry to the last, was standing at the bedside when I arrived. No one enjoyed more of the old King's confidence.

A clause of the will created him Duke of Somerset. It provided for other ennoblements also, including that of John Dudley Lord Lisle who became Earl of Warwick. [I hope that I shall not confuse my readers if in the pages that follow I refer to Edward Seymour Earl of Hertford as Duke of Somerset, and to John Dudley as

Earl of Warwick till a final promotion—to which I shall come later —made him Duke of Northumberland.]

King Edward VI was crowned in Westminster Abbey on Quinquagesima Sunday, an auspicious day whose order of service is my favourite in the year, containing the great chapter from the Epistle to the Corinthians: "Though I speak with the tongues of men and of angels and have not charity, I am even as sounding brass or as a tinkling cymbal." My heart leapt as I recited the words, hearing in them the keynote set for the new reign.

My hopes were no less ardent as I watched the young King, observed the grave attention with which he played his part in the proceedings. Although the ancient ritual had been shortened it was a formidable ordeal for a boy of his age; but he betrayed no signs of weariness, either at the service in the Abbey or later at the banquet where he entertained the chief dignitaries of England and all Europe. He had his reward on the following day when the celebrations ended with a great tournament. The chief prizes were won by his younger uncle, Thomas Seymour, recently promoted Baron Seymour of Sudeley. His exploits made him a hero in the King's eyes, laid the foundation of an influence destined to bear bitter fruit.

In these early months of the reign however no conflict interrupted the harmony. The council accepted Somerset's leadership with goodwill, and even Gardiner who was excluded seemed to bear no grudge; he was very affable when he joined me to officiate at King Henry's funeral. Somerset did not renew the order for the execution of the Duke of Norfolk, he let him know that his life would be spared. Soon afterwards I received a message from the duke asking me to visit him in the Tower. I went unwillingly, knowing that he wanted me to plead with Somerset for his release. He greeted me with much civility. When he spoke of Lord Wiltshire and his family he brought tears to my eyes; but indignation followed as I thought of the way in which he behaved to his niece and her brother Rochford while they were alive. I left the Tower in no mood to be his advocate.

Somerset who was fond of his sister could not be expected to weep for the Boleyns, but he shared my disgust at the duke's hypocrisy. In any case, as he told me, it would be dangerous to set him free. The Pope's emissaries were going about Europe proclaiming that King Edward was born in schism, urging the Emperor to intervene to put Princess Mary on the throne. All that saved England from invasion was the lack of a leader to foment rebellion, either Norfolk himself, or Surrey if he had not been beheaded.

Among those active in public affairs there was no one whose attitude aroused uneasiness, with the possible exception of Somerset's own brother, Lord Seymour. In spite of his recent elevation to the peerage, and the post of Lord High Admiral granted to him, he was a disappointed man. To strengthen his position he took advantage of the favour which he enjoyed with the young King, dazzling him with his athletic prowess and swaggering magnificence. It was easy for the younger uncle, amusing, adventurous, irresponsible, to become the boy's favourite. The elder was grave by nature, careful of his duty as guardian.

Seymour's success with the King so encouraged his audacity that he sought permission from the council to marry Princess Elizabeth. She was not quite fifteen and in any case unwilling. Somerset refused consent. Seymour was indignant, and without informing his brother he renewed his suit to his old love, the Queen Dowager. They were secretly married and there was a stormy interview between the brothers when the news became known.

The marriage did not interrupt the Queen's relations with her stepchildren, all of whom were devoted to her. The King was jubilant when he heard that she had become his uncle's wife, even Princess Mary congratulated her. For Princess Elizabeth there was some embarrassment in the situation, a difficult choice. She had been living with her stepmother since her father's death, and now when Seymour asked her to stay on in the household she agreed. The Queen remained ignorant that he was her rejected suitor.

It was an association demanding the utmost tact and prudence, and Seymour possessed neither. Stories began to spread of his unseemly behaviour. There was nothing really immoral, much that was indiscreet. The princess liked to lie late asleep in the morning, and he would come into her room to rouse her, pull her across the bed, smack her bare buttocks, romp with her in a way that had more than its share of lasciviousness. Other incidents were of a similar sort, and at first the Queen saw no harm in them; but details of his earlier proposal seem to have reached her, opened her eyes. She arranged for the princess to move into an establishment of her own.

When Parliament met a bill was prepared to permit the marriage of priests, and although no time could be found for it in the first session it became law in the following year. Meanwhile, as it was certain that permission would be granted, I informed married clergy in my diocese that subterfuge was no longer necessary, and Margaret set the example by presiding openly over the household at Ford. I waited however to bring her to Lambeth till the measure received Parliamentary authority. After that the last barrier was removed. She sat with me at the head of the table, helped me to entertain my guests.

The new dignity of her position did not greatly appeal to her. She disliked the formality of public functions; but it pleased her as much as it did me to know that the world at last accepted her, that her existence was no longer a secret of which to be ashamed. Most of all she enjoyed the freedom of movement now available to her. She had little chance before to see what England was like. An expedition, which she often made alone, was to the island of Sheppey, where Alice still lived in a house saved from the dissolution of the priory, retaining a community of her former nuns to continue their pastoral work.

Both in Church and state Somerset's policy was bearing fruit worthy of his humane and enlightened principles. The Act of Six Articles was revoked, the death penalty for heresy abolished. It was a welcome sign of the spirit guiding events that Nicholas Ridley was elevated to the see of Rochester. Somerset also vigorously opposed the enclosure of common lands. He soon became immensely popular among the humble, who acclaimed him as the Good Duke.

If I watched his progress with misgiving, it was because he was too sure of himself, too impatient. He had a talent for doing the right thing at the wrong moment, in the wrong way.

His faults had disastrous effect in his dealings with foreign nations. At a time when Pope and Emperor were conspiring to dethrone King Edward so that his sister might usurp his place, the utmost care was needed to conciliate the new King of France. It was not in Somerset's nature however to practise diplomacy; he despised the art, condemned it as dishonest. When dispute arose over the fortifications of Boulogne, he replied with high-handed defiance. Open war would have followed if Warwick had not intervened, meeting the French envoys in secret, assuaging their feelings.

He was equally clumsy in his treatment of Scotland. The effect was to unite every faction in Scotland against the common enemy and the two nations went to war. Before leading the army north he sent me a letter enclosing a written prayer. The benefit for which he asked was not victory, but peace and reconciliation, "the most happy and godly marriage of the King's Majesty our Sovereign Lord and the young Scottish Queen." Filled with goodwill for the Scots, he set forth to devastate Scotland.

He crossed the Tweed, advanced up the coast, found the Scottish army awaiting him on Pinkie Cleugh near Musselburgh. Its forces outnumbered his own, but his tactics remained as skilful as ever in this last battle of his career. He won an overwhelming victory which was entirely barren.

The Scots carried their little Queen off to Dumbarton, safe from pursuit, sent envoys to Paris to arrange her betrothal to the French King's eldest son. The French wasted no time. A fast ship dodged the English fleet in the Firth of Forth, sailed on round the Orkneys and down the west coast to the Clyde, where the child embarked. She landed safely at Brest, lost to both England and Scotland. She has grown up a Frenchwoman in France.

When it was too late Somerset offered terms, proposing that after betrothal to King Edward she should be left to grow up among her own people, till she was old enough to be married. The Scots would have accepted the proposal if it had been made earlier; it would have kept their Queen at home.

On his return to England he was severely blamed for his failure to bring off the Scottish marriage. Few were more vociferous in reproach than his brother Thomas, who himself had remained at home during the campaign, neglecting his duty as Lord High Admiral, delegating the command of the fleet to a subordinate. His efforts to make mischief were the more dangerous because of his influence with the King, who was bitterly disappointed over the loss of his Scottish bride.

It was a relief when Thomas Seymour turned his attention from fomenting trouble in the present to ambitious plans to assure his position in the future. He acquired from Lord Dorset the legal custody of his eldest daughter, Lady Jane Grey, who, as King Henry's great-niece, granddaughter of the Duke of Suffolk and Mary the White Queen, stood next in succession to the Crown if King Henry's own line failed. Seymour's purpose was to betroth her to the King in substitution for the Queen of Scots, and it was on that condition that her father relinquished her to him. Both looked for great reward from the connection, the one as father, the other as guardian of the Queen consort.

Lady Jane went to live in Seymour's house under the Queen Dowager's care, occupying the rooms left vacant by Princess Elizabeth. I met her there often on my visits, little guessing in what tragic circumstances our acquaintance would develop. She was not quite eleven years old at this time, an intelligent child quick at her books, in which she took great delight, and of a gentle and retiring disposition. I was charmed by her eagerness to learn, still more by her unself-conscious modesty.

Seymour's plans met an unexpected obstacle. He counted with confidence on his influence with the King to obtain consent for the betrothal. There was a change in the King's attitude however when they were together. Perhaps Cheke, his tutor, warned him; perhaps the boy himself, who had his share of his father's shrewdness, began to take alarm, to suspect motives other than affection in the behaviour of his favourite uncle, who found time so obligingly to amuse him, provided money whenever it was needed, and was never stern like the elder, never rebuked or opposed. When Seymour announced that he wished him to be betrothed to Lady Jane Grey he flatly refused. He was still sore at heart from the ruin of his cloud-castle in Scotland. He was in no mood to be satisfied with his cousin Jane, his companion since the nursery.

Seymour made the mistake of trying to force him. He brought

him a letter and told him to sign it, a brief note addressed to the council.

"My lords, I pray you to favour my Lord Admiral my uncle's suit."

The King however stood firm. To Seymour's mortification he insisted that he must consult Cheke first. I had the whole story from Cheke, to whom he showed the document.

As things were, Seymour acted boldly to save what he could of his scheme. He introduced a bill in Parliament to split the duties of the Lord Protector, to transfer to himself the charge of the King's person, while his brother retained control of public affairs. It was a forlorn hope. His bill was left unheard, undebated.

The rebuff stung him to fury, and for a time he behaved as if he had taken leave of his senses, boasting of the grand revenge which he was preparing, of his plans to become master of the state. Somerset at first ignored him, still hoping to avoid a direct conflict; but the growing impatience of the other members of the council prevailed, and they summoned Seymour before them to answer to the offence, too notorious to be disputed, of neglecting his duty as Admiral, deserting the fleet during the Scottish war. He treated the summons with defiance, challenged them to send him to the Tower.

That would undoubtedly have been his fate if Somerset had not intervened, sending for him and talking to him in private. What passed between them I do not know; but he was restored to favour. It was the wrong way to deal with Thomas Seymour.

For the next few months however he gave no more trouble. The Queen Dowager was about to bear him a child, her first in four marriages, and as she was already thirty-five years old the outcome was awaited with anxiety. At the end of August she was safely delivered, and he himself so relieved that he forgot even to be disappointed that it was a girl. Somerset too was delighted.

The rejoicing was soon over. Within a week of the birth Queen Catherine contracted a fever of which she died. Harsh stories were spread about Seymour, and it was said that in her delirium she reproached him bitterly for his unfaithfulness; but in his own way he loved her, and in her last illness he was constant at her bedside, patient and considerate.

Her death left him more restless in pursuit of his ambition, less well equipped than ever to attain it. He no longer enjoyed the standing at court which she brought him as King Henry's widow. Already he was thinking of a new marriage to be the means of his advancement. At first his hopes turned again to Princess Elizabeth; but his suit was no more successful than before, and he had to console himself with the next in succession, his ward, Lady Jane, offering to marry her as soon as she was old enough. She was not yet twelve.

In spite of the wealth inherited from his wife, he needed money to carry out his ambitious plans. He went into partnership with the pirates whom he was employed as Admiral to suppress, received a share of the proceeds of their raids, even acquired an island in the Scillies where they could shelter. When this failed to enrich him as fast as he wished he conspired with Sir Thomas Sherington, master of the Bristol mint, to coin money for his disposal.

Although the full extent of these activities did not become known till his arrest and attainder he was of too boastful a habit of speech to be capable of keeping a secret, and rumours spread which provoked grave uneasiness in the council. The most disturbing were those which described his efforts to foment popular discontent against the government. Although he himself did not live to lead a revolt his work bore fruit in disorder later in the year, condemning the nation to the misery of civil war, great destruction and loss of life.

He proceeded boldly to the decisive stage in his plot, control of the King's person. Precautions had been taken however. Even when he was admitted to the Royal presence he usually found that Cheke or Somerset himself had forestalled him, that the King clung to their protection, shrank from meeting him alone. Seymour was offended, complained of it angrily, choosing Warwick of all people in whom to confide. Warwick, as events were to show, was already plotting Somerset's downfall, but he had no intention of working for Seymour's benefit. It would suit him much better to put both of the brothers out of the way, beginning with the younger. Although it can never be known I suspect that it was he who instigated the desperate exploit which cost Seymour his head.

The occasion was a night in January, heavily overcast so that the moon was obscured. Seymour came to Hampton Court with two servants, eluded the watch and let himself into the privy garden, to which he retained a key. It was familiar ground to him, even in the darkness he could find his way to the postern door leading into a lobby adjoining the King's bedroom. This was unlocked, and he and his accomplices slipped through.

A disagreeable surprise awaited them. The King had a little dog, Sammy, a wire-haired terrier, which usually slept in his room. On this one night, as if he had a premonition, he shut it out in the lobby to keep guard. When the intruders entered Sammy barked and rushed at them, catching the hem of Seymour's cloak in his teeth. He kicked out, strode on quickly to the inner door, that of the bedroom; but the bolt was drawn on the farther side, and he wrenched in vain. The barking continued, frantic, staccato, with the piercing shrillness of the breed. The noise exasperated him, threatening to wake everyone in the palace. He drew a pistol from his belt, shot Sammy dead.

The explosion, deafening in that confined space, woke those whose sleep the dog had not disturbed. Servants, soldiers came running, found Seymour with his pistol smoking and immediately seized him. The King himself came out in his nightshirt, frightened but resolute. When he saw Sammy's body he paused in dismay, his eyes filled with tears. He sank to his knees beside it sobbing uncontrollably.

Seymour was sent under arrest to the Tower. Few believed his explanation that he wished to see how well the palace was guarded, but it is equally unlikely that he intended the King's murder. His purpose was almost certainly to seize the King's person and carry him off by force. Somerset urged the appointment of a special tribunal, hoping to be able to exercise mercy; but he failed to persuade the council, and we proceeded by bill of attainder.

Warwick was especially vehement in demanding this, and he was among those who did most to prevent the brothers from meeting while the debate lasted. Somerset expressed bitter regret to me later, declaring that, if he had visited his brother in prison, he could have won him over to plead contrition and be forgiven.

This was what Warwick and his friends most wished to avoid. The depositions revealed no extenuating circumstances, the bill was enacted. When at last Somerset signed on the King's behalf his hand shook so that his name was barely legible.

Few of his actions while he was Lord Protector incurred as much reprobation as his brother's execution. Yet if anyone deserved to be punished for treason it was Seymour, a man so devoured by ambition that the safety of the realm meant nothing to him in comparison, a desperado capable of violence to the King himself.

There were clouds visible on the horizon in that spring of 1549; but I paid them little attention, engrossed in the benefits that we enjoyed. Reform of the Church advanced without interruption, steadily whittling away clerical privilege, superstitious abuse. On Whitsunday the new English liturgy, the book of common prayer, on which I began work in King Henry's reign, was due to be read for the first time in all the churches of the realm. I looked forward to the event with pride and excitement.

Our reforms were not achieved without opposition; but the Lord Protector's government shrank from harsh measures to coerce the ignorant and backward. Only when an opponent became too dangerous was he put under restraint. This was what happened to Gardiner. When he refused to admit the visitors whom I appointed to inspect churches in his diocese of Winchester, the council committed him to the Fleet prison. He was free again in a few months but he learnt no humility from the lesson. On St. Peter's day Somerset gave him permission to preach before the King, on condition that he said nothing to impute a sacrificial meaning to the mass. His sermon disobeyed the order so flagrantly that the defiance could not be ignored. He spent the rest of the reign in the Tower.

That was in the summer before Seymour's treasonable activities began, and as events grew to a climax I was thankful that Gardiner was out of the way, unable to snatch advantage from Somerset's troubles.

21

Whitsunday came, the new liturgy was read in the churches. Although my own part in it was only that of translator and editor I could not help exulting over the accomplishment and public recognition of a task that had taken so long. My self-congratulation was short-lived. The first reports that I had of the book's reception were disturbing, and as the week went on the news became worse and worse.

The dissatisfied were not content to protest, they turned to violence. A priest in Devonshire was surrounded by his congregation carrying pitchforks and scythes and compelled under threat of personal injury to substitute the Latin mass. Armed revolt spread quickly through the western counties, and while hasty preparations were made to deal with it similar outbreaks followed in places as far apart as Yorkshire and Norfolk.

My prayer book bore the blame for the upheaval; but as on an earlier occasion the true causes lay elsewhere and had little to do with religion. The rebels themselves were in fact widely divided on religious policy. All alike complained however of the burden of poverty which oppressed them, of the falling value of money, the enclosure of common land, the unemployment among rural labourers as the lord of the manor diverted his fields from tillage to sheep-grazing.

These were long-standing grievances, and no one was more anxious than Somerset to alleviate them. His efforts indeed aroused false hopes. The people believed that the Good Duke was capable of miracles, and the inevitable disappointment offered fertile ground for troublemakers.

As it happened, there were forces not usually available in the country on which Somerset could call. He had hired large numbers of foreign mercenaries, mainly Germans, in preparation for a renewal of the Scottish war. He was very unwilling to use them against his fellow countrymen; but as the rebellion gathered strength his scruples provoked mounting impatience in the council. Even so his obstinacy might have prevailed if the western rebels had not issued a proclamation, denouncing him not only for his reform of the Church but also demanding the reintroduction of the Act of Six Articles. The perversity of the attack stung him to the quick, and in his rage he ordered the army into Devonshire.

The reinforcement put fresh heart into the loyal gentry holding out there, and after several anxious weeks peace and order were restored; but he himself earned lasting resentment in the west, blamed for every act of indiscipline of which the soldiers were guilty. Malice accused him of letting loose a rabble of foreigners to run riot in England.

The task of pacifying the eastern counties fell to Warwick. He had personal courage, was a skilled and enterprising general. He gained great credit from the success with which he conducted the campaign. When the danger at last was over and the rebellion crushed no one could vie with him in reputation. He had long been a member of the party jealous of Somerset's authority, and now he aspired to the leadership. His ambition was the more dangerous because much that he asserted was true. Nevertheless, as I argued in the council, the worst blunders of a humane and honest ruler are less harmful to the state than unscrupulous talent bent on self-seeking.

My advice would have carried more weight perhaps if I had not been put to shame by an incident arising in my own department, the affairs of the church. Bonner, the ill-mannered priest whom Pope Clement threatened to stew in molten lead, and who had risen in the course of the years to become Bishop of London, was ordered to preach a sermon at Paul's Cross reaffirming the Royal supremacy, to banish any doubt of its validity during the King's minority. He failed to obey, and as he persisted in his defiance a commission was appointed over which I presided to decide whether to expel him from his see.

The examination to which we summoned him at Lambeth is an occasion painful to recall, so ill was I able to cope with him. He relied for defence on the loudness of his voice, the

insolence of his bluster, digressing from the simple issue of loyalty
to the Crown into the field of controversial doctrine, and shouting
me down when I tried to keep him to the point. He behaved indeed as if he were the judge, I the offender.

At the next sitting I swallowed my pride and asked Sir Thomas
Smith, my fellow commissioner, secretary to the council and a
friend of Somerset's, to preside in my place. He repaid Bonner
in his own coin, replied to rude insult with fiercer reprimand and
threat, and when the argument still dragged on, he ordered him
to be arrested for contempt, committed to the Marshalsea prison.
I pronounced judgment depriving Bonner of his see, and soon
afterwards Nicholas Ridley was moved from Rochester and installed in London to succeed him.

The outcome was satisfactory, but it was a humbling experience.

I had more important concerns soon to occupy my mind than
wounded self-esteem. In the first week of October an urgent message came to me at Lambeth, that the Lord Protector needed
help to defend the King, whose life was threatened by enemies
in the council. The news astounded me, but there was no time
for questions, for explanations. I collected as many horsemen as
I could at short notice, about sixty in all, and we rode at once
to Hampton Court where Somerset awaited us with the King
in his charge.

When I met him my bewilderment was not diminished. He was
frantic with rage, unwilling to talk, barely articulate when he did.
I gathered however that a dangerous conspiracy had been uncovered, that traitors were in correspondence with the Emperor
to dethrone the King, subvert religion and set up Princess Mary
as Queen. It was clear whom he meant when I saw that neither
Warwick himself nor any of his close associates joined us.

On the following day he was calmer and agreed when we urged
him to send an envoy to London to visit the conspirators gathered
in Warwick's house in Holborn and demand an account of their
intentions. Sir William Petre was chosen and set off, and we
waited with what patience we could for his return. As the day
wore on without news of him the suspense became intolerable.
Some declared that he was a renegade, that Warwick had cor-

rupted him, others that he was detained by force, perhaps killed. Somerset, confirmed in his belief that armed rebellion was intended, fretted over the inadequacy of the defences at Hampton Court, a palace built by Wolsey for comfort and pleasure, no fortress to withstand a siege. He insisted that we should remove the King to a place of greater safety, and with the approach of darkness, in the anxious despondency that oppressed us, few opposed his decision to collect our forces and in spite of the lateness of the hour to set out at once for London to occupy the Tower.

The King was already in bed; but he was woken up, dressed quickly and came downstairs carrying a jewelled dagger given him by his father on the occasion of Admiral d'Annebault's visit. He was within a few days now of his twelfth birthday. He gripped the dagger firmly, as if the pretty toy were a weapon of war that inspired him with confidence. I could see the effort that he was making, barely yet aroused from sleep, to play the man in the ordeal awaiting him in the chilly night.

There was bustle everywhere in the palace as the garrison made ready to leave. Word of our plans spread among the population outside, and crowds poured into the courtyard to see us off. The night was heavily overcast; but many carried flaring torches, and as the King came out he was clearly seen in their lurid glow, standing with his uncle in the arch beneath the clock tower. Somerset drew him forward and made a short speech appealing to the people's loyalty, declaring that it was the King himself, not merely the Lord Protector, against whom the conspiracy was directed. There were murmurs of sympathy, rising to a full-throated roar when the King waved his dagger in the air, calling in his high boyish voice:

"Will you help me against those who want to kill me?"

It was difficult at first to distinguish the words shouted in reply. When I understood them my eyes filled with tears:

"God save your Grace. We all would die for you."

We set off in a great cavalcade on the road to London. At Kingston we received bad news. The Constable of the Tower, disobeying Somerset's orders, had opened the gates to Warwick.

We were advancing into a trap. The column halted while we conferred in the marketplace among the darkened houses. Rain was falling, the autumn night bitterly cold. I glanced anxiously at the King, he had borne himself with great courage; but this sudden check was a strain beyond endurance. It wrung my heart to see how he tried in vain to hide his dismay.

Then Somerset, who had been talking to his officers, came back and announced that we must turn and make for Windsor. I pointed out that we should not arrive before the early hours of the morning, that no preparations had been made to receive us, asked him whether we were not tasking the King beyond his strength. He brushed the objection angrily aside, declaring that there was no other castle where we should be as safe from attack. Nevertheless, as was usual with him, my argument took root as he thought it over, and after a few minutes he suggested that he should ride on ahead with his nephew to reach Windsor as quickly as possible, while the rest of us followed with the baggage. The King looked more cheerful when he heard this. Taking only a small escort, they spurred their horses into a canter and clattered over the cobbles out of sight into the darkness. They were well on their way before the column was marshalled to face back the way that we came, and we began our own slower journey.

A long ride at night stimulates thought. It was clear that Warwick controlled London, that he already had the majority of the council on his side. He could only be overthrown at the cost of a civil war, in which we should rely for our chief support on undisciplined partisans. Was it right to inflict such distress on the nation barely recovering from the violence of the summer? I could not believe that so many lords of the council, responsible men who served King Henry with loyalty, would lend themselves to Warwick's plans if the purpose was treason, submission to the Pope and Emperor. It was possible that they intended only to reorganise the government, to prevent Somerset from making more disastrous mistakes.

When we reached Windsor I was told that the King was safe in bed, having arrived with his uncle soon after midnight. He was suffering from a cold when I saw him the following morning.

The effect was to depress his spirits, especially in the grim discomfort of the castle, which had fallen into disuse since his grandfather's day. He asked anxiously what we were doing there, how long we should stay. I was unable to reassure him.

Somerset veered to and fro between conflicting impulses. At one moment he planned to put himself at the head of an army and carry the King off to Wales. At another he talked of reconciliation with Warwick, recalling their old friendship. The latter mood was reinforced when a train of waggons arrived from the dissident lords, bringing furniture and other supplies for our comfort in the bare fortress. Conciliatory messages followed, including a letter addressed to Paget (the foremost councillor on our side) and myself asking us to use our influence to persuade Somerset to surrender his office peacefully.

We took it to show him and found him much subdued, reproaching himself for the King's cold, his impulsive flight to Windsor and the impression given to his enemies of irresponsible panic. He agreed to receive an envoy from the council to discuss terms, and to allow yeomen of the guard sent from London to enter the castle to serve as the King's attendants. Appropriate action was taken, and negotiations began with every hope of success. We insisted only that his life must be spared, our opponents were inexorable in demanding his resignation; there was nothing incompatible between us. We were indeed on the verge of an understanding when he suddenly took fright, expelled the yeomen and replaced them with his own retainers.

The council read a sinister motive into the change of guard, feared that he was preparing to escape with the King to lead resistance from some remote fastness. I received a letter of stern remonstrance to warn me that unless the yeomen were restored the castle would be attacked and stormed. When I went with it to Somerset he already regretted his error, listened with contrition while I spoke of the danger of involving the King in the dispute. Rather than damage his nephew's interests he withdrew of his own accord to one of the towers, remained there while Warwick and his supporters entered unopposed and took possession. A meeting of the council was held at which I presided in his absence, and he was committed under arrest to the Tower of London.

In view of what happened two years later I have blamed myself for the part that I played in his downfall. Yet the alternative, as he himself recognised, was civil war; the surrender was made with his consent, and he bore me no grudge for it. The assurance given us that his life would be spared was observed. Within three months or so he was released from prison, even allowed to occupy a place again in the council, no longer of course as Lord Protector. Few men have fallen from supreme office with so little hurt to themselves, or so it seemed at the time.

Warwick took over the duties of the King's guardian. His soft-spoken manners made a favourable impression at first; but as the King became aware of the ruthless purpose which they disguised his feelings turned to alarm and resentment, and he longed regretfully for the stern gravity, even the vagaries of temperament of the uncle whom he loved and trusted. Yet the policy of the new administration was in many respects a pleasant surprise. Warwick's correspondence with the Emperor led us to fear that when he came to power he would put an end to reform, restore the traditional structure of the Church. It is probable indeed that he promised as much to gain the support of those whom Somerset's measures offended. But after Somerset's voluntary surrender, which reconciled almost every variety of opinion to the change of government, there was no need to depend on the Emperor and his English adherents, every reason to retain the goodwill of the friends of reform.

To my astonishment he went farther even than Somerset in favouring the cause of the reformers, and if I had a fault to find it was that the pace was too rapid, that the Kingdom of God cannot be built in such haste, least of all on a foundation of political expediency. I ought to have been pleased by the vigour with which doctrine and ceremony were purged of degrading error, and yet even at the time my satisfaction was marred by doubts. There was too much impatience, opinionated complacency among us; too little care was taken to find an adequate substitute for what was destroyed. Men were taught to reject the familiar forms of piety, to condemn what they used to revere, and they concluded in their bewilderment that nothing was sacred, religion itself a hollow deception. The result was a sickness spreading through every grade of society. No scruples restrained them from flouting the law whenever they could with impunity. Landlords evicted their tenants, merchants swindled their customers, adulterated their goods. The dispossessed and unemployed turned in revenge to crime for a living.

Warwick was anxious to demonstrate to the world at large that his zeal for reformation was untainted by disreputable heresy. He appointed a Royal commission to investigate suitable cases. Joan Bocher was among the first of the victims, a noisy zealot from Essex.

When Somerset was Lord Protector he enacted a measure abolishing the death penalty for heretics; but Warwick contended that not even an Act of Parliament could deprive the King of his right to extirpate enemies of the realm, and the prisoners were now on trial for their lives. I presided with a heavy heart. Joan Bocher was a tiresome woman, a pernicious influence; but I shrank from the prospect of condemning her to the stake. I tried to persuade her to save her own life; she persisted however in her errors, left me no choice but to convict her. She was condemned to be burnt.

When the woman was put to death I was with Margaret and the children at Ford, hoping that distance would banish the guilt that haunted me. There was no business to claim me there, so I fulfilled a long-standing promise to Meg (she insisted that at fifteen she was old enough, that I had no excuse for putting it off) to ride with her to the coast and take a boat across to the Isle of Sheppey to visit Alice. It was the last week in April with lovely spring weather, and she enjoyed the expedition with an exuberance of high spirits which reminded me of her mother in the early days at Nuremberg. I enjoyed myself too when I put the thought out of my mind of the scene impending at Smithfield; but as the day approached, the second of May, the strain was as much as I could bear to hide my distress, not to spoil her happiness. Alice was not deceived, and in the evening when Meg was in bed she asked what troubled me, and I told her. Her answer comforted, strengthened me:

"The only way never to be wrong is to make no decision, but that means giving up your authority, every chance that you have to do good."

Another comfort was the knowledge that Joan Bocher had no doubts of her own, that she entered the flames secure in the armour of impregnable righteousness. It is a protection which I shall myself have to do without.

At this time I saw a great deal of Somerset. He was free from prison, restored to membership of the council; but when he spoke it was almost as if we listened to the voice of a ghost, so incongruous was his figure sitting humbly among the rest of us, where formerly he reigned supreme as Lord Protector. Whatever humiliation he felt he kept rigorously controlled, only in private with me he expressed his discontent. He shared my fear of the breakneck speed of reform, insisted that the builders were scamping their work, that a restraining influence was needed, and that no one could exert it more ably and honestly than Gardiner. We discussed means of opening negotiations.

The opportunity came when Warwick was in France, presiding over the surrender of Boulogne in accordance with terms recently concluded between France and England. The council made haste to send a deputation to the Tower, led by Somerset himself, offering to set Gardiner free and let bygones be bygones if he agreed to a number of not unreasonable conditions, of which the chief was acceptance of the prayer book. He received the party with great cordiality, and in the course of further visits his attitude became so accommodating that we already looked forward with confidence to the success of our efforts. He himself was so sure of his release that he sent word to his servants to get his house ready for him at Southwark.

Then the blow fell. News of our doings reached Warwick in France, and he sent orders forbidding any decision till his return. He hurried home, retracted the conditions offered by Somerset and replaced them with a list of his own so uncompromising that only a Protestant of the strongest persuasion could accept them with an easy conscience. Gardiner's comment when he read them was reported:

"I'd sooner tumble myself into the Thames."

The effect was to put the prisoner into greater danger than before. Warwick was thoroughly alarmed by the overtures made in his absence, believed that a plot was on foot to undermine his authority. He ordered all the available evidence against Gardiner to be collected, and arranged for him to be brought to trial on the original charge, on which he had not yet been formally arraigned, of acting in malicious contempt of Royal authority. The offence to which this referred was already two years old, the sermon preached before the King on St. Peter's day imputing a sacrificial meaning to the mass. The Royal authority which it defied was vested at the time in Somerset as Lord Protector.

In further complication of the issue Warwick insisted that I should preside at the trial. It was of course my plain duty, much as I wished to be excused. Gardiner was still Bishop of Winchester, a leading figure in the Church, and it would be grossly irregular to arraign him before any lesser judge than the Archbishop of Canterbury.

My hope was to persuade him to make a formal admission of guilt and expression of contrition, which we could accept. I might have known however that this was not in his character. He was a hot-tempered man, smarting under disappointment, and he came into court in a mood of passionate defiance. He turned the dock into a pulpit, denouncing us, judges and witnesses alike, as heretical, partial and corrupt. As the farce dragged on into its second month my patience gave out, and I ended up as exasperated with him as he with me. When at last I was able to give judgment I felt no compunction in sentencing him to remain in prison, to be deprived of his see.

With Gardiner safely out of the way Warwick seemed to be satisfied, willing to say no more about the action taken in the council in his absence. It was no pleasure to watch his conduct of affairs, and I spent most of the spring and summer away in the country, working on books that I was writing. Circumstances arose indeed which forbade me to return for a time. This was the year of the sweating sickness, the worst epidemic of plague since early in King Henry's reign. I was at Croydon with my family, entertaining a party of guests who included many distinguished foreigners, Protestants seeking refuge here from the Emperor. I was especially glad of the company of John à Lasco, a Polish nobleman, whose advice I wanted on the doctrine of the Real Presence. His visit ended disastrously, his wife fell sick of the plague while she was in the house.

I packed Margaret and the children off in trepidation to Ford, and mercifully they were none the worse; they escaped infection. I myself, having reached an age when I was probably immune, stayed on to look after my guests, to make arrangements for most of them to leave, to provide medical attention for the sufferer. It is a terrible illness usually resulting in death, and her husband's distress was pitiable to see. They were a devoted couple; it was for her sake that he fled abroad, giving up the see of Veszprém in Hungary and many other rich benefices, which he forfeited by his marriage. She had a strong constitution however, and good care was taken of her. Luckier than many, she recovered her health.

When she was well enough to travel they returned to London, and I remained on at Croydon alone. I took advantage of the enforced solitude to make progress with my writing, but not without interruption. As if the plague were not misfortune enough the summer brought also an earthquake, an experience familiar in a country like Italy, but in England a portent, presage of evil.

It was about sunset. I was sitting reading in my study. The light was fading, but I had no need yet to send for a lamp, luckily as things turned out. Suddenly my chair tilted forward as if someone tipped me out on to the floor, and as I lay there the books fell scattered from the shelves, glass from the broken window, showering over me. I suffered nothing worse than bruises and a scarred nose; but for long I dared not move, not knowing what had happened and expecting the whole house to collapse. Then servants came running into the room, exclaiming in relief when they found me alive. They told me that the house was undamaged, no one in it badly hurt; but my steward who was a sailor in his youth, much travelled in distant parts of the world, declared that there had been an earthquake. I refused to believe him till I went out into the village, where the effects of the shock were far graver. I saw the road blocked with rubble, cottages with walls caved in, roof timbers sagging. People were in a state verging on panic. I helped them as well as I could to search the ruins, dig out the wounded and dead.

Fear of the plague kept most of the lords of the council away from London, spending the summer at their seats in the country. Meetings of the council were held wherever sufficient members could be gathered, as they travelled to and fro between each other's homes. The casual informality of the arrangement was of great convenience to those who had business from which they desired Somerset to be excluded. News of the meeting place seldom reached him till the meeting was over.

Much of vital importance to him was thus decided in his absence. He was not even consulted when Warwick and his friends used the Royal authority committed to them to promote themselves in the peerage. Warwick assumed the title of Duke of Northumberland, the name by which, with renewed apologies to the reader, I must henceforward call him. I myself found it difficult at first to think of him as Northumberland, associated as the name was in my mind with the last Earl, Henry Percy, who so nearly married Lady Anne Boleyn. When Percy died childless within a year of her execution the direct line of the ancient family became extinct.

In view of Somerset's rank it was plain rudeness to deny him a voice in these changes. This was not the end, however, of the plot hatched behind his back. Less than a week afterwards I received an urgent message summoning me to Westminster to a meeting of the council. There was a full company present except for Somerset himself, who was said to be on his way, and we began without him. The business was quite unimportant, and the familiar monotony lulled me.

Somerset's entrance woke me from a doze. He was very late, it was nearly time for us to rise for dinner. His manner was relaxed, indifferent as he strolled in.

Then in a moment everything changed. The lord treasurer sprang to his feet, accused him of treason. I slipped back eleven years into the past, listening to the humiliation of my friend, Thomas Cromwell, watching him arrested in the council chamber, led away to prison by officers of the guard. Somerset was at least spared the unseemly violence which Cromwell had to suffer. He had too much dignity to struggle, and Northumberland (as I must call him) remained suave and polite. The very restraint with which the scene was conducted made it the more inexorable.

A proclamation was issued immediately announcing the offences with which he was charged, including a plan to murder the Duke of Northumberland and other lords of the council. In much that was false one small grain of truth could be discerned. I knew that he often spoke rashly to me and probably to others, abusing Northumberland freely. Wild words were nothing new; but it is a long step from them to cold-blooded murder. No evidence was offered of preparations of the sort on which an armed uprising depends for success. His wife and family and a few of his friends were alone arrested as accomplices.

Nothing could save him. His popularity had earned him a respite of two years since his surrender at Windsor, during which his enemy feared to press the victory home; but now all necessary precautions had been taken, and Northumberland was ready to strike the final blow. It was typical of him that, when the trial was over and the prisoner condemned, he addressed him in words that reeked of hypocrisy, posing reproachfully as the friend who had already intervened once to save his life and was anxious to do so again.

I could not bear to sit still doing nothing to save my friend. Although no one could be deceived by Northumberland's profession of sympathy I made it the pretext to visit him at his house in Holborn and add my own entreaties. I tried to choose arguments that would appeal to him, urging on the one hand the gratitude that he would earn if he spared the people's Good Duke, on the other the absence of danger in view of Somerset's manifest unfitness for political intrigue. He listened with his usual suave attention and answered in a tone of regret, which hardly troubled to disguise its insincerity, that the issue no longer rested with him but with the King. The pretence was an insult to my intelligence, and I asked him sharply whether I might have audience of the King alone to try to persuade him. For a moment his urbanity lifted, his voice was almost a snarl:

"You can keep your breath to pray for your Good Duke's soul."

His unwillingness to allow me an interview with the King was explained when I heard of the struggle which he had to reconcile him to his uncle's execution. The King was now fourteen years old, beginning to develop his own ideas and to assert them with all his father's pertinacity. In addition, as I knew, he had a tender heart, and he was very fond of his uncle. There were various stories told of the means by which Northumberland obtained his consent. It was even suggested that he never consented at all, that his signature was obtained by a trick.

The chaplain attending Somerset at the scaffold was Richard Cox, my old friend and chancellor at Canterbury. He had since become chancellor of Oxford University, where he had much to do with Somerset, who took a great liking to him, asked for him especially to be with him at his death. After the execution Cox came to see me and described the scene.

He bore himself, Cox told me, with the same dignity and gravity, was dressed with the same sober elegance as when he presided at a meeting of the council as Lord Protector. In spite of Northumberland's orders forbidding any demonstration a great crowd filled the streets converging on Tower Hill. People flocked there from miles away in the country, drawn not by idle curiosity, but to mourn and protest. Everywhere the procession leading the prisoner to the scaffold was greeted with shouts of anger, wails of despair from the road, from windows, from rooftops.

When Somerset reached the place of execution he knelt to pray, then rose, bowed to the people and addressed them. The din hushed at once, and he spoke in a silence of reverent attention observed even by those who were out of earshot. He was still speaking when a noise arose in the distance; it approached, grew louder, a clatter of running feet, and a posse of armed men began to thrust its way forward. A frantic hubbub of voices cried "Rescue," "Reprieve." The soldiers guarding the scaffold were barely able to hold back the mob. Many people were badly hurt in the riot. Still the shouts persisted loud and triumphant: "Rescue," "Reprieve."

Then Somerset raised his hand, and such was his personality that silence was immediately restored. Every word that he uttered was distinct:

"There's no such thing, good people, no such thing."

What he said was true. There was no rescue, no reprieve. The whole cause of the uproar was the late arrival of a detachment of guards.

22

How could I serve with any self-respect, hold office as Archbishop in a Church controlled by a man like Northumberland? Nothing would have pleased me better than to resign, to retire perhaps to Cambridge even if I were unable as a married man to resume my fellowship. I was sixty-two years old, could spend what remained of my life happily with my family, surrounded by my books, fully occupied in reading and writing.

It was too attractive a prospect to be easily accepted as my duty. Even as I dreamt of it the thought nagged me of the harm that my resignation would do to the cause in which I believed. Everyone would say that reformed religion was shown to be a failure in England, that the Archbishop himself could endure it no longer and abandoned the task. No distinction could be drawn to convince the world between Northumberland's personal behaviour and the policy which he upheld. Both at home and abroad he was regarded as the Protestant leader. Any discredit that fell on him would exalt the Pope and Emperor, encourage Cardinal Pole's seditious designs.

Another argument even stronger to keep me at my post was my duty to the King himself. He was growing up quickly, showed intelligence and character beyond his years, and it was widely believed that he would be fit to rule, would insist on his right, before the term of his minority was completed. If I could only hold on with patience for a year or two I should have a King to serve commanding my whole-hearted devotion.

Meanwhile I had work which demanded my attention, kept me from brooding on events. I was preparing a revised edition of the prayer book to satisfy those who complained that the first clung too timidly to traditional patterns. In addition I had a project cherished in my mind ever since my association with King Henry in the annulment of his first marriage. The incongruity troubled me that civilized society in this sixteenth century of the Christian

Era should still depend for canon law on rules of behaviour appropriate to a tribe of primitive nomads. I could not believe that God revealed to Moses all that is necessary to a good life. My wish was to arm the reformed Church with a code responsive to modern conditions, which would restore respect for moral principles, check the callous disregard shown for others in the struggle for wealth and consequence.

These were tasks that demanded freedom from distraction, furnished excellent reason to be absent from Westminster, and I took advantage of it gladly to spend as much time as I could in my diocese.

The quiet which I sought was not unbroken even in Kent. A sect of Anabaptists was established at Ashford, and complaints reached me of their doctrine and behaviour. They called themselves the Family of Love and as they lay within my jurisdiction I went to Ashford to examine them. Two members of the sect, a man and a woman, were accused of adultery, caught, as I was told, *flagrante delicto*. Both were married, but it was an odd feature of the case that neither the husband of the one nor the wife of the other joined in the outcry, both professed unshaken confidence in the fidelity of their respective partners.

The man, John Kettle, was in his early thirties, a blacksmith by trade. I was favourably impressed when I saw him. He answered my questions civilly and fearlessly, was neither the ranting preacher nor the whining culprit. His frank quiet bearing was of the sort hardest for guilt to counterfeit. The woman, Anne Puxley, was several years younger, sturdily built with limbs plainly accustomed to heavy work. The skin was coarse where her short-sleeved dress left her arms bare. My attention was held by her face, framed in hair of that rich copper-red which a girl seldom retains beyond childhood. There was something luminous in her serenity; poverty and drudgery were lit with beauty.

From what I heard of the doctrine of these people there was nothing in it of the arrogance and exclusiveness to which Anabaptists are addicted. The impression was confirmed when they described the order of their worship. They told me that it was the custom of the sect to meet in each other's houses for prayer.

There was no fixed ritual, no apparatus of piety. They assembled at will without appointment, usually at a late hour when they were free from work. If there were chairs they sat, if not they stood. They prayed in silence.

On the night to which the charge referred Anne Puxley was alone in the house. Her husband had gone out to the byre where a heifer was due to calve. She did not expect him to be long, and when John Kettle came to the door about eleven o'clock to ask if there would be a prayer meeting she invited him in to wait, knowing that one or two other friends were likely to join them. He sat on a bench in the entrance, and she sat beside him. They sat in silence to pray.

The night was dark and there was no light in the house. When a group of people peered in, she supposed that they were the friends whom she expected. It surprised her that they went away again; but soon afterwards her husband entered, then others whom she knew, and the meeting proceeded as usual. The unexplained incident passed completely from her mind, till several weeks later the town bailiff came with an order to arrest her. He led her off to the gaol where Kettle was already held prisoner.

That was the story told for the defence. On the other hand the witnesses for the prosecution swore with unshakable assurance, each corroborating the other, that when they looked in at the door they saw the man and woman in an attitude incapable of innocent explanation. The details embarrassingly explicit were repeated by each in turn without variation, and as the prisoners did not deny that they were together at the time the weight of evidence was heavily on the side of guilt. If I hesitated to convict it was because I liked the faces of the accused and refused to believe them guilty.

I put off a decision as long as I could. There were questions at any rate which the witnesses must answer. What were they themselves, men of substance in the town, doing in that humble quarter at such an hour, eleven at night? Why did they not intervene at once or at least report the shameless behaviour to the proper officers, instead of keeping their knowledge concealed for weeks? Finally, if it was dark in the house, how were they able to see what was happening there? They replied to each question without hesitation. They visited the house on purpose, having heard rumours of the way in which the woman behaved and feeling that it was their duty to investigate. When they found their suspicions confirmed they delayed from compassion. As for the visibility of the proceedings, there was no difficulty at all; the moon was up and shone clearly in.

Their answers had a plausible coherence, although I doubted the compassionate motive which they professed. Then as I turned the facts over in my mind an odd discrepancy occurred to me. Anne Puxley agreed that while she sat alone in the house with Kettle some people looked in at the door; but according to her it was too dark to recognize them. How could that be so if the moon was shining clearly?

As it happened I remembered the night well on which the witnesses saw adultery committed here. I had to ride over on business from Ford to Canterbury and did not start back till late. The road was very dark. I was nearly home before the waning moon rose. To make sure I sent for the watchman who was on duty that night in the town. When he confirmed from his own memory that moonrise was not till eleven, I read guilty alarm on the faces of the witnesses. We established the fact beyond possibility of doubt that, when the prowlers peeped in at the open door of the cottage, the whole room lay in darkness, they could not see who was there, let alone what anyone was doing. I warned them that criminal proceedings would be taken against them for perjury. The prisoners were acquitted and released.

On the following morning when I was about to return to Canterbury and was getting ready for the journey I was told that four people, two men and two women, were waiting to see me downstairs. I came down and found Anne Puxley and her husband, John Kettle and his wife. The purpose of their visit was to thank me for my verdict.

I was touched by their courtesy, very satisfied too that justice had been done; but when they asked if there was any way in which they could serve me to show their gratitude I was at a loss what to reply. Then inspiration came to me. I thought of my sister Emmet, of the desolation of her life since her husband's death. The children by her first marriage were all grown up, and had left her to make homes of their own; she had none by the second. Although she was much younger than I was she seemed already to be an old woman. Could she not find peace again if she came to Ashford and were received into the Family of Love?

The pleasure with which the four visitors listened to my proposal convinced me that a true spirit guided me. I wrote to Emmet, took her to Ashford myself and introduced her. She is still there, and I know that she is happy.

My work on the revision of the prayer book was at last complete, and I submitted it to the council for approval. It provoked a number of objections, and amendments were demanded which I had to accept, reconciling myself to the compromise for the sake of unanimity. Even if the outcome was not all that I hoped I was pleased that we had a version able to command agreement, and it was with a sense of relief that I sent it to the publisher. Copies were printed and a few even distributed in anticipation of Royal assent.

This was the moment chosen to intervene by John Knox, a Scottish refugee of whom Northumberland made a great favourite. He was a Protestant of the severest persuasion, whose truculence of manner afforded reason enough for his expulsion from Scotland, apart from the intransigence of his views. He was useful however to Northumberland, refuting by the violence of his preaching any suspicion that the government was not in earnest in its religious policy. Although his comments were not sought on the new prayer book he obtained access to a copy through a friend, and his indignation was aroused by the rubric prescribing a kneeling posture for communicants at the altar. He insisted that to kneel for the bread and wine is the attitude of a heathen abased before his fetish. It was useless to argue with him, to point out that idolaters in fact lie prostrate on the ground. He was determined to make mischief over a custom which is no more than an act of seemly reverence.

He inveighed against us furiously in a sermon preached before the King, who, brought up strictly to abhor whatever smacked of idolatry, was greatly distressed to find it in his new liturgy. An urgent message reached me to say that the rubric must be changed.

I was appalled, disapproving of the change on principle and knowing that the book was already printed. The King was at Windsor, where the amenities were much improved since our midnight flight there. I suggested, and Northumberland grudgingly agreed, that we should meet and discuss the issue in his presence.

Knox was not invited to the debate, so we were spared his tirades. Northumberland who argued on his behalf spoke with less firmness than I expected. The fact is that he was growing tired of Knox, whose rudeness defeated the purpose for which he was employed. What encouraged me even more as the debate proceeded was the keen intelligence shown by the King. He seemed to be fully recovered from an attack of measles which aroused anxiety in the spring, and the tour which he made of the southwestern counties in the summer left him bronzed but without any mark of undue strain. Every one said that he greatly enjoyed it, taking part in the festivities with exuberant energy. My spirits rose as I looked at him. He was a boy no longer, he stood on the verge of manhood, a King whose reign would foster religion and social justice.

He followed the speeches with eager attention, inheriting his father's love of theological argument. When I sat down he offered a suggestion which seemed to be excellent sense:

"Why can't just a few words be added to show that nothing idolatrous is meant?"

No one ventured to oppose. Northumberland made haste with his accustomed suavity to congratulate him on his wisdom. The printer did his best, setting the added material on a separate sheet and gumming it into the copies waiting to be sent out. In his agitation he inserted many in the wrong place. The book however appeared on time.

This was the origin of the "black rubric," as my opponents called it. If anyone earns credit from the whole episode it is the King. With a strength of mind rare at his age he listened to both sides of the case, refused to be blinded by prejudice or dominated by Northumberland. I could give many other examples from my own experience of his high principles, the quickness of his understanding; but the most outstanding is that which I heard from Nicholas Ridley, who described how he preached once at Westminster la-

menting the hunger, filth and disease suffered by the poor, and how
the King sent for him afterwards, showed him a sheaf of notes
that he had taken of the sermon, sat alone with him for hours de-
vising practical means for the relief of distress. The outcome of
their talk was the conversion of two empty houses of religion—
the priory of the Black Canons of St. Thomas in Southwark and
the convent of the Grey Friars close to Newgate—the former to
become a hospital for the sick, the latter known since as Christ's
Hospital to be a home for orphans and a school for the children
of needy parents.

Fifteen was a dangerous age for the Tudors, the age of the King's
uncle, his father's elder brother, Arthur, Prince of Wales, when he
died. The King's birthday fell in mid-October, and little more than
three months later, at Candlemas, disaster came. An entertainment
was planned at court for the festival, and Princess Mary was invited by her brother to attend. When she arrived he was in bed
with a high fever, scarcely able to breathe. Day by day the reports
of his condition grew more alarming. The doctors could not say
what the trouble was, except that his lungs were affected. He was
in great pain, and everyone admitted to his room was appalled by
the suddenness of the change in him. Many doubted whether he
would live.

I was too stunned by the shock to take it in, to admit the
possibility of his death. Then the news improved, hope revived. He
was well enough to receive official visitors, to take leave of the retiring Venetian ambassador, who reported that he looked as handsome as ever but still pale and weak. Those were the words made
known in public, but I heard that in private conversation the ambassador confessed that he saw already on his face the shadow of
death.

Northumberland, whose own ambition was threatened with mortal danger, did all that he could to reassure public opinion, to
create the impression that the illness was over, and when Parliament assembled in March he insisted that the King should open
it in person. Spirits rose when this was announced; but I myself
attending the ceremony, which was transferred for the King's convenience to the palace from Westminster Hall, found little in his

appearance to comfort me. He performed his part with careful dignity, with the strained expression of one to whom every movement is an effort. He staggered, and I feared that he would fall, under the weight of the immense train of crimson velvet.

The business of the session put anxiety for the time out of my mind. It was an important occasion as I came ready to introduce my new code of ecclesiastical law, which was to replace the Pentateuch. The need was more urgent than ever to restore a Christian standard of behaviour in public and private life. If I was in a mood to lay most stress on the former it was because I smarted from a recent incident in my diocese when a consignment of goods of great value was intercepted on Northumberland's orders and diverted to his use. My plan had been to found a school at Ashford from the proceeds of sale.

In my speech introducing the code I refrained from specific accusation; but his face flushed as he listened, his eyes glared. He leapt to his feet and interrupted me:

"Attend to your own business, my lord," he shouted, "and keep your preachers in order. If they snivel at their betters they'll hang."

He referred, as I knew, to Knox, who had recently turned on him, reviling him fiercely in a sermon, and the ingratitude rankled. I was about to retort that he promoted the man against my advice; but my eyes fell on the chair where the King sat listlessly watching us, and the angry words died on my lips. The quarrel faded into insignificance in comparison with the gravity of the issue of the King's health. It was not a time for recrimination but for prayer.

Northumberland, who hated to betray himself, already regretted his outburst. He tightened his mouth, listened in cold composure while I finished my speech. When he replied he adopted a tone of conventional piety, deploring the vicious habits of the people, the meagre evidence of fruits of the Gospel. The effect was to turn attention from the abuse of public authority to the humble sins of the cottage and the street. The measure proposing my code was not put to the vote.

Formerly I could have borne this with patience, trusting to the King to put everything right when he came to rule; but now a sickening doubt obtruded, I dared not think of the future. The

frail figure haunted me, drooping in the great chair of state as
he strove to fix his attention on the business of his Parliament.

When the session was over he was carried by barge to Greenwich
in the hope that the fresher air and the quiet would do him good.
Encouraging bulletins were issued from time to time; but as he fulfilled no engagements, was kept strictly secluded, they failed to
banish anxiety. It was known that the doctors diagnosed consump-
tion of the lung, and alarming stories spread of his fits of coughing,
of discharge of blood from his mouth. The nation waited in suspense.

At the end of May, Northumberland celebrated the marriage
of his fourth son, Lord Guildford Dudley, to Lady Jane Grey.
He had acquired Durham House, Lord Wiltshire's old home on
the strand of the Thames, and the sumptuous entertainment provided there for the wedding outraged taste and good feeling, jarring
rudely on the anxiety felt by the nation while the King lay dying
at Greenwich. I remained away deliberately, unwilling to revisit
in such circumstances a place endeared to me by happy associations.

In any case I heartily disapproved of the match. The boy was
of weak character, self-willed, bad-tempered and conceited, who declared openly that he cared nothing for the girl. I was devoted to
Lady Jane, whose sweetness of disposition, beauty and learning
exceeded even the hopes which I formed of her when she was a
child. The wedding distressed me, but I had no idea of the even
greater mischief that was intended. I saw only what was obvious to
all, that Northumberland was linking the Royal family with his
own.

Meanwhile heartrending stories spread of the King's condition.
The doctors no longer even spoke of his recovery. Their visits became less frequent. Then I heard that they had been dismissed,
that Northumberland relied on a witchwife with a secret nostrum.

On the 21st of June I received a message at Ford from Northumberland summoning me to Greenwich. I set out at once, choosing my fastest horse, expecting to find the King dead, the council
gathered to make arrangements for his sister's succession; but on
my arrival Northumberland received me alone, told me that the

King still lived. Then he led me into the inner quadrangle where chairs were set ready for us.

I remembered the place well. It was here that I found Queen Anne brooding, while Mark Smeaton played to her on the spinet and King Henry rode hunting with Lady Jane Seymour in the woods; it was here that Amanda triumphed over the Seymour poodle.

There was time to reflect as we sat there, so long was it before Northumberland spoke. The strain of the past weeks could be read in his face. When he turned to me at last his words took me by surprise, so strangely they echoed my memories:

"The next Queen will be Lady Jane. It's the King's will."

His tone was abrupt, almost curt, disguising his nervousness, and when he went on to explain his meaning, bringing me back into the present, I understood that he had good reason for trepidation. He told me that the King had executed a new device for the succession, upsetting the terms of his father's will, disinheriting the two Princesses Mary and Elizabeth, so that the Crown would pass on his death to the next heir, Lady Jane Grey, now Lady Jane Dudley. The new settlement overrode not only King Henry's will but also the Act of Parliament which gave it validity, and legislation would normally be necessary to support it; but Northumberland dared not wait till Parliament met. He proposed that the change should rest on the authority of Royal letters patent, to which, as he told me, the council and all the judges of the realm had already subscribed. My signature alone was needed to complete the document.

The whole proceeding appalled me. I understood the purpose readily enough and could even share the concern which prompted it. If Princess Mary came to the throne all reform of the Church was in danger, and I myself had especial ground for fear, having pronounced the annulment of her mother's marriage. The fact remained that by preventing her accession I should be guilty of both perjury and treason, and there was not even reason of state to recommend the exclusion of Princess Elizabeth.

Northumberland frowned angrily when I gave him this answer. He asked whether it was not my duty to obey the living King Edward rather than the dead King Henry. I was convinced in my own mind that no such conflict arose, that King Edward would be the last to show disrespect to his father's wishes. Although I did not express my thoughts Northumberland seemed to read them in my face. He broke out into a storm of protestation, swearing that he put no pressure on the King, who feared what would happen to the realm if a woman ruled it. I asked whether Lady Jane was not a woman also, but he brushed the objection aside impatiently:

"Lady Jane has a husband to guide her. Either of the Princesses is likely to marry a foreigner."

I marvelled at the impudence with which he admitted that the effect of the new device would be to make Lord Guildford Dudley a King, whether or not he wore the Crown.

At this stage one or two lords of the council who were his supporters came out into the quadrangle to join us. They added their arguments to his, confirming his statement that the highest judicial officers of the realm from the Lord Chief Justice downwards were satisfied and had already subscribed to the document. Such a weight of legal opinion impressed me, but I was not convinced. Perhaps I let it rankle more than it should that they decided so much before I was even informed. I refused to say more till I had spoken to the King himself.

My purpose was to see him alone, to plead with him; but Northumberland took care to deny me the opportunity. Two of the lords followed me into the King's room and stayed there as long as I was with him. In any case when I saw the wasted figure on the bed every thought in my mind yielded to sorrow. I barely recognised him, so shocking was the change in his condition. I heard afterwards that he had eaten nothing for ten days.

He greeted me with friendly words; but his voice was a barely audible croak, and I was aware of the effort that it cost him to speak. Every instinct of compassion urged me not to tire him with legal dispute. Yet the issue was of too great importance to be put aside; the fate of the kingdom hung on his decision. I forced myself to tell him that he was bound by his father's will, and that I, having sworn to uphold it, could be no party to a device which upset the order of succession, disinherited his sisters.

The film of pain and weariness lifted from his eyes as he listened. A gleam of fire flashed there, a warning to which I was accustomed in his father's when opposition provoked him. What arguments were used to convince him I cannot say; but it was plain that he had set his heart on the new settlement. His weakness however betrayed him; the words of anger were lost in his throat, inarticulate, stifled by gasping and coughing. He looked at me pleadingly as he murmured that the judges approved of his action, that if I talked to them they would answer all my objections.

Many of the judges including Sir Edward Montague, the Lord Chief Justice, were still in the palace, detained there, as I guessed, for this very purpose. I left the King and went downstairs to meet them. At the time I knew nothing of the pressure applied to obtain their own agreement to the new device, of Northumberland's threat to fight anyone who refused. They were all together in one of the state rooms when I joined them, and Montague spoke on their behalf. He was an old man learned in the law, whose judgment I respected. He assured me that before giving his approval he had taken the utmost care to satisfy himself of the legality of the proceeding. His words carried weight, but whenever I was on the point of yielding the reproachful image of King Henry intervened, reminding me of the solemn duty which he laid on me. I returned sorrowfully to his son to tell him that I could not break my word.

He was waiting for me eagerly, and when I knelt in homage at his bedside he nodded to me at once to rise. I do not know what gave him the impression, but he assumed that I came to consent. The tortured look left his face, a smile of happiness lit it:

"I couldn't have borne it," he declared, "that you alone of the council should stand out against me."

My resolution melted. I had not the heart to disillusion him. Bowing in silence I turned to the table where the document lay ready. A list of signatures extended almost to the bottom of the page, the names of the judges and councillors who had already subscribed. There was room for my own at the head, and that was where I signed. It was right that the first name should be that of the Archbishop of Canterbury.

Others claimed after the event that they signed with reservations. They themselves are the best judge of their behaviour to accommodate it with their conscience. I know that when I wrote my own name I acted with the full intent of recognizing Lady Jane as next heir to the Crown. I was wrong perhaps, and I have been heavily punished for the error. Yet I cannot wholly regret it when I remember King Edward's expression of gratitude, the joy in his face as he watched me obey his will.

When I left Greenwich I rode to Lambeth. It was Northumberland's wish that we should all remain close at hand. Signs of his preparations for the King's death were to be seen everywhere on my journey. A fleet was gathered in the river, and on the road I kept overtaking detachments of soldiers moving towards London, through whom my escort with difficulty made me a way. My heart sank. It was as if the country were on the brink of war.

At Lambeth I shut myself up with my books, vainly seeking escape from the present. When a week passed without news from Greenwich a faint hope even came to tantalize me.

I was forbidden to speak to anyone of the constitutional changes in store. Northumberland intended to keep them secret till he was ready to hold Princess Mary in custody, to forestall her supporters. But my birthday fell on the Sunday, and Nicholas Ridley dined with me on the Saturday evening to celebrate it. A sixty-fourth anniversary calls for no sumptuous festivity, it was an appropriate occasion however for a quiet dinner with an old friend, an exchange of reminiscences over a bottle of good wine. We enjoyed ourselves, conversation flowed freely, and I was unable to refrain from telling Nicholas more than I should of Northumberland's plans. I even forgot to warn him to keep to himself what I said, and on the following morning when he preached at Paul's Cross he pointedly omitted the prayer for Princess Mary, assuming that she was no longer entitled as heir to a place in the liturgy.

Everyone present noticed the omission, and conjecture throve on it. The town was already buzzing with rumours. The most disturbing were those which declared that the King had been poisoned. I could not believe that Northumberland wished to kill him; his interest was to keep him alive, at any rate till his plans were complete. What I feared was that the witchwife left in charge was administering drugs with this sole purpose, heedless of the torment that they produced. I prayed God to release him quickly, to let him die.

Thursday the 6th of July brought a sultry heat with thunder brooding in the air. It was oppressive weather sufficient in itself to account for my restlessness, the presentiment distracting me. Towards evening black scrolls of cloud crept up from the west, blotting out the sun. Then suddenly as I stared out of the window a flash dazzled me, so close and vivid that the garden seemed to be aflame. The storm broke, and rain fell in torrents. Soon hail as well as rain battered the window panes, a deep crust of hailstones piled up on the ledge outside. I attributed it to a trick of the light or to my imagination that they seemed to be stained red; but I heard afterwards that a similar effect was observed almost everywhere in the town. Not even the fury of the gale provoked such terror among the people as the hail of blood.

In the middle of the night before the storm abated a horseman struggled through to Lambeth. He was brought up to my room, drenched and bedraggled as he was, and I recognized one of Northumberland's most trusted retainers. The note that he gave me was in his master's handwriting. It was very short:

"The King died just before nine. Keep it to yourself."

I thanked God that King Edward was in heaven, but I knew that the message heralded cataclysm.

23

For two days Northumberland kept the news of the King's death secret. He hoped in the meantime to arrest Princess Mary and sent his two elder sons to ride at once to Hunsdon, her house in Hertfordshire, to seize and hold her. A day went by, the second began, and still nothing was heard from them. Rumours were fast spreading through the country, and he dared wait no longer. He summoned the Lord Mayor and aldermen of London to Greenwich and informed them, swearing them to secrecy, that the King was dead and that his successor appointed by letters patent under his own hand was his cousin, Lady Jane.

A public announcement followed on the Sunday, read in every church, and preachers were told to add suitable exhortations in the sermon. The response was far from enthusiastic, but there was little active expression of discontent. Everyone was bewildered, uncertain what was happening and fearful of Northumberland's power. He had occupied the Tower of London with strong forces and was gathering as many as possible of the lords of the council around him. I received orders to join them there.

Having accepted King Edward's new device for the succession, committed myself to Northumberland's cause, I could not refuse to support him to the utmost of my influence; but I went reluctantly as if at every step fate drew me in the wrong direction under a leader whom I distrusted. I was worried too about Margaret and the children in the unsettled state of the country, on the brink perhaps of civil war. They were still at Ford, where I left them when I was called away to King Edward's bedside.

There was a feeling of uneasy expectation in the Tower, as if in a beleaguered garrison. Yet those present were the most powerful men in the land, the supreme source of authority in the interregnum created by the King's death. They maintained an impressive appearance of dignity, all the ritual of state as when the King was alive; but I was not deceived by it, I knew that in their hearts they were as confused and frightened as I was. King Edward had no successor yet, the throne was empty. We were about to proclaim Queen Jane; but the people of England, regarding her as the tool of Northumberland whom they hated, rejected her, gave their allegiance to Queen Mary.

Confidence was at its lowest on my arrival because Northumberland himself was not present to sustain it with his dominating will. He had gone to Isleworth to fetch Lady Jane from Syon House, and on the following day he brought her to the Tower, travelling in great splendour down the river. In spite of her gorgeous clothes, the pomp and ceremony surrounding her, my heart ached for her as she stepped from the barge. Her face was as sad as if she thought of the two Queens in whose steps she trod, and foresaw that the path led her to the same fate.

As soon as she was safe with us in the Tower heralds rode out into the city to proclaim her Queen. It was an inauspicious opening to her twelve-day reign. The heralds and their escort of archers cheered "God save Queen Jane," but no one else. London listened in grim silence. The only comfort that we had was that at least the event passed off without a riot.

The new Queen was not disliked for herself, and in other circumstances she could have been accepted with favour; but now she had to bear the unpopularity earned by her father-in-law. It was assumed that her husband would share her Crown, that the Dudleys would rule England. Events denied her the opportunity to confute the assumption; but I am by no means sure that sitting on the throne she would have been as submissive as Northumberland hoped, and people believed.

An incident that occurred on the first evening after her proclamation offered a foretaste of her spirit. A crown made to her size was brought by one of the lords for her to try on, and as he waited he remarked that another like it was being made for her husband. She refrained from comment, except to express satisfaction with the fitting of her own; but when Guildford Dudley himself joined her a few minutes later she told him gravely that the late King appointed her alone to succeed him, that she had no authority even if she wished to allow another to share her coronation. The boy took great offence, insisted on his right to be crowned, threatening her with chastisement unless she obeyed. She paid no attention to his reproaches, refused to answer, and at last exasperated by her silence he rushed out of the room, screaming insults, to find his mother.

The duchess was taking part with her husband in an informal but none the less grave conference, at which most of the council including myself were present. A letter had just arrived from Princess Mary, revealing that she was already in Norfolk, safe in country held by the Howards. Nothing was said about the two young Dudleys sent to arrest her; but it was clear that their mission had failed, and indeed we heard later that they had a narrow escape from death, deserted by their own men, attacked and pursued by her retinue, owing their lives to the speed of their horses.

Princess Mary wrote in temperate and conciliatory terms. She reproved us for disobedience to her father's will, but offered pardon to anyone who repented and acknowledged her as Queen. It was a skilful letter, appealing to ancient loyalty as well as to immediate interest, and Northumberland feared that many of his colleagues would be tempted to submit. We were discussing what answer to make, how to present our case in the most favourable light, when his son Guildford, his own candidate for monarchy, interrupted us.

The boy—he was eighteen years old, but the word is appropriate —ran straight to his mother, burst into a violent tirade against his wife, demanded an assurance that he himself would be crowned. He spoke at the top of his voice, clearly audible to everyone. I saw Northumberland's face darken with anger; but the duchess rose quickly, grasped her son by the arm, led him out soothing him while he wiped his nose with his handkerchief. They retired to her own quarters, and a servant was sent to collect his clothes from his wife's bedroom, to inform her that he would not return. After two months of marriage he fled back to celibacy.

Behind Northumberland's back comment was outspoken. I remember Paget's rueful smile when we were alone together.

"If we must have a woman to reign let's have one of the right sex."

The next day, Tuesday, passed quietly without news either to disturb or to reassure us. Northumberland declared that the fugitive princess was making for the coast to escape to Flanders, and he ordered the fleet to sail out to intercept her. He called the French ambassador to discuss French support if we were led into conflict with the Emperor, especially to guard against an attack on Calais. The ambassador was friendly and cooperative, the French were much alarmed themselves at the danger of a change of government which would place the Emperor's cousin on the English throne. For the present our interests were theirs; but I suspected that if opportunity arose they would press the claims of their own candidate, the young Queen of Scotland, who was about to marry their King's eldest son.

Our peace of mind was of short duration. On Wednesday Northumberland received a message from his sons describing the ignominious outcome of their errand, and other reports followed warning us that the eastern countries were flocking to Princess Mary's standard, that she herself was advancing on London with a strong force. The need was urgent to send an army to stop her.

If this had been the only demand on our resources there would have been little difficulty. The town was full of Northumberland's troops; but he was too uncertain of the temper of the citizens to take the risk of drawing any away, to weaken the garrison. He preferred to raise fresh levies, offering extravagantly high pay. The collection of riffraff attracted by such means was not of a sort to inspire confidence. The only men of decent appearance among them could be recognised by their livery as retainers of nobles already wavering in his cause.

A stream of soldiers and waggons poured out into the country, heading for Newmarket. The question remained for him, who was to command it. Of the nobles assembled to pay court to Queen Jane there was no one on whom he could rely for the task except himself. The others either lacked military competence or were of doubtful allegiance. It was a cruel dilemma in which he was placed. If he left London with the army it was probable that disaffection would spread there behind his back, unchecked by his ruling spirit. On the other hand, defeat on the field of battle would be fatal to his cause, and his presence was indispensable to avert it.

His natural inclination was to take action rather than to sit still, and his associates urged him in the same direction, some from honest conviction, many because they wanted him out of the way. When at last he made his decision it was on condition that the whole council signed his commission, so that all bore responsibility for the campaign conducted under his command. It was difficult to feel that we were the lawful government of the country when so much care was taken by our leader not to be found guilty alone of treason if he failed. He set out on Friday at dawn, accompanied by his sons, except Guildford. Many citizens lined the streets to see them off, but no voices cheered.

For a day or so we waited in suspense, cut off in the Tower from the populace, uncertain whether to regard ourselves as rulers or prisoners. The reins of power were still in our hands, we performed the duties of government; but we knew that if we left our stronghold to return to our homes we should be pursued and arrested by our own soldiers, or waylaid by armed supporters of the princess who abounded everywhere in secret. Except in material comfort, our condition differed little from that of the occupants of the dungeons beneath.

I do not know how I could have borne the strain if the Queen had not been there to share it, if I had not enjoyed the refreshment of her conversation. The faith to which she clung rested on a sure foundation, not that God would change the course of events to suit her, but that he would always be with her, accompanying her in every misfortune.

Two disasters became known to us at the weekend. The fleet sent to watch the coast of Flanders was driven by adverse winds into Yarmouth, where the crews mutinied and forced their officers to declare for Princess Mary's cause. Soon afterwards the threat of a similar mutiny in the army held Northumberland up as he advanced on Cambridge, and an urgent request came from him for money to allay discontent. There were few of us by now who did not know in our hearts that we were fighting a losing battle. Nicholas Ridley alone refused to give up hope. He preached a rousing sermon at Paul's Cross warning his hearers that if Princess Mary became Queen the reformation of the Church in England was doomed. What he said was true, but he was interrupted by cries of dissent. A time came when he paid a cruel penalty for his courage and outspokenness.

News reached us from Northumberland at irregular intervals, and every message increased our despondency. Princess Mary awaited him in Framlingham Castle, guarded by strong forces of devoted supporters, and as he could not tempt her out to fight in open country he advanced to lay siege; but his troops were as unreliable as I feared when I saw them in London, many even had orders from their feudal lords to betray him. At Bury St. Edmunds they mutinied, refused to go farther. Witnesses described how he blustered, pleaded, forgetting even dignity in his agitation. The most that he could persuade the men to do was to return to Cambridge under his command.

Despair provoked him to a crime that completed his downfall. His brother, Sir Andrew Dudley, was caught in Calais with a train of waggons loaded with plate and jewels stolen from the Royal treasury. He confessed that he was carrying the treasure into France to bribe the French King to invade England, with a promise to cede Calais as a final inducement.

When this treason became known in London even his closest supporters were appalled. Several of the council contrived to slip out of the Tower, either eluding the vigilance or relying on the complaisance of the guards, and gathered at Baynard's Castle at the mouth of the Fleet, where the Lord Mayor and other officers of the city joined them. I myself was not among them, I could not make up my mind. It was evident that Queen Jane's cause was lost, that only harm would come from plunging the country into civil war. Yet I could not bring myself to desert her, I felt that my place was at her side.

Prompt action followed the meeting at Baynard's Castle. An

armed force was sent to the Tower to demand the keys, and we had neither the means nor the will to resist. I pleaded in vain for time to warn Northumberland to give him a chance to escape. Already they were proclaiming Queen Mary in Cheapside, the applause was in distressing contrast to the gloomy silence that greeted the proclamation of Queen Jane. Even from the Tower I could hear the outburst of cheers, and a few minutes later the whole town rang with exultation as every bell left in the churches was pealed. It amazed me that so many survived the measures which I enforced to remove them.

I had little attention however to spare for them. I was anxious for the safety of Queen Jane and hurried to her rooms. She was sitting in the great chair of state under the Royal canopy with a book in her lap. When I entered so unceremoniously she looked up without surprise. Her father followed me, tore the canopy away, informing her that she was Queen no longer, and she nodded as if she expected the news. Her smile was joyful:

"Does that mean," she asked, "that I can go home?"

He did not wait to reply, hurried out again to join his colleagues who assembled to proclaim Queen Mary on Tower Hill. I was left alone with her to explain that not even a twelve-day Queen can slip away from her throne as simply and safely as a schoolgirl from her desk.

That evening two letters went out from the council. The first was addressed to Northumberland, ordering him to lay down his arms, and I put my signature to it with the others, knowing that resistance was fruitless. He was no longer the commander but the prisoner of his army, which acknowledged no authority except Queen Mary's. When she sent officers from Framlingham to arrest him he threw himself on her mercy and surrendered.

The other letter was addressed to Queen Mary herself, offering submission and allegiance. Although I was ready to serve her, no longer disputed her right, I could not subscribe to the language used by the writers to exculpate themselves. They declared that they accepted the new device for the succession only under duress, with secret reservations intending to upset it as soon as they could. I do not know whether they lied to King Edward or to Queen

Mary, but I was unwilling to do either. How could I pretend that I had perjury in my heart when I yielded to King Edward's dying wish, earned his smile of gratitude? I was shown the letter to Queen Mary and invited to sign, but I refused.

During the next few days my friends were arrested one after the other, Nicholas Ridley, Cheke, Queen Jane herself, and from hour to hour I expected my own summons; but for some reason that I cannot understand no notice was taken of me. I went back to Lambeth and shut myself up there, not wishing to be a spectator of the shame put on Northumberland when he was brought as a prisoner to London through jeering crowds. He was no friend of mine, but I pitied him in his humiliation.

My seclusion saved me also from witnessing Queen Mary's triumphal entry into the town. I was reconciled to her accession, to the restoration of the order prescribed in King Henry's will; but it was more than I could bear to take part in a scene of public rejoicing, no matter what disapproval my absence aroused. She had bishops enough to attend her, having released Gardiner and Bonner from prison and given them back their sees.

There was one matter however for which I neither could nor wished to disclaim responsibility. During these troubled weeks no one seemed to think of King Edward's funeral. His coffin would have remained at Greenwich if I had not gone there myself and brought it up the river to Westminster, where it lay now awaiting burial. My heart ached when I saw how little respect was shown to his memory, and my conscience pricked me. I was still Archbishop of Canterbury, still had my duty to perform, whatever the future might hold for me.

I was about to write to the Queen to remind her of her brother when a formal notice forestalled me, announcing that the funeral would be held in Westminster Abbey and ordering me to officiate. It was difficult to learn the truth when I was in the anomalous position of an Archbishop without effective authority; but it seems that the delay arose less from lack of affection for her brother than from her unwillingness to consent to a Protestant ceremony. She was persuaded when it was pointed out that, as he died a heretic, he was not entitled to the Roman rite. Even so, she refused to be present at the funeral herself, and arranged that at the very time that the service was performed a requiem mass should be sung for his soul in the Tower chapel, which she and her court attended while Gardiner presided.

Her absence could not mar the solemn dignity of the procession bearing the coffin from the palace to the Abbey church, or of the ceremony with which we committed our beloved King to his last resting place in the tomb built for his grandfather. The liturgy that I used was from the recent prayer book. Most of the phrases were my own, and there were tears in my eyes as I uttered them. It was not only that, as already I foresaw, I was performing my official duties for the last time; I had worthier ground for sadness in the fear that the reformed Church itself was doomed, that this service of farewell to King Edward was its swan song.

A week or so later the Protestant cause suffered a blow the more crushing because it was among the least expected. Northumberland, condemned to death for treason, announced that he had undergone a change of heart, that he accepted the traditional doctrine of the mass, repented of his apostasy and asked for a confessor to be sent to the Tower to reconcile him to Rome. Gardiner himself was given the duty, and he reported so favourably on his penitent's state of mind that the Queen was anxious to grant a reprieve. Her advisers dissuaded her, and Northumberland was beheaded, dying in the Roman faith.

The defection of so notable a Protestant, leader of the most advanced party of reformers, brought great triumph to our enemies and discouragement to our friends, disarming much of the opposition aroused by the Queen's reversal of her brother's policy. It was generally assumed, in the bitterness of the indignation felt against him, that he acted with cynical insincerity, submitting to the mass only in an attempt to save his life. His career was that of a man who regarded religion rather as the means of political aggrandisement than as the way to truth.

Except for himself and two of his closest associates, no one suffered death on the scaffold. Queen Jane was pardoned, condemned only to live under surveillance in the house of the new

Constable of the Tower, Sir John Brydges, a kind-hearted gaoler who did his utmost to make life agreeable for her. She deserved no punishment at all; Queen Mary's forbearance redounds nonetheless to her credit, so few in her position would have been as indulgent. A favourable impression of magnanimity was created, boding well for the opening reign. It was said that, however widely the Queen's policy differed from her brother's, she resembled him in her hatred of shedding blood.

Even now, three years later, when so much has happened to refute it, I cannot believe this estimate of her character to be wholly wrong. She is a sick woman often prevented by ill-health from attending to public affairs, surrounded by bigots who egg her on against her better judgment. I doubt whether she knows of all the crimes committed in her name.

It was a relief that the change of government came about with so little bloodshed, but nothing else afforded satisfaction in the course of events. The mass was restored, marriage of clergy forbidden. Most of my friends were deprived of their sees, many arrested. If there were fewer prisoners than offenders it was because repression was still flavoured with mercy, especially where Gardiner was concerned. He took care to give ample notice to those about to be charged, so that they had time to escape if they wished. Many fled abroad, and this seemed to be what the authorities intended, so little effort was made to guard the ports. The effect was to strip the kingdom of a large number of leading Protestants.

When they consulted me I encouraged, implored them to go. Their departure in fact suited both sides. It diminished the risk of civil war which everyone was anxious to avoid, but it also preserved the seeds of religion in safe refuge ready to flower when conditions became more favourable again. The Queen was thirty-seven years old and still unmarried. No doubt a husband would be found for her, rumour was busy already with the name of the Emperor's son, the Prince of Spain; even so, in view of her age and health, there was reason to suspect that she would be unable to bear an heir. If she died childless, and was succeeded by her sister, the whole outlook for the Church would be transformed.

Most of the German reformers who came to England at my invitation to escape the Emperor's persecution fled back now to the continent, finding refuge in free cities or with princes willing to protect them. They begged me to go with them, but I could not agree. They themselves, German and English alike, were needed abroad to guard our teaching till England was able to receive it again; but if I followed their example the scandal suffered by the cause would be out of all proportion to any benefit accruing from my arrival, to swell an already adequate force of Protestant exiles. When the Church is in danger its defence assigns different duties to each of us. That of the Archbishop is to stand fast at his post. In any case, incomprehensible as it seemed, I remained unmolested at Lambeth.

My most pressing anxiety was on behalf of Margaret and the children. I dared not join them at Ford, for fear of drawing attention to them. We were back in an atmosphere of prohibition and concealment, and at any moment the harsh penalties of the Act of Six Articles might be reimposed, threatening not only the priest himself but also his wife with death. I felt myself a prisoner at Lambeth, with the authorities ready to pounce. Even a letter written to Margaret would be intercepted.

Ralph Morice was with me, helping to sort my papers, choosing which to destroy, which to put aside in hiding, records which might be of use in better times. When I could bear the anxiety no longer I turned to him, told him to go himself into Kent, pick up my family and escort them across the sea. He demurred at leaving me, protested that the task which occupied us was urgent, that there could be no immediate danger at Ford while all was quiet at Lambeth. We had a heated argument; I had seldom known him so stubborn. At last we agreed on the compromise, that he would pay a short visit to Ford and return to tell me what was happening there. Disguised as a vagrant soldier he rode down through the night, and in less than two days he was back. He reported that everyone was safe, that they were left in peace, and that he had strict orders from Margaret to stay at my side. For the time being I had to be content. We resumed work on the documents, but I extracted a solemn promise that, if need arose, he would rush off at once, convey the three of them to the continent.

Early in September I was visited by Bonner, who was back again as Bishop of London, taking Nicholas Ridley's place. He was sent to find out how far I was willing to cooperate with the government, and I had the impression that he hoped that his errand would be fruitless. He was much put out to learn that I could swear allegiance to Queen Mary with an easy conscience, and when he asked whether my obedience extended to matters of religion I told him that the Queen as supreme head of the Church had the right to impose what rules she pleased. No other answer would be consistent with my belief that the function of the clergy is purely spiritual, the administration of the Church the province of the secular ruler.

Bonner visited others as well, and the outcome was more rewarding for him, if his true purpose was less to encourage cooperation than to elicit damaging evidence. When I heard that many were punished with arrest and imprisonment I was ashamed, contrasting the hardihood of their principles with my own perhaps too easy acquiescence. It is painful to one's vanity to gain a reputation for subservience.

The climax came when news reached me of the celebration of mass in Canterbury Cathedral. Thornton, my suffragan Bishop of Dover, officiated, a former monk whom I myself chose for promotion, impressed by his apparent zeal for the new learning, but in whom I was gravely disappointed. Everyone assumed that he acted on my orders, and the wildest rumours spread, that I accepted not only the mass with its doctrine of transsubstantiation but also Papal supremacy. Here was an issue at last on which my mind was clear. The Queen had power to abrogate the law forbidding the mass, but she could not change the meaning of the ceremony. There was no room for compromise in my abhorrence of a sacrifice which offers an innocent victim to appease divine anger and atone for sin.

I composed a statement defining my belief, explaining the part played by Thornton in the incident at Canterbury, and concluding with an appeal to the Queen to allow me to debate in public against any leading divines of her choosing, to prove that the doctrines contained in the book of common prayer and held in respect in the reign of King Edward VI conform most purely to those established by the Apostles in the primitive Church. My intention was to have a copy of this statement affixed under my seal to the door of every church in London, beginning with St. Paul's. The idea was inspired by Luther's example, when he nailed his theses to the church door at Wittenberg.

I had just finished writing when John Scory came to see me. He was one of the preachers whom I appointed at Canterbury when the priory of Christ Church was dissolved, one of those who shared my sympathy for reform. He rose to be Bishop of Chichester, but Queen Mary deprived him of his see. The stories of my responsibility for Thornton's mass greatly disturbed him, and the purpose of his visit was to ask if they were true, and to expostulate if I were guilty. I assured him that I disapproved as strongly as he did, and I pointed to the statement lying on the window sill and told him what I meant to do with it.

Soon afterwards I left him alone while I went to fetch a book to show him. He stayed talking over a glass of sack, did not depart till dinnertime. It was late in the afternoon that I went to the window sill for my statement, to read it through again to correct any copyist's mistakes. I could not find it, the sill was empty. Even then I did not connect Scory with its disappearance. I thought that I must have put it away inadvertently in a drawer or cupboard. I called Ralph, and we spent the whole afternoon and evening searching, but without success.

The following day my views on the mass were known throughout London. There were copies on sale in the shops, others hawked in the streets. Scriveners had been busy all night, and it did not take me long to find out that Scory was the source of information, that he slipped the document into his pocket while I was out of the room.

Perhaps he distrusted my resolution, feared that without his intervention the statement would never be published. I bear him no grudge, the effect was the same as if my own plan had been carried out. He robbed me only of the pleasure of a theatrical gesture.

Whatever the council intended after Bonner's report, my statement on the mass put leniency out of the question. Foreseeing what was in store I took the precaution of paying off the tradesmen and others to whom I owed money. There would be nothing for them if their debts remained outstanding when my goods were confiscated. Hour by hour I awaited the summons to appear before the council, uncertain when I sat down to a meal whether I should finish it, and when I went to bed how long I should be allowed to sleep uninterrupted. Already I felt myself a stranger in the rooms at Lambeth, as if they ceased to be mine.

It was time, if not already past time, for Margaret and the children to escape. I reminded Ralph of his promise, tore him away from his archives, hurried him off on his errand to Ford. At his own suggestion he carried a packet of the most precious of the documents that we had been sorting, letters from my correspondence with King Edward defining our plans for the future of the Church. He hid them in the bundle of clothes tied to his saddle.

Soon after his departure the summons came. I was rowed across the river to Westminster under escort, no longer a councillor but a prisoner, and when I entered the Star Chamber my colleagues sat to examine me, with Gardiner as their president. He treated me with courtesy, saying nothing to remind me of his own trial when our positions were reversed, and I was glad to arouse no comparison, knowing that I was incapable of his thunder in defying the court. I answered his questions as civilly and exactly as I could about my attitude to the mass, and when they rose for dinner they allowed me to go home to Lambeth for mine.

It was the last night that I spent in my own house. I had no illusions about the outcome. It was as though my judges were waiting for instructions, for a decision taken elsewhere. On the following day when the hearing was resumed there was a fuller attendance of councillors, including many who shared responsibility with me during the brief reign of Queen Jane, and I was aware of a change in the atmosphere. The discussion went on for a long time, but when it was over I was told that by circulating my statement I revived the charge of treason outstanding against me for my part in Northumberland's plot. I was committed to the Tower, lodged in the cell occupied by Northumberland himself till his execution.

No visitors were admitted, but on the day after my arrival a letter was smuggled in to me. It was from Ralph Morice, and the first sentence appalled me, announcing that on his way into Kent he was recognised, arrested, thrown into prison. I reproached myself bitterly for putting off till so late my plans to send Margaret and the children out of the country. What chance was there now of a rescuer at Ford? It puzzled me however that the message was written from Sandwich, and I read on.

Ralph explained that on the night of his imprisonment a friend bribed the gaoler to leave a rope tied to the window, so that he was able to climb out and let himself down. Remembering his portly build, I could not help smiling as he described with what difficulty he accomplished the feat. He confessed with much humble apology that he had to leave his bundle behind, and the papers which it contained were lost to us and in the hands of the authorities. The choice lay between them and his neck.

I forgave him readily for choosing the latter, both for his own sake and for that of the errand on which he travelled. He borrowed a horse from the prison stables and hurried on under cover of darkness to Ford. His account of his reception there was brief, he said nothing of the arguments that he used; but I knew his bustling methods too well to doubt that he descended like a whirlwind, wasted no time on remonstrances, carried them all off, Margaret, Meg, Tom and the servants, in phantom cavalcade to the coast. He assured me that they were already safe on board ship, that as soon as he found someone to deliver his letter he would embark too and see them across to Flanders.

There was great relief in the news, but also great sadness. It was not only that I was not there as before to see them off, to wave goodbye. This time I knew that they were sailing out of my life, that we should never meet again till God himself brings us together beside the rivers of Paradise.

24

I could bear to be punished for my religious opinions, which
still seemed good to me, even if those who succeeded to power
in the Church condemned them as heresy; but it broke my heart
to be convicted and sentenced to death on a charge of treason
which I loathed above all others. I had plenty of time to brood
on my guilt as I awaited the gallows, to ask myself how else I
could have behaved when King Edward lay dying, what else I
could do after his death but keep my word. It was hard not to
yield to self-pity when I reflected how little I knew of the plot
prepared by Northumberland, for which I must suffer.

Bodily discomfort aggravated the heaviness of my thoughts. My
cell was cramped and ill-ventilated, and I was not allowed outside
even into the yard. My health deteriorated from lack of exercise,
depriving me of self-command, weakening those faculties of mind
and spirit which I needed to endure the fate in store. There is
nothing to fear in death, but much in dying, especially if one must
suffer the tortures inflicted on a traitor. I dared not recall the dreadful ritual, to be hanged, to be cut down alive, mutilated, disem-
bowelled.

In my despair I decided to write to the Queen herself to implore mercy. I knew that she bore me a grudge for annulling her
mother's marriage, but it might be that she remembered the occasion also when I interceded to save her from her father's anger.
So I composed a letter admitting that I did wrong to deny her
right to the Crown, but explaining that the source of my action
was love for her brother, my anxiety to gratify his dying wish. She
made no reply, but I believe nevertheless that she was moved by
my appeal. Orders were given shortly afterwards alleviating the conditions of my imprisonment, allowing me freedom of movement
in the grounds of the Tower.

My greatest joy was an announcement of which I heard at the end of the year, that she pardoned my treason and would proceed against me only on the charge of heresy. I could face that with self-respect.

In January the country was shaken by a rebellion which broke out in Kent under the leadership of Sir Thomas Wyatt, son of my old friend whom I knew at Durham House. In my prison I received little news of the progress of events, till an influx of prisoners so enormous that there were not cells enough in the Tower to accommodate them revealed that the rebellion was over, had suffered crushing defeat. Wyatt himself was captured, would soon die on the scaffold.

The most innocent of all the victims of the rebellion was my dear companion and comforter, the former Queen Jane. She played no part in the conspiracy, was not even aware of it, and her first impulse when it was crushed was an immense relief that her cousin, the Queen, was out of danger. Her own danger however became acute. As long as she lived her place in the succession to the Crown, the memory of the few days when she wore it, offered temptation to malcontents, a symbol round which they could rally to subvert the government. I believe that the Queen desired to save her life; but her heart was set on marriage to the Prince of Spain, and he refused to come to England for the wedding as long as the danger remained of a living rival to the throne. Queen Jane died on the scaffold so that Queen Mary might be married. How could the Spaniard be worth such a price?

The lack of sufficient accommodation in the Tower brought unexpected advantage to me. I was told that I must share my cell with others, and the companions allotted me were Hugh Latimer and Nicholas Ridley. The latter was among my dearest friends, and although Latimer and I disagreed on occasions in King Henry's reign I had great respect for his warm humanity. I was a year older than he, but he felt his age more, was in failing health.

Infirmity of body had no effect on the resolution of his character, and as Nicholas was equally vehement in his principles, much clearer-headed in defining them, I drew strength from their company, doubt was banished. We heard that a boon long requested in vain was to be granted, that we should be allowed to defend our opinions in public, to engage in dispute with a panel of divines chosen by the Queen and her council. The prospect greatly encouraged us, and we were scarcely aware of the discomfort of our cell, so engrossed we became in preparation for the task, rehearsing our arguments, collecting evidence from the few books available. We were told that we were about to be moved to Oxford, the scene appointed.

In the Bocardo prison I was put in a separate cell, but we were allowed to meet and talk together on the roof of the building. I was the first to be summoned to dispute before the Royal commissioners in St. Mary's Church. My views on the sacrament of the altar and the doctrines arising from it are known from other books that I have written, where I expound them in detail. There is no need for me to repeat them here or to describe the arguments with which I upheld them. I received a courteous hearing, as did the other two when their turn came; but when my opponents spoke I was allowed no opportunity to answer and rebut them. In any case it made no difference what I said. The decision was fixed beforehand. I was told that I failed to establish my case, that my views were condemned.

On the following day all three of us stood together in the church, and were brought in turn before the commissioners and invited to recant. We refused, were pronounced heretics. There were no more meetings after that, no more conversations on the roof of Bocardo. I was kept strictly guarded and alone. I never saw my friends again till I was made to watch them die.

I shall not weary the reader by describing at any length the ensuing year and a half of solitary confinement at Oxford. When writing materials were available I worked on the earlier chapters of this book, also the treatise on which I was engaged to refute Gardiner's views on the Real Presence; but the conditions in which I lived were not favourable to coherent thought, least of all the recurrent interruptions when orders were sent from the council to deprive me of paper and ink. At such times I sat idle, wondering how much longer I should be given before I suffered as a heretic at the stake. Little news reached me from the outside world; but

I heard that Pole was recalled from exile, arriving in state as Papal Legate, that he was already installed at Lambeth, busy in my library, sorting and taking possession of my books. I tried not to let the thought rankle.

He was not yet consecrated Archbishop of Canterbury in my place. An obstacle stood in the way, and its nature was revealed when I received notice to appear for trial before a commission nominated by the Pope. My own appointment was confirmed by a bull of Pope Clement VII, and the Queen scrupulously faithful to the rules of the Roman curia was unwilling to remove me without Papal authority. I had the right to be tried in a Papal court, to appeal to the Pope himself, and she would not let me escape it.

Far from insisting on the right I denied that the Pope had any jurisdiction in England. From the outset my trial was confused by irreconcilable antinomy. I recognised no authority in the Papal commissioner who presided, but the Queen's proctors who brought the proceedings against me represented the Crown and were entitled to respect and obedience. If I defended myself with lamentable weakness, stumbled and strayed in argument, was guilty at times of prevarication, if not worse, I like to think that part of the blame can justly be laid on my bewilderment, my uncertainty whether or not to plead at all. In any case there was little inducement to careful reasoning when I recalled the treatment which it received at the disputation in the previous year. Witness succeeded witness, bent on malice: Croke on whose behalf I intervened with the Papal governor of Bologna, Serles whom I imprisoned at Canterbury on the council's orders. It would have been more dignified for me to remain silent when such evidence was offered; but that would have been an affront to the Queen by whom the proceedings were instituted.

I was never in any doubt of what the verdict would be, so was neither surprised nor shocked when the commissioner found me guilty of heresy. His findings however had to be confirmed by the Pope himself, and I had a right of appeal, with eighty days in which to exercise it. I wrote to the Queen to seek permission to travel to Rome to plead my case, not that I wished to throw myself on the Pope's mercy, or believed that it would save my life, but I hoped that if I explained the purpose of the reforms carried out in England I could promote a better understanding in the Church, perform a mission for the Queen similar to that which I tried to accomplish for her father when his great matter came before the Court of Rota.

Back in my cell in Bocardo I waited for her reply, but the days passed and none came. The only relief from solitude was a visit paid by a Spanish friar, Pedro de Soto, sent to persuade me to recant. He was courteous, gentle, sincere and I enjoyed the companionship, the renewed experience of theological debate. As far as conscience allowed, even farther perhaps than was right, I encouraged him to persevere, and he became a frequent visitor.

A day came when he entered my cell with a grim face, the set expression of a man who acts with reluctance. A sudden dread gripped me as I stared at him, saw in his black mantle and cowl and white habit no longer the familiar companion to whose visits I looked forward with pleasure but a spectre, a harbinger of evil standing in silence in the doorway, beckoning me to follow. He led me in haste along the stone corridor, up the stairs to the roof, to the corner of the parapet overlooking the city gate and the open ground towards Balliol. The sun shone brightly from a clear sky, it was a morning such as October brings to make amends for the approach of winter.

A crowd of people was gathered outside the wall. Over their heads I could see what they were watching, a small group guarded by soldiers between the college and the wide channel of the drain. A tall stake like a maypole was fixed in the ground, with heaps of fagots and brushwood surrounding it. Although I had never been present at such a scene before, could never be induced to attend for any purpose, I knew very well what was going to happen. These were preparations for burning a heretic.

I knew that the victim would not be myself. Not yet; but as the crowd caught sight of me on the roof of Bocardo excited faces were raised, fingers were pointed, and I heard the odds shouted predicting me no long respite. To avoid the eyes fixed on me I looked across at the actors grouped beneath the college. They were fanning out, drawing apart from two protagonists, who knelt with their backs to me, their heads bowed. A third mounted a platform hung with black cloth under the projecting corbels of the college entrance. I could not hear from that distance what he said, but it was evident that he was preaching a sermon. De Soto made the sign of the Cross.

At last the sermon was over. The preacher stepped down, the victims rose to their feet, I could see their faces and recognised them. In my heart I had known it all along, there was no surprise in the horror that petrified me. The men whose death I was forced to witness were Hugh Latimer and Nicholas Ridley.

The two were taking off their outer garments. Latimer had the same old gown of shabby frieze that he wore in the Tower, and his head was muffled in a handkerchief under his leather cap as if it had been midwinter. His rags fell to the ground, and no one troubled to take possession of them as he wound himself in the waxed sheet that he had brought to be his shroud.

In contrast, Nicholas, as always, was neatly, even elegantly dressed. His gown was trimmed with fur, his cape and cap were of black velvet. As he removed them he handed them to a man whom I recognised as Shipside, his brother-in-law. Then the victims were led to the stake and chained to it back to back.

I tried to shut my eyes, but it was as if a spell held them open, forced me to look. Everyone was looking, the crowd beneath me surged forward. A servant came out of the college carrying a lighted brand. He kindled a heap of furze soaked in tar, it flared up at once with clouds of smoke. I could see the smoke clearly, but the flames were pale in the sunlight. Other men forked more brushwood on and brought armfuls of fagots to feed the fire as it gained hold. For a moment the smoke hid the stake mercifully from me, then a gust of wind caught and scattered it. The wind blew from behind Latimer, and the flames enveloped him. The bag of gunpowder tied round his neck exploded, and his body sagged forward dead.

With thanksgiving for the speed of his release I stared anxiously to see what had happened to his companion. Lying upwind the fire burnt more slowly there, but it was hard to distinguish anything through the intervening blaze. Then my blood ran cold;

screams of pain repeated and repeated rang in my ears, the whole air shuddered with them between the college and the city walls, screams more animal than human such as I have heard when a hare is caught in a trap, or a horse falls in the shafts with its back broken.

A man staggered towards the fire with a load of brush. He approached as close as he could and pushed it towards the stake. It was Shipside, Nicholas' brother-in-law. I could see that his purpose was merciful, to make the flames shoot up and put an end to the torment; but the stuff must have come from a heap less dry than the rest, instead of quickening the fire it damped it down. The flames crept and crackled underneath with a heat to sear the flesh beyond endurance, but not enough to kill.

On and on went the screams, and I could distinguish words, the tone distorted by agony of the familiar voice:

"Let the fire come to me, I cannot burn."

At last someone, probably Shipside, succeeded in stirring up the flame to reach the gunpowder. A great sigh rose from the watching crowd. The soul of Nicholas Ridley was with Jesus Christ.

I cannot remember how I returned to my cell. De Soto must have had almost to carry me downstairs. When I came to myself he was still with me, sitting in silence. I am sure that he disliked his duty, but was convinced that it was for the good of my soul to witness the terrible example. Now that it was over he had the compassion to say nothing, and I was grateful to him.

On the following day however he visited me to point the lesson. No amount of tact could soften the theme which he was sent to preach, that what I had seen was the punishment inflicted on heretics not only by human law but also divine justice, and that full recantation was needed to reconcile me to God as well as to man. I never felt less like recanting than I did then, and I told him so. There was no room in my mind for anything but anger, hatred of those who murdered Nicholas so cruelly.

Since then my thoughts have travelled farther. Nicholas died as a martyr, fulfilling his duty no less bravely than those whom the Church reveres in the past. Of that I am convinced, it is my one rock of certainty among waves of doubt. But he died for clearly defined principles cherished with ardent faith. Are my own clear enough, compelling enough to be worthy to inspire a martyr's death? At times I envy Latimer to whom no such questions even occurred. Spectators who stood within earshot reported his last words as he was chained to the stake:

"We shall this day light such a candle by God's grace in England as I trust shall never be put out."

They are magnificent words, truly heroic; but like so many heroes of legend he simplifies the view of things to an extent which conflicts with experience. What is the candle that he lit? Is it free inquiry revaluing the doctrines of religion? Or is its flame only that of a new prejudice which substitutes for Papal authority a no less unreasoning dependence on the words of the Bible? I doubt whether he himself knew. The danger of heroic faith is that it can serve error as effectively as truth. Mankind has often suffered great harm from candles lit by heroes and never put out.

Alone in my cell I sat waiting while the eighty days allowed for my appeal ebbed inexorably away. I no longer expected the Queen to reply to my letter, to give me leave to go to Rome to plead. In my absence the sentence of excommunication would be confirmed, I should die like my friends at the stake. The prospect became more dreadful, clothed in vivid detail now that I had seen with my own eyes what it meant.

Then on a dark afternoon in early December the door opened and Alice came in. It was as if the whole room were suddenly flooded with sunshine. I expected no miracle from her presence, it stirred no hope of reprieve. All my happiness lay in having her with me. I awoke from nightmare.

She told me that she was unable to get permission to come before. She herself was kept under guard after my arrest, was forbidden to leave the island of Sheppey. The precautions became still tighter at the time of Wyatt's rebellion; but gradually as things grew more settled her freedom was restored. She found witnesses to vouch for her character, the orthodoxy of her principles. There was nothing that could be held against her, except that she was sister to the heretic Archbishop.

For two years however her efforts to see me were in vain. Strict orders were given not to admit her, either when I was in London at the Tower or in Bocardo at Oxford.

She owed her success at last to Stephen Gardiner. For a long time it did not occur to her to approach him. She knew how vehemently we were opposed in doctrine, what rivalry there was between us, that I presided over the court which committed him to the Tower in King Edward's reign, he over that which committed me when the tables were turned. He was the last man, she thought, whose heart she could soften, and it was indignation alone that led her to seek him when she heard of the burning of Latimer and Ridley, of my being forced to watch. Since the Queen's accession he had not only been restored to his see of Winchester, he held also the office of chancellor. She went to him, to the chief officer of the government, to reproach him for lack of charity.

He was at Westminster for the session of Parliament. Wearing her nun's habit, which the change in religion made acceptable again, she was able to gain access to the building and waylay him. His first impulse was of courteous attention, which turned to surprise when he learnt her purpose and who she was. He beckoned her to follow him into his room and as he sank into a chair she was shocked to see how ill he looked. For the past month, as she heard later, he had in fact been lying on the brink of death, and if it had not been for his great strength of will he would not have come to Westminster at all. He was so far out of touch with recent affairs that he seemed to know less than herself of the events which she described at Oxford.

He spoke of me, she said, with much kindness, recalling pleasant incidents of our early acquaintance. When she led the conversation on to more controversial ground his comments became guarded; but she had the impression that he resented the influence which Pole exerted on the Queen, dazzling her with his titles of Cardinal and Papal Legate, to which that of Archbishop of Canterbury would be added as soon as I was eliminated. That Gardiner was jealous of Pole I might have guessed; but I am sure that there was more than that in the distaste which he expressed for the prevailing harshness of persecution. I remembered the reputation which he bore even in King Henry's reign, that of hunting the head deer only, sparing the herd.

While I myself was the head deer I was the favourite target of his bitterest eloquence; but now I was a prisoner no longer to be feared, and it was typical of him that his enmity melted in compassion. He and Alice, it seems, hatched great plans for my conversion. He gave her permission to visit me and himself suggested a change in my circumstances, the news of which filled me with delight. She told me that he agreed to my removal to one of the colleges—Wolsey's foundation was chosen, the present Christ Church—in whose favourable atmosphere my ears might become attuned to persuasive arguments.

On the morning following the interview he broke down in the middle of a speech in the House of Lords, was carried up the road on the Queen's orders to the palace and put to bed there. In a day or two he was dead. Alice wept as she told me this, recalling the kindness shown her by a dying man.

His death did not interrupt the arrangements made on his authority to move me to Christ Church. The dean who greatly respected him obeyed his orders all the more devotedly when they came from the grave. I left Bocardo, and at first it was hard to believe that I was not dreaming, suddenly transported into a haven so rich in comfort for body and mind. Is it ingratitude to Gardiner that I used the freedom which I owed him, the quiet walks by the river under a wintry sky, to complete my treatise refuting his arguments on the sacraments? In a few hours now, when I meet him among the immortals, I am sure that he will not reproach me, that he retains even there his enjoyment of theological dispute.

Alice was a frequent visitor while I was at the college. She was determined to fulfil her part of the compact, to reconcile me to the traditional doctrine of the Church. If anyone could convert me it was she; I could almost have brought myself to accede only to please her. Yet always when I was on the point of yielding to her explanation of the mass an obstacle rose in my mind to check me, the vision of a stone altar, the priest's knife dripping blood. I could not tell her what it was that nourished my obstinacy.

To reveal it would have been to inflict wanton hurt, to defile the symbol that she revered, source to her of comfort and love.

She had however a line of reasoning which I found hard to resist because she linked it with my own fundamental ideas. She asked whether I was not inconsistent in rejecting the claims of the Pope when the Queen, whom I recognised as supreme head of the Church, declared them to be valid. What assurance is left of good order in religion if the Archbishop disobeys the Queen in the exercise of her lawful power?

I had no answer to offer that even convinced myself. Yet I knew in my heart that, if once the tie with Rome were renewed, superstition, priestcraft, all the evils against which we had been fighting for twenty years would flow in again and engulf us.

I said so to Alice, and she shook her head sadly, then suddenly she smiled:

"We all try so hard to put truth into words. We must bear with each other if we don't choose the same ones."

We were standing in the meadow below the college where the Cher meets the Thames. Alice stooped to dip her hand in the water. The emerald ring, a Queen's jewel, sparkled on her dripping finger in the wintry sun.

She stared at it as she spoke: "No words truly describe what we know in our hearts. We choose the best that we can, and they can't be wholly wrong if they lead people to God."

"What if they reveal God to some," I asked, "but hide him from others? Don't we serve him as well in denying as in affirming them?"

She frowned: "Who can be sure enough of his own judgment?"

"Latimer was," I reminded her, "and Nicholas Ridley."

She did not reply, but I knew what she was thinking, that they died in error. We moved away, walking beside the river, and as she clasped her hands the ring still glittered, catching my eye. Our minds, as so often when we were together, followed the same train of thought.

"She died in idolatry," I muttered, "in a rite of abominable witchcraft; but God was honoured in her death, her willingness to give her life for something greater than herself."

"Yes," Alice agreed. "That's what her ring tells me too."

Others as well as Alice tried to convert me while I was at Christ Church, many indeed of the canons acting with the friendliest intentions. De Soto came to visit me, and he introduced me to another friar, John de Villa Garcina, who had just been appointed professor of divinity in the university. I was greatly impressed by Garcina's penetration and learning, the patience with which he strove to overcome my hesitation. There were times when I was on the point of yielding to his persuasion, but I was restrained when I thought of all that it implied. How could I renounce the purpose to which I had devoted my life?

Alice left Oxford. Emmet was ill at Ashford and needed her care. I wondered how Alice would adapt herself to the Family of Love. She smiled however when I warned her of their heresies, she showed more interest in my report of the improvement of Emmet's spirits among these new friends. In any case we both had other concerns to occupy our minds. I went with her to see her off at Osney wharf on the barge that would carry her as far as London. We knew as we kissed goodbye that we should never meet again.

I was glad that she was no longer with me, was spared the distress when I received orders to leave Christ Church and return to prison. The period of grace allowed for my appeal to Rome had expired, judgment was given against me by default in the Court of Rota, and I was excommunicated, relegated as a heretic to the civil arm of the law for punishment. Henceforth anyone associating with me would be guilty of grave offence. I went back from my brief respite of happiness to the inexorable logic of Bocardo.

A month later I revisited Christ Church in circumstances the more painful for the contrast which my memories evoked. Whether by chance or design, the collegiate church was chosen for the ceremony in which I was deprived of archiepiscopal rank and holy orders, cut off, as the ritual prescribes, from the body of Christ. Those who officiated were the Bishops of London and Ely, Bonner and Thirlby. The former dislikes me as much as I dislike him, and it was not unnatural that he made the most of the opportunity to inflict humiliation. I found much harder to bear, and not to re-sent, the part played by Thomas Thirlby. I had known him since the old days at Cambridge, where he occupied the rooms below Bilney at Trinity Hall—a pest however unintentional to his neigh-bour because of his addiction to practice on the flute. Our friend-ship drew closer in the years that followed, and he was often my guest at Lambeth. In King Edward's reign he wrote to me to seek my help when his see of Westminster was abolished, and I was able to get him transferred to that of Ely. No doubt it embarrassed him now to preside over my disgrace, and unlike Bonner he tried to be civil, even addressing me more than once as "my Lord."

When the archbishop's pall and vestments put on for the pur-pose were stripped off me, my fingers scraped to desecrate the unction given to celebrate the sacrament of the altar, I felt that every comforting semblance clothing my self-esteem was taken away, leaving my soul naked, exposed to contempt and derision. After nearly forty years as a priest I came out into the street a layman; less than a layman, a condemned heretic and an outcast.

I walked back to prison in a shabby cloak and cap of the sort worn by tradesmen, which I was made to put on when my own ecclesiastical gown was removed. It was bitterly cold, and I shiv-ered in clothes so much thinner than those to which I was ac-customed. I was exhausted in body, having eaten nothing, having no appetite before I set out; but the exhaustion of spirit was more terrible, the sense of being alone, despised, abandoned.

A gesture of pity from one of the guards escorting me recalled me from my misery, cheered me by its utter unexpectedness. He had been given my gown when it was taken from me, and now seeing how chilled I was he put it over my shoulders, insisted on my wearing it. He even offered to buy wine to refresh me, and when I told him that I craved for food rather than drink he said that he would get me some fish. I believe that he gave the money for it to one of the turnkeys; the fish was brought to my cell, and I ate it with gratitude. Even more than the assuagement of hunger, the renewed assurance of human kindness, of fellow-feeling raised my spirits.

Neither the turnkey who brought me the fish, nor the guard

who provided the money escaped Bonner's anger. He summoned them before him, stormed at them, threatened them both with arrest. Thus a bishop rewards an act of charity.

There was nothing more to do now, it seemed, but wait for death. If the prospect had been utterly inescapable I could perhaps have borne it with greater fortitude. What tormented me, shook my resolution, was the thought still persisting that if I recanted I should live. Although Alice never put it into words I knew that the hope stimulated her efforts to convert me at Christ Church. Garcina himself, chiefly concerned as he was for the salvation of my soul, encouraged me with cautious promises to reinforce his arguments. Even here in Bocardo he continued to visit me.

When he left me, and I brooded alone over the doctrines which I upheld, none seemed to be sure enough to carry the terrible importance attached to it. Nothing but words, words groping in the dark, the inadequate attempt of human reason to define eternal mystery.

I longed for distraction to relieve my solitary brooding, and my wish seemed to be granted when the keeper of the prison, a man called Woodson, pitying my loneliness, took to coming into my room from time to time to talk. He was honest and good-natured, a countryman by birth, a grazier's son from the sheep-rearing land in the Cotswolds. He came inspired by evangelical zeal, earnestly persuaded that his mission was to rescue me from heresy. It distressed him however when he found that his efforts bore no fruit. I tried to explain my difficulties, but he could not understand them. He assumed that I was deceiving him, left the room greatly offended and did not come back.

I missed him when he was gone. Left to myself I wondered uneasily if I had not been wrong to disappoint him. In other circumstances perhaps my judgment would have been more balanced; but in prison it is hard to resist conclusions biased by personal need. I felt that there would be no harm in urging Woodson to another visit, in professing a new willingness to listen. The invitation would earn me a respite from solitude.

I failed to allow for his eagerness. He came hastening to see me with a recantation already drawn up for me to sign, and was sadly put out when I explained that he took too much for granted. As he thrust the document towards me I turned away, shook my head.

The effect was disastrous. He was reproaching himself already for his neglect of duty, and my recalcitrance stung him to the quick. He stormed at me with bitter recriminations and strode out, slamming the door.

On occasions when the mind and will are no longer able to cope with events the body takes charge. As I stood alone in the room the ground seemed to sway beneath me. I just had strength to stagger to my bed, fell there and fainted. It appears that I lay unconscious for a long time, and even when I came to I was not fully in control of myself. My servant who slept next door said that he was woken by the sound of my groans, and went off at once to arouse Woodson.

By then I was recovering my wits. In the confusion of feelings overwhelming me I cannot distinguish clearly which motive prevailed, whether the force of reason, the fear of a terrible death or sheer weariness that longed to be rid of an intolerable burden. While I waited for Woodson to come I rose unsteadily to my feet, walked across to the table and picked up and read the document which he had left there. It was not at all to my liking, and I took pen and paper to compose a version of my own. I wrote:

"Forasmuch as the King's and Queen's Majesties by consent of their Parliament have received the Pope's authority within this realm, I am content to submit myself to their laws herein and to take the Pope for chief head of this Church of England, so far as God's laws and the laws and customs of this realm will permit."

I was adding my signature when Woodson arrived. I handed him the paper bearing my name. He took it suspiciously, but as he read it his whole expression changed. He was delighted, thanked God aloud. In the exuberance of his relief he embraced me.

That was a month ago. The events that followed are painful to recall. My recantation which gave such pleasure to Woodson failed to satisfy the authorities, in whose view it was not enough to acknowledge the supremacy of the Pope when I made it depend on the Queen's command. Garcina came to see me to add his own efforts, to complete the process of my conversion. He pressed his advantage, and I felt that I was fighting a losing cause. Having taken the first step to retreat I could only yield more and more.

At his prompting I have signed at least five recantations, each of which in turn has been rejected as inadequate. Always I tried to choose phrases conceding no more than conscience allowed; always the ambiguity was detected, and a fresh version demanded to close the loophole of escape. This evening the provost of Eton, Dr. Cole, has been to see me, bringing a final statement prepared for my signature. There is no room in it for reservations, for quibbles. It declares complete and abject submission, renunciation of everything that I have said and thought since I began my career.

Tomorrow—today, for it is already long past midnight—I must read this document aloud before the congregation assembled in St. Mary's Church. If I refuse I go to the stake to be burnt. If I consent shall I save my life? Cole was careful not to commit himself. He was more concerned to gather information useful for the sermon which he will preach at my execution, if I have to die.

25

Since I wrote the last words a man has been here, bringing a letter from my sister Emmet. It is nearly four o'clock in the morning, not an hour at which visitors are usually admitted to the prison; but Woodson has given orders that on this occasion the rules may be relaxed in my favour. The messenger had ridden without pause all the way from Ashford in his anxiety to arrive in time. He told me that Emmet implored him to hurry.

The letter contains heavy news. Alice is dead. When she left me at Oxford to nurse Emmet at Ashford she found the whole town stricken with plague, of which Emmet was one of many victims. Emmet herself recovered, but Alice still went on caring for the sick, going from house to house to visit them. For some time she seemed to be immune to the disease, but when she caught it the attack was fatal.

She died the day before yesterday. If I am burnt this morning she at least will be spared the distress.

The purpose of the letter was not only to tell me of her death, it was also to enclose a small packet, of which Emmet wrote:

"She asked me to send you this. She said you'd know why."

I unwrapped the twist of paper. It held Queen Anne's emerald ring.

Alice added no message of her own. She left the ring to speak for itself, and now as I watch the emerald gleaming in the candle-light images take shape, answer my question as clearly as if I heard her very words. I am caught up in spirit to another prison, to a room much more sumptuous than the present, to the state apartments at the Tower, and I kneel to take leave of a Queen dressed in black damask, Proserpine, the bride of death. Her eyes shine with secret knowledge like those of a goddess.

"Some day," she foretells, "you'll think better of me."

Not for idolatry, witchcraft, but because she gave herself as a willing sacrifice. Whether a cause be true or false, great courage is needed to die for it.

Day is breaking. Balliol looms outside the window, indistinct through sheets of rain beyond the swollen ditch. The fagots prepared for my burning will be soaked through, hard to kindle. Out there in the desolation the stake was set up for Nicholas Ridley, and his screams ring in my ears when the fire lacked heat to kill him, to put him out of his torment:

"I cannot burn, I cannot burn."

Yes, but through the din I hear another voice, still and small and sweet, like a wave of silence in which terror and indecision are drowned. Alone in the depths of my soul the kind stranger, my familiar friend talks to me. He speaks without words, no words can express his meaning; but I think of Margaret and the children safe in Germany, of Alice waiting to greet me on the other side of the flames.

"If a man will keep still and listen, he will hear what the Spirit witnesses within him."

Help me, Lord, to listen when my hour comes.

EPILOGUE
(Added by an unknown hand)

I was among those present in Oxford on Saturday the 21st of March, 1556, to hear the former Archbishop make public recantation of his heresy. The ceremony was to have taken place at the stake; but the rain compelled a change of plan, and he was brought into St. Mary's Church to stand on a stage set up beside the pulpit. Remembering him in his prosperity as a man always neat and scrupulously clean in his dress I was shocked by his neglected appearance, his ragged gown and cap, his unkempt beard reaching to his waist. He looked even older than his sixty-six years.

Tears rolled down his cheeks while Dr. Cole preached the sermon, and when his own turn came to speak, to read the statement prepared for him, we expected him to affirm his conversion and express penitence for his errors in the most abject terms. It was known that he had recanted several times while he was in prison, that he yielded principle after principle to satisfy the authorities. The first part of his speech did nothing to disturb the general expectation, exhorting his hearers to obey the Queen, to behave to each other with brotherly love, appealing especially to the rich to show charity to the poor. He expressed belief in every article of the Catholic faith, every word and sentence taught by our Saviour Jesus Christ, and when he went on to allude to "the great thing which troubles my conscience more than anything that ever I did or said in my whole life," few doubted that he referred to the leading part which he played in the schism of the Church, beginning with his judgment annulling the marriage of the Queen's mother.

I myself was so sure of this that my attention wandered, but it was recalled abruptly when I heard him speak of "bills and papers which I have written or signed since my degradation, wherein I have written many things untrue." He added that as his hand had offended, writing contrary to his heart, it should be the first to suffer punishment when he came to the fire. No uncertainty was left of his meaning when he declared:

"And as for the Pope I refuse him as Christ's enemy and Antichrist, with all his false doctrine."

The words startled me the more, they were so out of keeping with his usual moderation; but violence of expression can be forgiven in a man when he knows that less than an hour lies between his living body and the flames.

An angry hubbub interrupted him. He tried to continue his speech, but his voice was drowned, and the friars and other clergy surrounding the stage seized and pulled him down to the floor. It was difficult in the confusion to see what was happening; but he shook himself free, and something that he said seemed to satisfy them. They drew back and made way, and he strode out of the church. We all flocked after him.

He turned up Brasenose Lane and round the college into Turl Street, making for the open ground outside the walls where the stake, fagots and furze awaited him. He walked so fast that his escort had to run to keep pace, and two friars who tried to plead with him, shouting exhortations to repent, gave up at last out of breath, dropped back and were left behind.

At the place of execution he took off his gown of his own accord and stood ready in a long white shirt reaching to his feet, while a soldier fastened him to the stake with a steel band. One or two people came up and spoke to him, but I was too far off to see who they were.

Then the furze was heaped round him. It had been stored in shelter from the rain, and when fire was applied it kindled readily. As the flames leapt up he stooped to them and thrust his right hand into the blaze, the hand that signed his recantations. For a moment he drew it back, wincing from the pain, but quickly thrust it in again and held it there till the flesh was charred to the bone. Once he raised his other hand to wipe his brow, but no cry, not even a groan escaped him. I should have heard it, the crowd was so still. There was no sound except the crackle of the flames as they gathered strength to envelop him.

Then suddenly he called out: "I see heaven open and Jesus waiting."

He never spoke again. He died quickly.

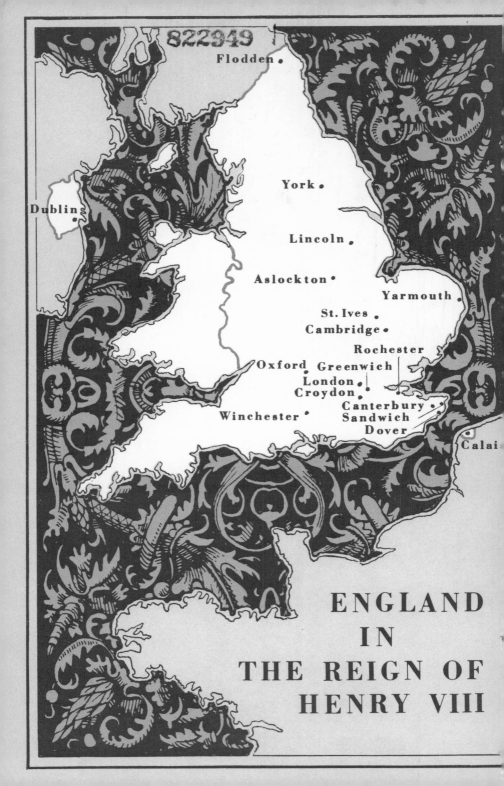

822949

Flodden •

Dublin

York •

Lincoln •

Aslockton •

Yarmouth •

St. Ives •
Cambridge •

Rochester

Oxford • Greenwich
London •
Croydon •

Winchester •

Canterbury •
Sandwich
Dover

Calai

ENGLAND
IN
THE REIGN OF
HENRY VIII